D0363951

ANATOMY AND PHYSIOLOGY FOR NURSES

EVELYN C. PEARCE

S.R.N., R.F.N., S.C.M., T.M.M.C., C.S.P.

Formerly Senior Nursing Tutor, The Middlesex Hospital; Member of the General Nursing Council for England and Wales, and for many years Examiner in Nursing to the Council; Examiner in Fever Nursing and Epidemiology for the Diploma in Nursing, London University.

---

other books by Miss Pearce

A General Textbook for Nurses

Medical and Nursing Dictionary

Fevers and Fever Nursing

A Textbook of Orthopaedic Nursing

Instruments, Appliances and Theatre Technique

A Complete Handbook of Hygiene
in Questions and Answers

ANATOMY AND PHYSIOLOGY FOR NURSES

a complete textbook for the preliminary state examination

by

EVELYN C. PEARCE

ninth edition

FABER AND FABER LIMITED

24 Russell Square

London

1948

First published in June 1929
by Faber and Faber Limited
24 Russell Square, London, W.C.1
Eighth edition, March 1943
Reprinted, February and October 1944
July 1945 and April 1946
Ninth edition, 1948
Printed by Purnell and Sons, Ltd.
Paulton (Somerset) and London

PREFACE

This book was first written several years ago, to meet the need of student Nurses preparing for the Preliminary State Examination. It is based on the syllabus issued by the General Nursing Council and on lectures given in preparing Nurses for this Examination.

In the present Ninth Edition, some of the text has been rewritten, a few additions made, a number of illustrations redrawn, and many new illustrations have been added. I hope that these changes and additions will make the subject clearer to the student, and I desire to thank Miss Peggy Hodge for her interest and co-operation in producing the new illustrations. Professor T. B. Johnston and Messrs. Longmans, Green and Co., Ltd., kindly gave permission for the diagram of the *Interior of the Heart* (fig. 95) to be based on an illustration in Gray's *Anatomy*.

By courtesy of the Registrar of the General Nursing Council for England and Wales questions included in recent examination papers are given in an appendix and in order to help students as much as possible the page references where information relating to these questions will be found in the text have been added.

EVELYN C. PEARCE

January 1948

CONTENTS

LIST OF ILLUSTRATIONS

Chapter 1

INTRODUCTION TO THE HUMAN BODY

Anatomy is the term used to describe the study of the position and relationship of one part of the body to another. In *regional anatomy* a geographical study is made and each region, e.g. arm, leg, head, chest, etc., is found to consist of a number of structures common to all regions such as bones, muscles, nerves, blood vessels and so on. From this study it follows that a number of different systems exist. These have been grouped together and described under the heading *systematic anatomy*.

A study of the position and relationship of one part of the body could not be separated from a consideration of the use of each structure and system. This study led to the employment of the term *functional anatomy* which is closely allied to the study of physiology. Then again it was found that certain structures could be examined by the naked eye and the term *macroscopic anatomy* was introduced to describe this study, in distinction to *microscopic anatomy* which necessitates the use of a microscope. Closely allied to the study of anatomy are *histology* and *cytology*. The former deals with the fine structures of the body, and the latter with a study of the cells.

Physiology is the study of the functions of the normal human body. It is closely linked with the study of all living things in the subject of *biology*; with the chemical reactions and behaviour of cells under different conditions in biochemistry, and with physics in the study of the physical reactions and movements taking place in the body.

The body is made up of many parts, each having its own particular function to perform. The *cell* is the *unit* or the smallest element of the body of which all parts are comprised. Cells have distinctive functions. They may be *secretory* as when manufacturing an essential substance, such as the glands of the digestive tract, or *excretory* when separating some substance which has to be eliminated from the body as do some of the cells of the kidney. Cells may also be *nervous*, *connective* or *protective* in function.

From characteristic cell units a great variety of body tissue is developed. These tissues in turn are built up into organs. For example the liver is an *organ* made up of liver *tissue* and the tissue is composed of liver *cells*.

Terms used in Anatomy. Many parts of the body are *symmetrically* arranged. For example the right and left limbs are similar; there are right and left eyes and ears, right and left lungs, and right and left kidneys. But there is also a good deal of *asymmetry* in the arrangement of the body. The spleen lies entirely on the left side; the larger part of the liver lies on the right side; the pancreas lies partly on each side.

The human body is studied from the erect position with the arms by the sides and the palms of the hands facing forwards, the head erect and eyes looking straight in front. This is described as the *anatomical position*.

The various parts of the body are then described in relation to certain *imaginary lines* or *planes*. The *median plane* runs through the centre of the body, and corresponding lines on the front and back of the body are known as the *anterior* and *posterior median lines* respectively. Any structure which lies nearer to the median plane of the body than another is said to be medial to that other. For example the hamstring muscles which lie on the inner side of the thigh are nearer the median plane than those which lie on the outer side and are therefore *medial* to the other group which are described as *lateral*. Similarly the inner side of the thigh is described as the *medial aspect* and the outer as the *lateral aspect*. The terms *internal* and *external* are used to describe the relative distance of an organ or structure from the centre of a cavity. The ribs for example have an internal surface which is near the chest cavity and an external surface which is on the outer side, farther away from the cavity. The internal carotid artery (see fig. 107), is within the cranial cavity and the external is outside the cavity.

The terms *superficial* and *deep* are used to denote relative distance from the surface of the body, and the terms *superior* and *inferior* denote positions relatively high or low, particularly in relation to the trunk, such as the superior and inferior surfaces of the clavicle.

The terms *anterior* and *posterior* are synonomous with *ventral* and *dorsal*. These terms are only applied to man in the erect attitude or "anatomical position". For example the anterior and posterior tibial arteries lie in front and behind the leg (see fig. 111).

In describing the hand the terms *palmar* and *dorsal* are used instead of anterior and posterior, and in describing the foot the terms *plantar* and *dorsal* are similarly employed.

The terms *proximal* or *distal* are employed to describe nearness to, or distance from a given point, particularly in relation to the limbs. For example the proximal phalanges are nearer to the wrist and the distal ones are the farthest away. When three structures are in a line running from the medial plane of the body outwards, they are described as being placed in *medial*, *intermediate* and *lateral* positions. An example of this is seen in the arrangement of the three cuneiform bones of the foot (see page 87). Similarly when three structures run from front to back (anterior to posterior) or from above downwards (superior to inferior), these are described as anterior, middle and posterior as happens in the arrangement of the three fossae of the skull (see page 41); and superior, middle and inferior, as occurs in the arrangement of the superior, middle and inferior radio-ulnar joints (see page 96).

THE SYSTEMS OF THE BODY

Systematic anatomy or the division of the body into systems is arranged (*a*) according to the functions they perform and (*b*) under the heading of the different terms employed to indicate the knowledge of certain parts.

Osteology is a knowledge of bones,
Arthrology „ „ „ „ joints,
Myology „ „ „ „ muscles,
Splanchnology „ „ „ „ organs or viscera,
Neurology „ „ „ „ nerves and nerve structures

When grouped according to functions the general arrangement is as follows.

The *Locomotor System.* This includes the parts concerned in the movements of the body. The *skeletal system* which is composed of the bones, and certain cartilages and membranes, the *articulatory system* which deals with the joints or articulations, and the *muscular system* which includes muscles, fascia and tendon sheaths.

The *Blood-Vascular System* includes the *circulatory system*, and *lymphatic system.*

The *Digestive System* consists of the alimentary canal and the glands and organs associated with it.

The *Respiratory System* contains the passages and organs concerned with breathing.

The *Ductless Glands* are grouped together because of the internal secretions they produce. The spleen is generally included in this group because it also has no duct, though as far as is known it does not produce an internal secretion.

The *Urogenital System* includes the organs of the *urinary system* and the *reproductive system.*

The *Nervous System* is composed of the *central nervous system* which includes the brain and spinal cord, the *peripheral nervous system* consisting of the nerves given off from brain and cord and the *autonomic nervous system.* The central and peripheral systems are often grouped together and described as the *cerebrospinal nervous system.* The autonomic nervous system includes the sympathetic and parasympathetic nerves. It is also described as the *involuntary nervous system.*

The *Special Sense Organs* include taste, smell, sight and hearing, and also the sensory function of the skin.

The *Excretory System* is the term sometimes employed to describe collectively the organs that deal with the excretion of waste products from the body. These organs include the *urinary system*, the *lungs* in their function of eliminating carbon dioxide, the function of the *skin* in so far as it too excretes carbon dioxide though only in minute quantities, and the *colon* which excretes certain insoluble substances such as iron in the faeces.

A TISSUE CELL

A cell is a minute living organism composed of protoplasm which is made up of water containing salts and protein; these substances form the basic material of all cells, differing slightly according to the type and function of the cell, as in nerve cells, muscle cells, liver cells, skin cells and so on, because each cell selects from the blood stream the particular amino-acids (protein material) which it needs.

Although the entire cell is composed of protoplasm, different parts of the cell vary slightly and are named according to the function of the part.

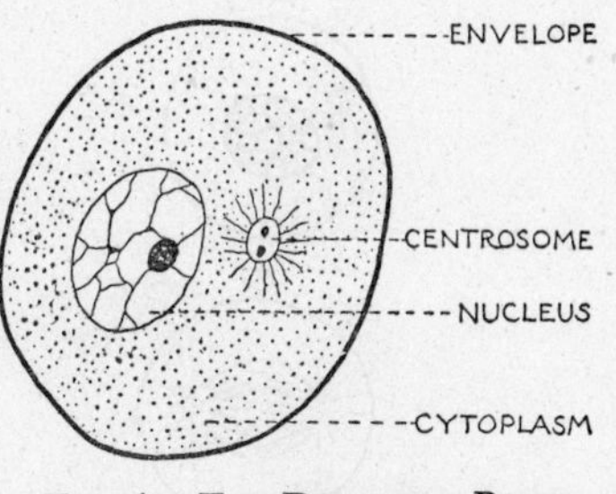

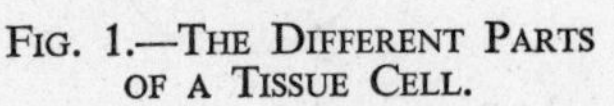
FIG. 1.—THE DIFFERENT PARTS OF A TISSUE CELL.

The *nucleus* lies at the centre of the cell.

Cytoplasm is the name given to the protoplasm immediately around the nucleus.

The *centrosome* is a minute part of the protoplasm very near the nucleus which is active in the changes that take place when the cell divides.

The *cell membrane*, envelope, or covering of the cell is slightly denser than the other parts.

A living cell possesses a number of characteristic properties:

Growth. During the growing years cell growth is very active; in adult life, when growth is complete, cell division is constantly replacing those cells which are worn out by work or destroyed by disease.

Metabolism. Cell metabolism includes the reception of the nourishment the cell needs, which it receives from the tissue fluids of the body. The cell absorbs and assimilates this food material to form new protoplasm to replace and repair the waste caused by the activity of the cell, and the breaking down of its protoplasm. Each cell takes in nourishment, uses it as fuel to perform work, and then returns the broken-down waste material to the tissue fluid. In addition to supplying food materials to the cell, the blood forms the medium of interchange between the lungs and the tissues, bringing the oxygen each cell needs and carrying away the carbonic acid waste.

Irritability and conductivity. By these two properties the cell is active. When a cell is stimulated either by chemical, physical, mechanical, or nervous means, the cell responds; it may contract as does a muscle cell (fibre); it may produce a secretion, as do the cells of the stomach, pancreas, and other organs and glands; or it may conduct an impulse, as in the case of the nerve cell. This last is the best example of cell conductivity, as a nerve impulse generated by the stimulation of a nerve cell

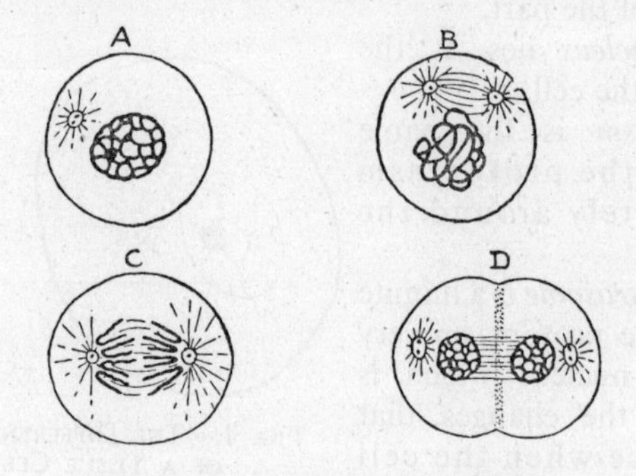

FIG. 2.—STAGES IN CELL DIVISION.

A. Cell with Nucleus and Centrosome.
B. Nucleus changes, Centrosome divides.
C. Two identical sets of Chromosomes being attracted to the Poles.
D. Two Cells separating.

may be conducted for a considerable distance, a yard or more, according to the length of the nerve fibre. But in all cases, a stimulus which *excites* a cell to action is *conducted* along the entire length, from end to end of the cell.

Reproduction. Most cells divide by a process described as *mitosis* or *karyokinesis.* Activity begins in the nucleus, the nuclear membrane disappears and the *chromatin* changes character and becomes long filaments called *chromosomes.* The *centrosome* divides and the *two new centrosomes* move away from each other to each end of the nucleus called the poles. The chromosomes are then attracted to the poles and lie near the new centrosomes. The *chromatin* of which the nucleus is formed now comes to rest and *two new nuclei* exist. Finally the *protoplasm of the cell constricts and divides* and the two new cells are complete.

THE ELEMENTARY TISSUES OF THE BODY

Four groups of tissue in the body are known as the elementary tissues. These are *epithelial* tissue, *muscular* tissue, *nervous* tissue, and *connective* tissue. Many of the tissues consist of cells joined together by some connecting substance.

Epithelial Tissue consists of cells which form the mucous membrane and skin covering the body and lining all the hollow organs, tubular organs, blood vessels, and the air cells. There

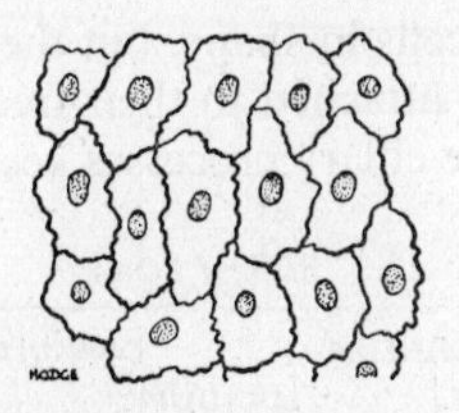

FIG. 3.—PAVEMENT CELLS OF SQUAMOUS EPITHELIUM.

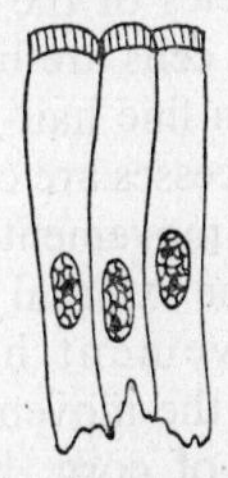

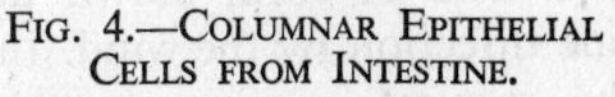

FIG. 4.—COLUMNAR EPITHELIAL CELLS FROM INTESTINE.

are two main classes of epithelial tissue, each containing several varieties. All epithelial cells lie on and are held together by a homogeneous substance called a *basement membrane*.

Simple epithelium. This class consists of a single layer of cells, and is subdivided into three varieties.

Pavement or Squamous Epithelium. Pavement epithelial cells are fine thin plates placed edge to edge like the particles in a mosaic pattern or the stones of a pavement. These cells form the alveoli of the lungs. They are found whenever a very smooth surface is essential as in the lining of the heart, lining of blood vessels and lymphatics, the serous membranes. When lining these structures the epithelial covering or lining is called *endothelium*.

Columnar Epithelium forms a single layer of cells which line the ducts of most glands, the gall bladder, the alimentary canal,

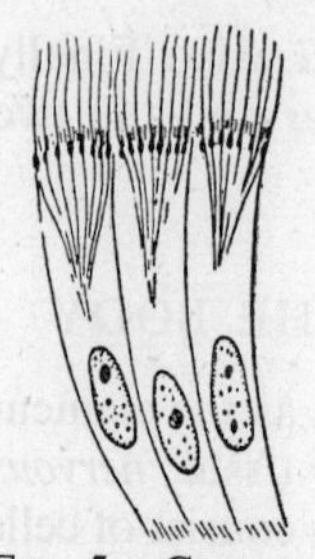

FIG. 5.—CILIATED COLUMNAR EPITHELIAL CELLS. Showing hair-like projections.

the genito-urinary tract and the surface of mucous membranes which open on to the exterior of the body.

The illustration Fig. 4 shows columnar cells from the intestine; these have a slightly striated border. In some situations, as when lining the alveoli of secreting glands, the cells of columnar epithelium are short and have a cubical appearance—they are then described as *cubical* cells (*see* Fig. 8).

Ciliated Epithelium, is found lining the air-passages and their ramifications such as the frontal and maxillary sinuses. It also lines the uterine tubes or oviducts and part of the uterus and the ventricles of the brain.

Ciliated cells are like columnar cells in shape, but they have in addition fine hair-like processes attached to their free edge. These processes are called *cilia*. The ciliary processes keep up a continual movement directed towards the external opening. This movement has been likened to the movement seen in a field of corn, blown in one direction by the wind. In the respiratory passages the constant movement prevents dust, mucus, etc., entering the lungs, and in the uterine tubes the movement conveys the ovum into the uterus.

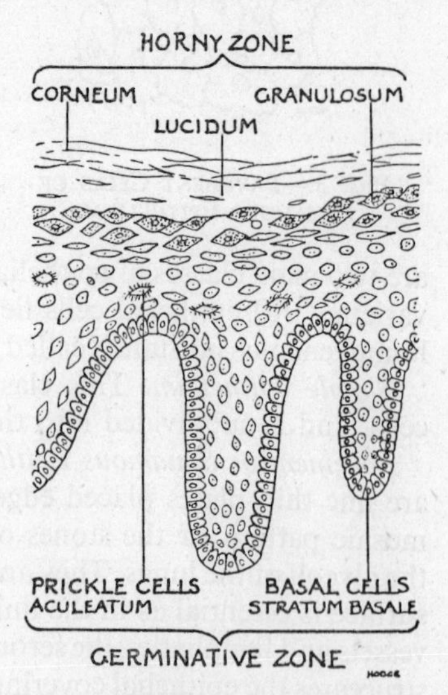

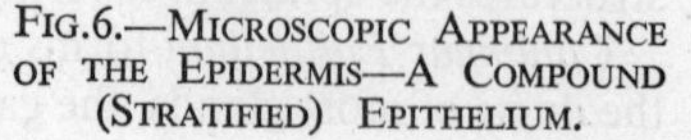

FIG.6.—MICROSCOPIC APPEARANCE OF THE EPIDERMIS—A COMPOUND (STRATIFIED) EPITHELIUM.

Goblet Cells are mucus-secreting cells which lie in the walls of glands and ducts lined by columnar cells, either plain or ciliated. Goblet cells secrete mucus or mucin and express it on to the surface, they act as mucus-secreting glands and are most numerous where a considerable amount of mucus covers the surface as in the stomach, colon, and trachea.

Compound Epithelium. This class of epithelial tissue consists of more than one layer of cells. There are two varieties.

Stratified Epithelium forms the epidermal layers of the skin; it also lines the mouth, pharynx, oesophagus and the lower part of the urethra, the anal canal and the vagina, and it covers the surface of the cornea.

The outer layers of cells near the surface comprise the *horny layer* of the skin; these cells are flattened and resemble scales. The deepest layer of cells are columnar in shape. These form the *germinative layer* and here the cells multiply by karyokinesis, pushing those above them nearer the surface until the superficial ones are cast off.

The cells between the basal layer and the horny zone are called 'prickly cells', they are connected to each other by fine tendrils which give them a prickly appearance when examined under the microscope.

Transitional Epithelium is a compound stratified epithelium consisting of several layers of cells. It lines the urinary bladder, the pelvis of the kidney, the ureters and the upper part of the urethra. The deeper layers of cells in transitional epithelium are of the columnar type of cell with rounded ends which make them pyriform or pear-shaped. As the cells in the deeper layers multiply by dividing, the superficial layers of cells are cast off. The superficial cell layers in transitional epithelium are less scale-like than those of stratified epithelium. Comparison of the illustrations Figs. 6 and 7 will make clear this point.

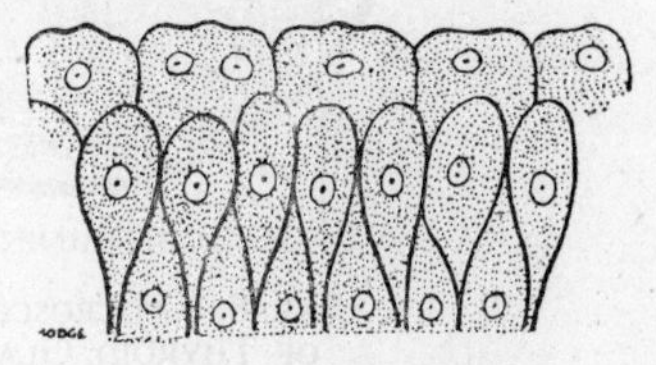

FIG. 7.—TRANSITIONAL EPITHELIUM FROM THE BLADDER.

FUNCTIONS OF EPITHELIAL TISSUE

Protective. The epithelial tissue which forms the covering of the body, the skin, and the lining of the cavities which open on to the surface is mainly protective. It prevents injury to the underlying tissues, prevents the loss of fluid from these tissues and also prevents the passage of fluid into the structures which are covered by skin. Micro-organisms cannot pass through healthy skin but they can and do pass through abraded skin.

Secretory. Most of the secreting glands and their ducts are composed of columnar epithelium. Very often the epithelium lining the gland and its duct is continuous with that of the surface in which the glands lie. Simple tubular and simple

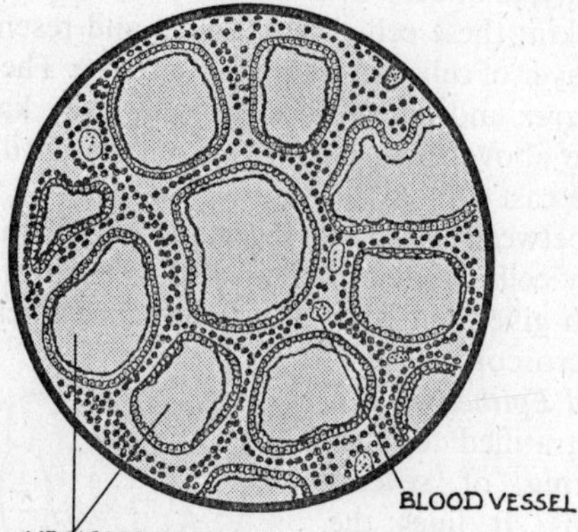

FIG. 8.—MICROSCOPIC APPEARANCE OF THYROID GLAND STRUCTURE.
The Vesicles are lined with cubical (culumnar) Epithelial Cells.

saccular glands are just involutions from the surface such as the simple tubular glands of the intestine as shown in Fig. 9. When these involutions branch, the structure becomes more complicated, as in the formation of *compound tubular glands* such as those of the kidney, and *compound racemose* or *saccular glands* such as the salivary glands and the pancreas.

The endocrine glands are also composed of epithelial cells which may be massed together or may line hollow vesicles as occurs in the thyroid gland where the vesicles are lined by columnar epithelial cells, cubical in shape. These cells produce their secretion—colloid—but there is no duct from these glands and therefore the secretion reaches the blood stream either directly or through the lymphatics.

Glands. A gland is a *secretory organ* which may exist as a separate organ such as the liver, pancreas, and spleen; or may be simply a layer of cells as the *simple tubular glands* of the alimentary tract (*see* Fig. 9). All glands are liberally supplied

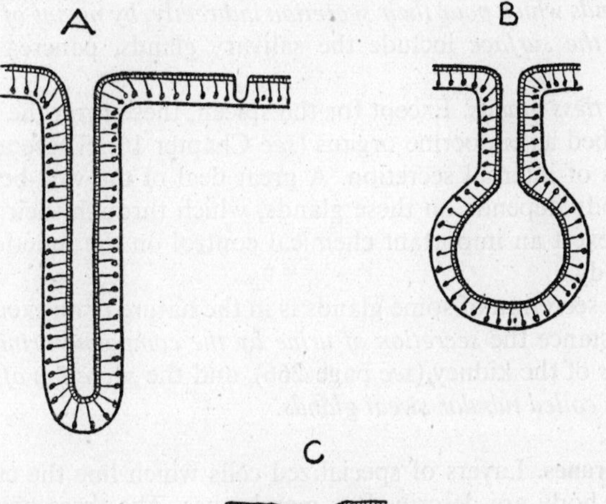

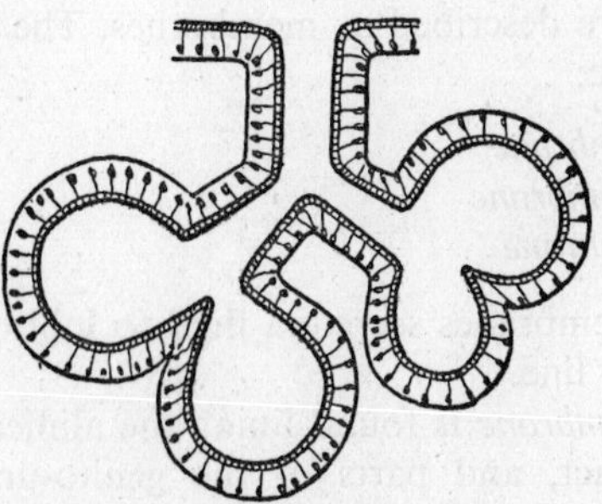

FIG. 9.—TYPES OF GLANDS.

A. A simple tubular gland such as is found in the intestine. Note the ruptured goblet cell.
B. A simple saccular gland.
C. A compound saccular or racemose gland such as the salivary glands.

with blood; their special function is to select from the blood stream certain substances, which they then elaborate into their important juices or secretions.

There is a tremendous variety of glands, each with its different function, making a collective description and classification difficult. A simple classification might be attempted as follows:

Glands which pour their secretion directly on to the surface include the sweat glands, sebaceous glands, and the gastric and intestinal glands.

Glands which pour their secretion indirectly, by means of ducts, on to the surface include the salivary glands, pancreas, and liver.

Ductless glands. Except for the spleen, these form the group described as endocrine organs (*see* Chapter 16). These are the glands of internal secretion. A great deal of the well-being of the body depends on these glands, which through their secretions exert an important chemical control on the functions of the body.

The secretion of some glands is in the nature of an excretion, for instance the *secretion of urine by the compound uriniferous tubules* of the kidney (*see* page 266), and the *secretion of sweat* by the *coiled tubular sweat glands.*

Membranes. Layers of specialized cells which line the cavities of the body are described as membranes. The three principal membranes are:

Mucous membrane
Synovial membrane
Serous membrane

All these membranes secrete a fluid to lubricate or moisten the cavity they line.

Mucous Membrane is found lining the alimentary tract, the respiratory tract, and parts of the genito-urinary tract. A mucous membrane is composed of columnar epithelial cells which may or may not be ciliated. These cells lie closely packed together. Some of them become distended with mucous secretion and are then called *goblet cells.* The cell becomes more and more distended and finally ruptures and discharges its secretion on to the surface (*see* Fig. 9).

Mucus is the secretion of the membrane and consists of water, salts, and a protein, *mucin,* which gives the sticky or viscid character to the secretion.

Synovial Membrane lines the cavities of joints. It consists of fine connective tissue, with a layer of squamous endothelial cells on the surface. The secretion of synovial membrane is thick and glairy in character.

Serous Membranes are found in the chest and abdomen, covering the organs contained therein and lining these cavities.

The pleura covers the lungs and lines the thorax.

The pericardium covers the heart as a double layer.

The peritoneum covers the abdominal organs and lines the abdomen. (These membranes are described in the chapters dealing with these various organs.)

The characteristics which are common to all three serous membranes are, that each consists of a double layer of membrane having an intervening potential cavity which receives the fluid secreted by the membrane. This *serous fluid* is very similar to blood serum or lymph. It acts as a lubricant, and in addition it contains protective substances, and removes harmful products, passing these on to the lymphatic system to be dealt with.

MUSCULAR—NERVOUS—CONNECTIVE TISSUE

Muscular Tissue. Muscle is a tissue which has the power of contraction and by means of this movements are performed. It is composed of cylindrical fibres which correspond to the cells of other tissues. These are bound together into little bundles of fibres by a form of connective tissue which contains a highly specialized contractile element. The chemical *composition of muscle* is 75 per cent water and 25 per cent solids; of these about 18 per cent is protein and the remainder gelatine,

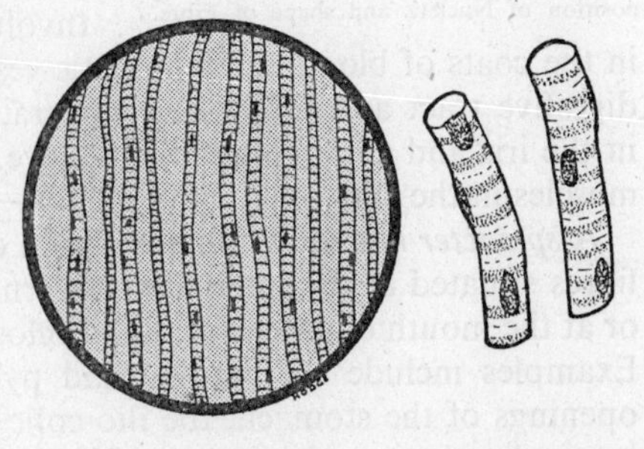

FIG. 10.—MICROSCOPIC VIEW OF VOLUNTARY STRIATED SKELETAL MUSCLE FIBRES. Inset, diagrams of two Muscle Fibres showing position of Nuclei.

fats, and salts. Muscular tissue is classified according to its function.

Voluntary muscle is under the control of the will. It is striped in appearance, as the individual fibres are transversely striated by alternate light and dark markings; for this reason it is also sometimes described as *striped* or *striated muscle*. Each fibre is enclosed in a fine membrane—the *sarcolemma* (meaning—muscle sheath). A number of fibres are massed together to form bundles; many of these bundles are bound together by connective tissue to form large and small muscles. When a muscle contracts it shortens, and each individual fibre takes part in the movement by contracting. This class forms the skeletal muscles.

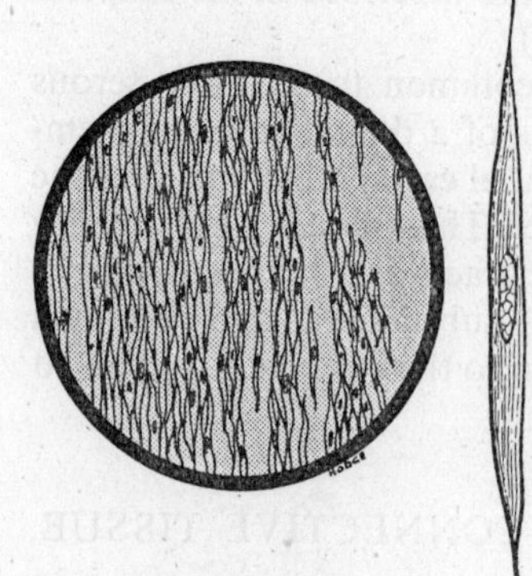

FIG. 11.—MICROSCOPIC VIEW OF PLAIN NON-STRIATED MUSCULAR TISSUE.

Inset, a smooth Muscle Fibre showing position of Nucleus and shape of Fibre.

Involuntary muscle is not controlled by the will. With the exception of cardiac muscle (*see* below) this variety is composed of elongated spindle-shaped muscle cells which retain the appearance of a cell. These have no markings and are therefore sometimes described as *plain* or *unstriped muscle*.

Involuntary muscle is found in the coats of blood and lymphatic vessels, in the walls of the digestive tract and the hollow viscera, trachea, and bronchi, in the iris and ciliary muscle of the eye, and in the involuntary muscles in the skin.

A *sphincter muscle* is composed of a circular band of muscle fibres situated at the internal or external openings of a canal, or at the mouth of an orifice, tightly closing it when contracted. Examples include the cardiac and pyloric sphincters at the openings of the stomach, the ilio-colic sphincter or valve, the internal and external spincters of the anus and urethra.

Cardiac muscle is found only in the muscle of the heart, and unlike other involuntary muscle, it is vaguely striated. Its fibres or cells are short and branching (*see* Fig. 12), they are arranged longitudinally as in striated muscles, are characteristically red in colour and not controlled by the will.

Cardiac muscle possesses the special property of *automatic rhythmical contraction* independent of its nerve supply. This function is described as *myogenic* as distinct from neurogenic. Normally the action of the heart is controlled by its nerve supply (*see* page 138), and this special myogenic function is only called upon under any adverse conditions when for some reason the nerve supply is interfered with.

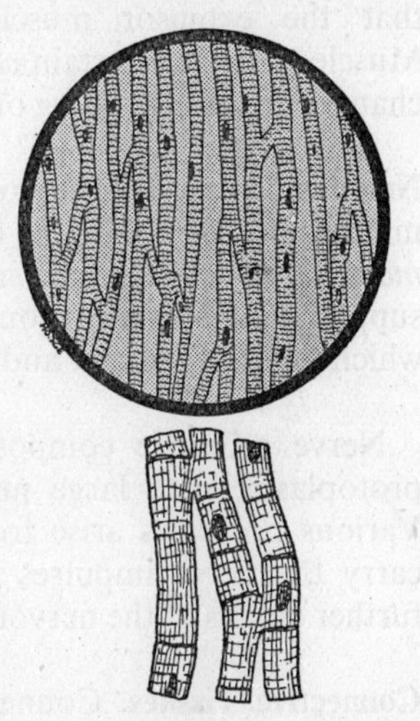

FIG. 12.—MICROSCOPIC VIEW OF CARDIAC MUSCLE SHOWING THE CHARACTERISTIC BRANCHING OF ITS FIBRES.
Above is design of Cardiac Muscle Fibres.

Muscular Contraction. Muscular tissue is extensible and elastic, which means it can be stretched and will then contract and return to its former size and shape. When a muscle is stimulated a short *latent period* follows, during which it is taking up the stimulus. It then *contracts*, during which it becomes short and thick, and finally it *relaxes and elongates*. The rate at which a muscle will contract is determined by a variety of factors, principally:

The *strength of the stimulus*, e.g. an electrical current may be applied weak or strong,

The *weight the muscle* is required to move, it can be imagined that a weight might be employed which would be difficult to move and therefore the muscle could only contract slowly,

Fatigue, as a muscle becomes tired its contractions get more sluggish,

Temperature. As a rule muscle contracts best in a warm environment. Generally speaking, cold stimulates the contraction at first, but if persisted in, a cold environment causes the subsequent contractions to become sluggish in character.

Muscle tone. Muscle is never completely at rest; it may appear to be, but it is always in a condition of muscle tone, which means always on the alert ready to respond to stimuli. The *knee-jerk* obtained by sharply tapping the patellar tendon results in slight extension of the knee joint, demonstrating that the extensor muscles are in a condition of tone. Muscle also has a certain *chemical tone*, meaning that chemical changes are always going on even when the muscle is at rest.

Nervous Tissue. The nervous tissue consists of three kinds of matter, (*a*) *grey matter*, forming the nerve cells, (*b*) *white matter*, the nerve fibres, and (*c*) *neuroglia*, a special type of supporting substance found only in the nervous system, which holds together and supports nerve cells and fibres.

Nerve cells are composed of highly specialized granular protoplasm, with large nuclei and cell walls as other cells. Various processes arise from the nerve cells; these processes carry the nerve impulses to and from the nerve cells. (For further details of the nervous tissue, *see* Chapter 20.)

Connective Tissues. Connective tissue makes up all the solid parts of the body which are not included in the previous three groups. There are several varieties of connective tissue.

Areolar tissue. This consists of loosely woven tissue which is distributed widely throughout the body. It is placed immediately beneath the skin and mucous surfaces forming the sub-cutaneous and sub-mucous tissue, and it also forms the sheaths of fascia which support and bind and connect together muscles, nerves, blood vessels, and other organs.

Areolar tissue consists of a matrix of intercellular substance in which lie connective tissue cells and into which are woven bundles of *fine white fibres*, composed of wavy strands, running through the matrix in every direction and so arranged that they form a network. These fibres consist of collagen, a gelatinous substance, and they are held together by mucin. *Elastic fibres* which are yellow in appearance and composed of elastin also form part of the structure. These fibres are fine and they appear taut and straight. The tissue spaces in which lymph collects are large, and it is from the lymph contained in them that most of the nourishment of areolar tissue is derived. These lymph spaces communicate with each other, and it is here, in these, that many of the immunizing substances which protect the body from disease are formed. The *ground-substance* of areolar tissue is an almost transparent fluid containing mucin. Different types of cells lie in this ground substance including the connective tissue cells (*see* Fig. 13).

Retiform (reticular) *lymphoid* or *adenoid* tissue is similar to areolar but the *ground-substance* is of lymph, and in some situations as in the tonsils it contains numerous lymphocytes. It contains fewer white fibres than areolar tissue.

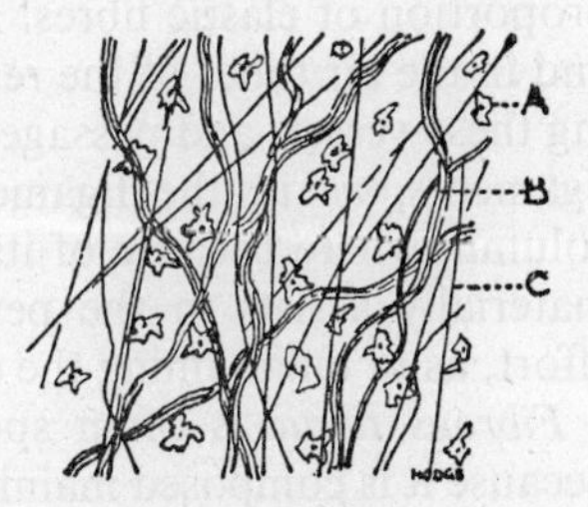

FIG. 13.—AREOLAR TISSUE.
A. Connective Tissue Cells.
B. White Fibres.
C. Elastic Fibres.

Jelly-like tissue or *mucous connective tissue* is present in many situations in the developing embryo and it is found at birth in *Wharton's jelly* of the umbilical cord. It is found in the adult *only* in the vitreous humour of the eye. It is a soft jelly-like substance, semi-fluid in character and it contains a few cells and collagen fibres but no elastic fibres.

Adipose tissue. Adipose or fatty tissue is deposited in most parts of the body. It is associated with areolar tissue by the deposition of fat cells and is present in all subcutaneous tissue except that of the eyelids and the penis, and inside the cranial cavity.

It consists of minute lobules composed of globules of fat surrounded by protoplasm, forming fat cells. The substance contained in the cell is made up of compounds of fatty acid and glycerin (*see* the digestion of fat, page 180). Adipose tissue has a very liberal blood supply; each lobule possesses a network of capillary blood vessels which closely surrounds the fat cells contained in it. Adipose tissue performs a number of functions.

To help support and retain in position the organs of the body. It is well known that the kidneys, for example, are deeply embedded in fat.

To form a protective covering for the body.

To act as a store of material which when required can be re-absorbed and, by combustion in the tissues during metabolism provide a source of heat and energy for the use of the body.

Elastic tissue. This form of connective tissue contains a large proportion of elastic fibres. It is found in the walls of arteries and in the air tubes of the respiratory tract and assists in keeping these vessels and passages open. It is also present in certain ligaments, as in the ligamentum sub-flava of the vertebral column, where because of its elastic and extensible qualities it materially assists in the performance of sustained muscular effort, as in maintaining the erect position of the spine.

Fibrous tissue is often spoken of as a *white fibrous tissue* because it is composed mainly of white collagen fibres arranged in definite lines. This arrangement gives great strength and fibrous tissue is found where resistance is required. Between the definite bundles of white fibres some areolar tissue lies, which contains the nerves, lymphatics, and blood vessels supplying the structure.

Fibrous tissue is tough and strong. It forms ligaments, except the elastic ones, and tendons. The dura mater lining the skull and neural canal, the periosteum covering bone, the strongest layers of fascia separating muscular sheaths, the fibrous layer of the pericardium, and the sclerotic coat of the eye, are examples of fibrous tissue.

Cartilage or gristle is a dense, clear blue-white substance, very firm but less firm than bone. It is found principally at joints and between bones. The bones of the embryo are first cartilage, then the growing centres persist as cartilage and when adult age is reached cartilage is found covering the bone ends. Cartilage does not contain blood vessels but is covered by a membrane, the *perichondrium*, from which it derives its blood supply.

There are three main varieties of cartilage which demonstrate the characteristics of this substance—firmness, flexibility and rigidity.

Hyaline cartilage, in which the ground substance or matrix is almost clear and does not contain fibres, is firm and elastic, it is found covering the ends of the long bones as articular cartilage, in the costal cartilages, in the nose, larynx, trachea, and bronchial tubes where it keeps open the orifices. It is also the temporary cartilage from which bone is formed. The cells of hyaline cartilage are arranged principally in small groups (*see* Fig. 14) set in a matrix of homogeneous substance.

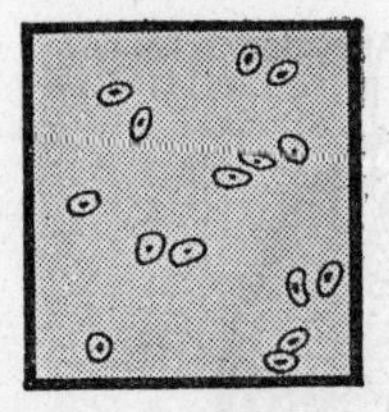

FIG. 14.—HYALINE, ARTICULAR CARTILAGE SHOWING CELLS LYING IN A HOMOGENEOUS MATRIX.

FIG. 15.—FIBRO-CARTILAGE SUCH AS THE INTERVERTEBRAL DISCS ARE COMPOSED OF, SHOWING THE CELLS ARRANGED BETWEEN BUNDLES OF FIBRES.

White fibro-cartilage which is composed of bundles of fibres having the cartilage cells arranged between the bundles of fibres. It is found where great strength is required. Fibro-cartilage deepens the cavities of bony sockets, as in the acetabulum of the innominate bone, and the glenoid cavity of the scapula. It also forms the inter-articular cartilages, as in the semilunar cartilages of the knee, and the connecting cartilages, as in the intervertebral discs of the vertebral column and in the pad of cartilage at the symphysis pubis.

Elastic cartilage is often called *yellow elastic cartilage* because it contains a great many elastic fibres which are yellow. It is found in the lining of the ear, the epiglottis and the

Eustachian (pharyngotympanic) tubes, when compressed or bent it is very flexible and readily springs back into shape.

The Structure of Bone. Bone forms one of the hardest of the connective tissues of the body. It is composed of nearly 50 per cent water; the remaining solid parts are divided into a composition of mineral matter, principally calcium salts 67 per cent, and animal matter 33 per cent.

The structure of bone may be examined by the naked eye when the gross structure is seen, and with the aid of a microscope, when the minute structure is examined.

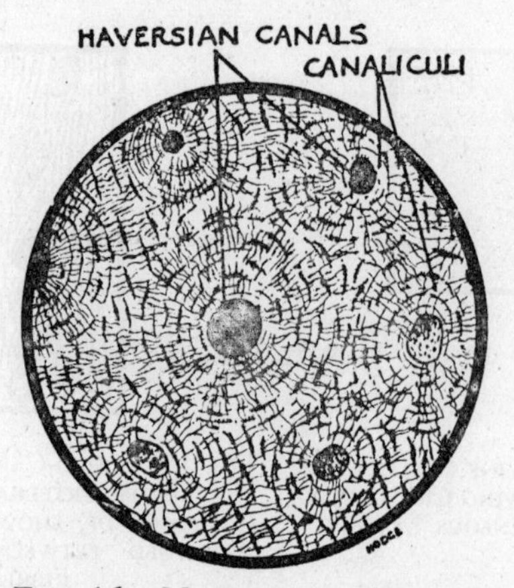

FIG. 16.—MICROSCOPIC VIEW OF TRANSVERSE SECTION OF COMPACT BONE SHOWING HAVERSIAN CANALS, LAMELLAE IN CONCENTRIC RINGS AND CANALICULI.

Bone consists of two kinds of tissue: compact tissue and cancellous tissue.

Compact bone tissue is hard and dense; it is found in flat bones and in the shafts of the long bones, and as a thin covering over all bones.

Cancellous bone tissue is spongy in structure. It is found principally in the ends of the long bones, in the short bones, and as a layer in between two layers of compact tissue in the flat bones.

The gross structure of a long bone. A long bone shows both varieties of bone tissue. The best way to examine the gross structure is to have a long bone sawn through longitudinally when the distribution of compact and cancellous tissue can be seen. It is divided into a shaft, the central part, and two extremities or ends of the bone. If the shaft is cut across, dense bone tissue will be seen and a hollow centre called the medullary canal,

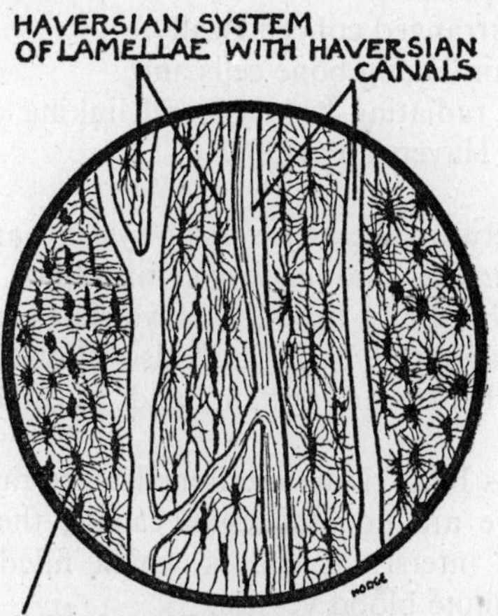

FIG. 17.—MICROSCOPIC VIEW OF LONGITUDINAL SECTION OF COMPACT BONE SHOWING HAVERSIAN SYSTEM OF LAMELLAE AND CANALS, AND ALSO THE INSTERSTITIAL ARRANGEMENT OF BONE STRUCTURE BETWEEN THE HAVERSIAN SYSTEMS.

containing yellow bone marrow. If the end of a long bone is cut, the spaces in the cancellous tissue will be seen containing red bone marrow. In the yellow marrow fat cells predominate; in the red marrow red blood cells are very numerous. The red bone marrow is the birthplace of the red blood cells.

Minute structure. A transverse section of compact bone (Fig. 16) shows a wonderful design mapped out in circles. In the centre of each circle is a *Haversian canal.* The plates of bone or *lamellae* are arranged concentrically around the central canal, in between these plates are minute spaces called *lacunae*, these spaces contain bone cells and the spaces are connected to each other and to the central Haversian canal by minute canals called *canaliculi*. Each pattern so formed is a *complete Haversian system* composed of:

A central *Haversian canal* containing nerves, blood vessels, and lymphatics,
Lamellae arranged concentrically,
Lacunae containing bone cells and
Canaliculi radiating between and linking up the lacunae and the Haversian canals.

The areas between these Haversian systems are composed of *interstitial lamallae*, and *canaliculi* arranged somewhat differently. Fig. 17 shows how the Haversian canals run longitudinally through the bone and also shows the difference between the Haversian system and inter-Haversian bone structure.

In cancellous bone tissue the lamellae are rather irregularly arranged, there are no Haversian canals, the blood vessels ramify in the interstitial spaces which filled with marrow support the minute blood vessels.

Bone is covered by a vascular membrane, the periosteum, except at the articular surfaces where it is covered by hyaline cartilage.

Periosteum. Periosteum is a fibrous membrane covering bone. It is rich in blood vessels, and invests the bone closely. The blood vessels from the periosteum ramify in the bone substance, and in this way help to supply the bone with blood. In growing bone a layer of bone-forming cells lies between the periosteum and the bone and from multiplication of these cells, the bone grows in circumference. In addition to blood derived from the periosteum the long bones are supplied with blood by a special nutrient artery, which pierces the bone obliquely at a protected part of it—in the case of the long bones of the upper extremity, in a direction towards the elbow, and those of the lower extremity, in a direction away from the knee. The *nutrient foramina* are well marked in the long bones.

The Development and Growth of Bone. Bone develops either from cartilage or from membrane. The flat bones ossify in membrane and are called *membrane bones* and the long bones in cartilage, called *cartilage bones.*

Membranous ossification. The connective tissue membrane from which the flat bones develop such as those of the skull, face and clavicle is very richly supplied with blood. As development progresses bone-forming cells are laid down. Ossification begins at defined centres, and proceeds by the mutliplication of cells within the membrane until a delicate network of bone is formed. Fresh osteoblasts or bone-building cells are formed and the bone increases in thickness. Eventually a flat bone is produced which consists of two layers of hard compact bone, separated by an interstitial layer of bone resembling cancellous bone tissue, and covered by periosteum.

Cartilaginous ossification. In the developing embryo all the long bones are first represented by rods of cartilage covered by perichondrium. A *primary centre of ossification* called the diaphysis appears at the middle of what will eventually be the shaft of a long bone and proceeds towards the ends. The cartilage cells change their character and calcium is laid down in the matrix, *bone cells* develop. The perichondrium becomes periosteum and from it bone cells are laid down so that the bone increases in circumference as well as in length. The growing bone now consists of a shaft, the *diaphysis* and two extremities, the *epiphyses.*

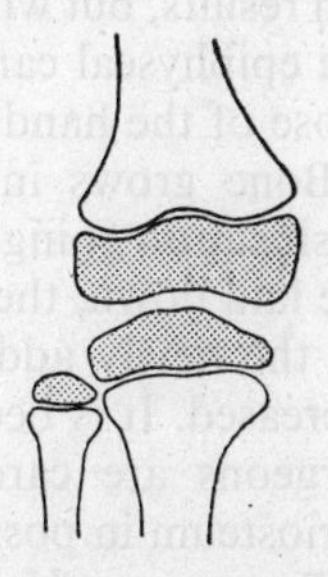

FIG. 18.—THE POSITION OF THE EPIPHYSEAL CARTILAGE IN THE LOWER EXTREMITY OF THE FEMUR AND THE UPPER EXTREMITIES OF THE TIBIA AND FIBULA.

Later in the process of development, a secondary centre of ossification appears at each extremity or *epiphysis* and ossification begins there and extends towards the shaft and also towards the end of each epiphysis. The ends of the bone remain covered by hyaline cartilage which becomes the articular cartilage. A layer of cartilage remains between the shaft or diaphysis and each extremity or epiphysis and this layer is called the *epiphyseal cartilage*. These epiphyseal cartilages persist until the bone is fully grown and then the cartilage ossifies and no further growth can take place. When the bones of a child are X-rayed there appears to be a gap between the shaft and epiphyses (*see* Fig. 18). There is no gap, the epiphyseal cartilage fills this area, but cartilage being less dense than bone it is not visible in the X-ray picture. If acromegaly occurs, which is brought about by disorder of the function of the anterior lobe of the pituitary gland (*see* page 246), before the epiphyseal cartilages have disappeared the condition of gigantism results, but when acromegaly occurs after the ossification of the epiphyseal cartilage then only certain bones are affected—those of the hands and jaw.

Bone grows in girth or circumference by the process of ossification going on beneath the periosteum; as the bone cells are laid down, the periosteum is pushed further from the bone by the newly added bone cells, and the girth of the bone is increased. It is because of this function of the periosteum that surgeons are careful, when removing bone, to replace the periosteum in position, for the formation of new bone from it.

Two types of bone cells set to work in the building of bone; *osteoblasts* which build bone, and *osteoclasts* which destroy bone. In this way the solid parts are formed and also the spaces, cavities and canals are constructed.

Chapter 2

THE SKELETON

The Skeleton is the bony framework of the body, which in certain parts is supplemented by cartilage. *Osteology* is the study of bones.

The skeleton is divided into:

The Axial Skeleton, comprises the head and trunk, and includes the following bones:

Skull, 22 bones Vertebral Column, 26 Hyoid bone, 1 Sternum and Ribs, 25	74

The Appendicular Skeleton, comprises the limbs.

Upper limb, 64 bones Lower limb, 62	126

In addition to these, there are six auditory ossicles in the middle ears, making a total of 206 bones.

Classification of Bones. The bones of the skeleton are classified according to their shape and formation.

Long Bones. These are found principally in the limbs. Each long bone consists of a shaft and two extremities. Long bones act as levers in the body and make movement easy.

Short Bones. Good examples of these are seen in the bones of the carpus and tarsus. They are composed largely of cancellous bone tissue as they require to be light and strong. They have a thin covering of compact tissue. Short bones give strength in support, as in the strength shown in the wrist.

Flat Bones consist of two layers of dense bone tissue with an intervening layer of spongy bone. These are found where protection is needed, as in the bones of the skull, the innominate bones, ribs and scapulae. Flat bones also afford large surfaces for the attachment of muscles, e.g. the scapula.

Irregular Bones are those which cannot be included in either of the other three classes. Examples of irregular bones are the vertebrae and some of the bones of the face.

The *Sesamoid Bones* are another group. These are developed in the tendons of muscles, and are found in the vicinity of a joint. The patella is the largest example of this type.

Terms used in describing Bones:

Border, a division between two surfaces of one bone,

Canal, or meatus, a bony tunnel, e.g. the external auditory meatus, the carotid canal,

Condyle, a large, rounded eminence usually at the end of a bone, as in the condyles of the femur and tibia,

Crest, a ridge on the top of a bone, as the crest of the iliac bone, or a narrow, sharp ridge in any position, e.g. the crest of the tibia,

Epicondyle, a projection above an articulating surface, as in the epicondyles of the humerus,

Foramen, a hole perforating a bone, e.g. the obturator foramen of the innominate bone,

Fossa, a depression in a bone, e.g. the olecranon and coronoid fossae on the humerus, the scapular fossae,

Groove, or *sulcus*, a furrow on a bone, e.g. the bicipital groove on the humerus,

Lamina, a thin plate of bone, as the laminae of the vertebrae,

Notch, an indentation in a bone; it may serve for the passage of blood vessels and nerves,

Process, a projection from a bone which may be sharp, as in the spinous processes of the vertebral column, or blunt, as in the coracoid and acromion processes on the scapula,

Spine, a sharp-pointed eminence, e.g. the spine of the scapula,

Surface, the flat parts of a bone, which may be divided by borders into anterior and posterior, superior and inferior, medial and lateral, surfaces, etc.,

Tubercle, a smaller process, e.g. the tubercle of the tibia, and,

Tuberosity or *trochanter*, a broad, rough process, as the tuberosities of the humerus and the trochanters of the femur.

THE SKULL

The bones of the skull are arranged in two parts—the *cranium* (sometimes called the *calvaria*) consists of eight bones, and the facial skeleton of fourteen bones.

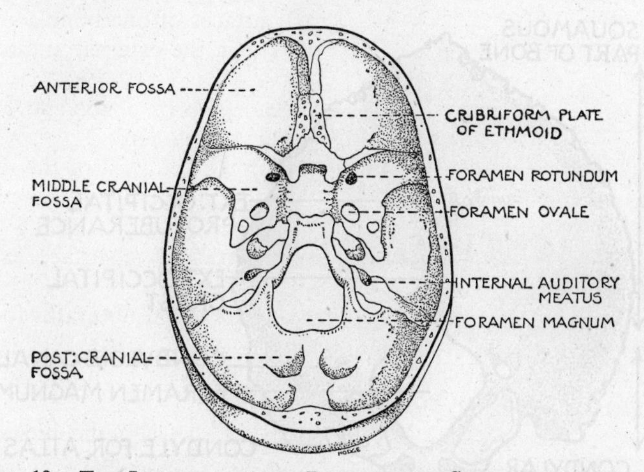

FIG. 19.—THE INTERIOR OF THE BASE OF THE SKULL, SHOWING THE ANTERIOR, MIDDLE, AND POSTERIOR CRANIAL FOSSAE.

The cavity of the cranium presents an upper surface known as the *vault of the skull*; this is smooth on its outer surface, and marked by ridges and depressions to accommodate the brain and its blood vessels on the inner surface. The lower surface of the cavity is known as the *base of the skull.* It is perforated by many holes for the passage of nerves and blood vessels. The base of the skull is divided into three fossae, an anterior, middle, and posterior fossa. The anterior fossa is formed by the horizontal plates of the frontal bone; the middle by the sphenoid bone and the petrous portion of the temporal bones; and the posterior fossa mainly by the occipital bone, *see* Fig. 19.

Cranial Bones:

1 Occipital	2 Temporal
2 Parietal	1 Sphenoid
1 Frontal	1 Ethmoid

The Occipital Bone is at the back and lower part of the cranial cavity. It is pierced by the *foramen magnum*, through

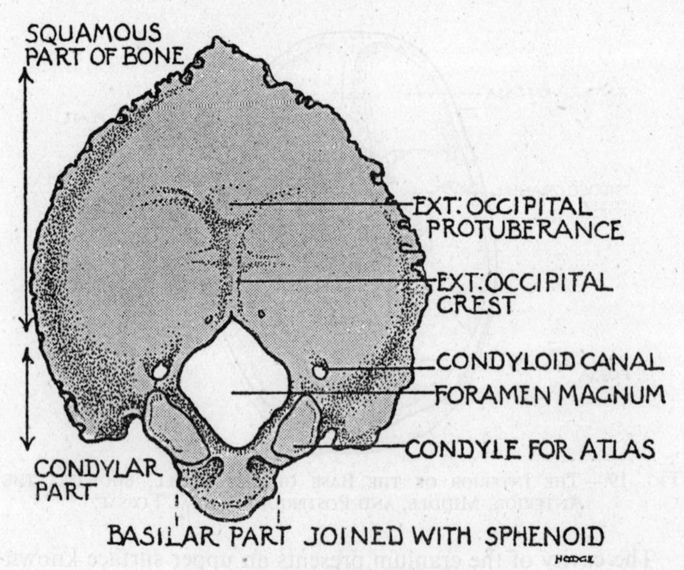

Fig. 20.—The Occipital Bone.

which the spinal cord passes from the brain. Each side of the foramen magnum are masses of bone which form the *condyles of the skull* and present articulating surfaces for the atlas. The flat surface behind the foramen magnum is named the *squamous part* of the occipital bone. The *basilar* part lies in front and fuses with the sphenoid bone when ossification is complete. The occipital bone is marked by lines and ridges externally, for the attachment of muscles and ligaments. Internally it shows four fossae; the upper two receive the posterior part of the cerebrum and the lower two the hemispheres of the

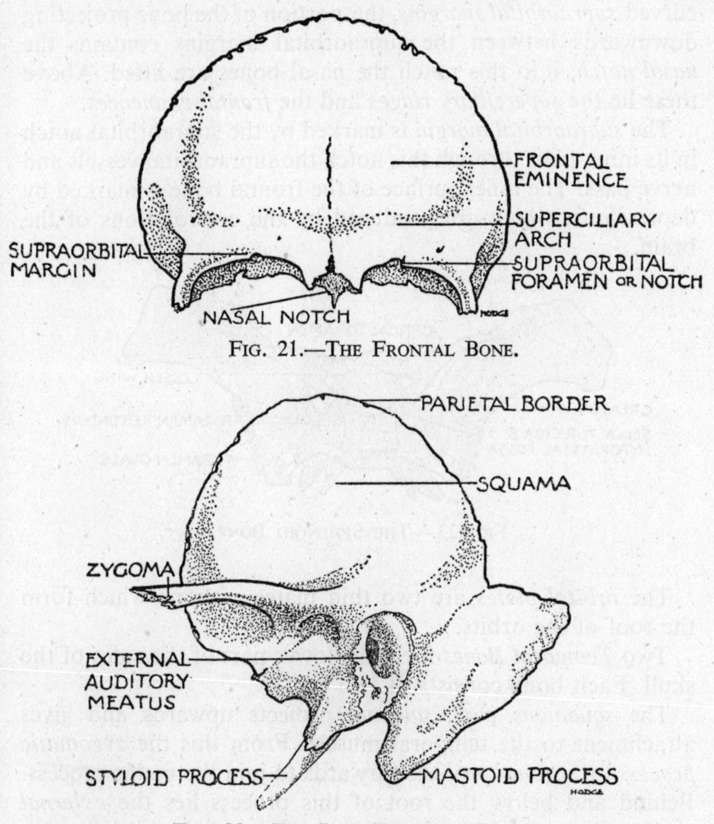

FIG. 21.—THE FRONTAL BONE.

FIG. 22.—THE LEFT TEMPORAL BONE.

cerebellum. Ridges between these fossae give attachment to portions of the dura mater.

The two Parietal Bones together form the roof and sides of the skull. The outer surface is smooth, but the inner surface is marked by deep furrows which lodge the cranial arteries.

A very large furrow about the middle of the bone lodges the *middle meningeal* artery.

The Frontal Bone forms the forehead and the upper part of the orbital cavities. The arches of the orbits are formed by the curved *supraorbital margins*, the portion of the bone projecting downwards between the supraorbital margins contains the *nasal notch*, into this notch the nasal bones are fitted. Above these lie the *superciliary ridges* and the *frontal eminences*.

The *supraorbital margin* is marked by the supraorbital notch in its inner half; through this notch the supraorbital vessels and nerve pass. The inner surface of the frontal bone is marked by depressions, which are produced by the convolutions of the brain.

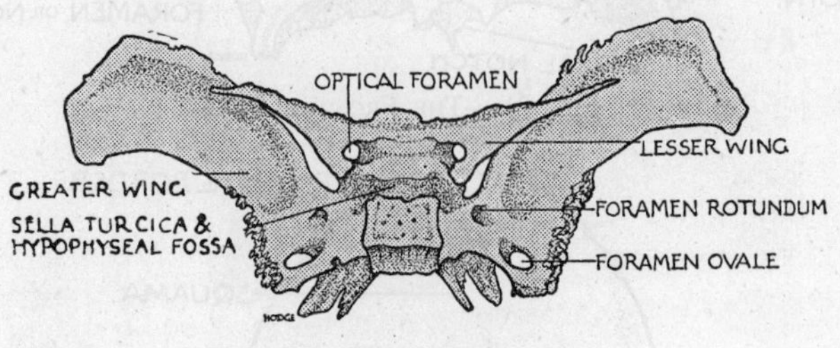

FIG. 23.—THE SPHENOID BONE.

The *orbital plates* are two thin plates of bone which form the roof of the orbits.

Two *Temporal Bones* form the lower part of the sides of the skull. Each bone consists of two parts:

The *squamous* part, *squama*, projects upwards and gives attachment to the temporal muscle. From this the *zygomatic process* or *zygoma* projects forwards to join the malar process. Behind and below the root of this process lies the *external auditory meatus*.

The *mastoid portion* lies behind and it is continued downwards as the *mastoid process*; its outer surface gives attachment to the sterno-mastoid muscle. The mastoid process contains spaces known as the *mastoid air cells* and a particularly large space lying a little in front of these is named the *tympanic antrum*, this space is lined with epithelium which is continuous with that of the middle ear or tympanic cavity. Infection spreading from the middle ear may lead to suppuration in the tympanic antrum.

Below the meatus a sharp process called the *styloid process* projects downwards.

The *petrous* portion of the temporal bone is wedged in at the base of the skull and contains the hearing apparatus.

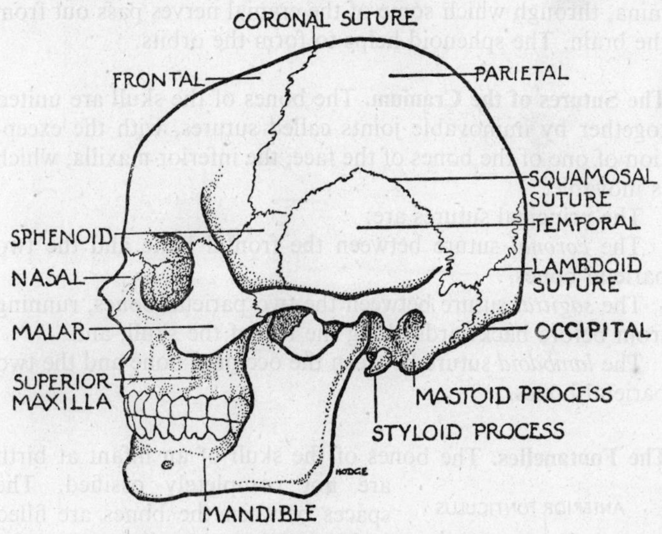

FIG. 24.—THE LEFT SIDE OF THE SKULL.

The Ethmoid is a light spongy bone, cubical in shape, situated at the roof of the nose wedged in between the orbits. It consists of two lateral masses or *labyrinths* composed of the ethmoidal cells or sinuses, which are closed except where they communicate with the nasal cavity. The ethmoid contains also a *perpendicular plate* and a *cribriform plate*. The perpendicular plate forms the upper part of the nasal septum. The cribriform plate fits into a notch in the frontal bone. Above this plate the olfactory bulbs lie, and through the perforations in the plate filaments of the olfactory nerves pass to the upper part of the nose (see page 316).

The Sphenoid is similar in shape to a bat with wings outstretched, it consists of a body and two greater and two lesser wings. The body shows a depression named the *sella turcica* which lodges the *pituitary gland* or *hypophysis cerebri.*

It lies at the base of the skull and forms a large part of the middle cranial fossa (*see* Fig. 19), and lies wedged in between the frontal bone anteriorly and the basilar portion of the occipital bone posteriorly. It is perforated by numerous foramina, through which some of thc cranial nerves pass out from the brain. The sphenoid helps to form the orbits.

The Sutures of the Cranium. The bones of the skull are united together by immovable joints called sutures, with the exception of one of the bones of the face, the inferior maxilla, which is movable.

The principal sutures are:

The *coronal* suture between the frontal bone and the two parietal bones,

The *sagittal* suture between the two parietal bones, running from before backwards along the top of the skull, and

The *lambdoid* suture between the occipital bone and the two parietal bones.

The Fontanelles. The bones of the skull of an infant at birth are not completely ossified. The spaces between the bones are filled in by membrane, and at the angles of the bones these membranes are called fontanelles. The largest of these is situated at the junction of the frontal and the two parietal bones, where the coronal and sagittal sutures meet. This is called the *anterior fontanelle*. It is shaped like a lozenge, measures about one and a half inches from back to front, and forms a soft spot on the head of an infant through which the brain can be felt pulsating. It

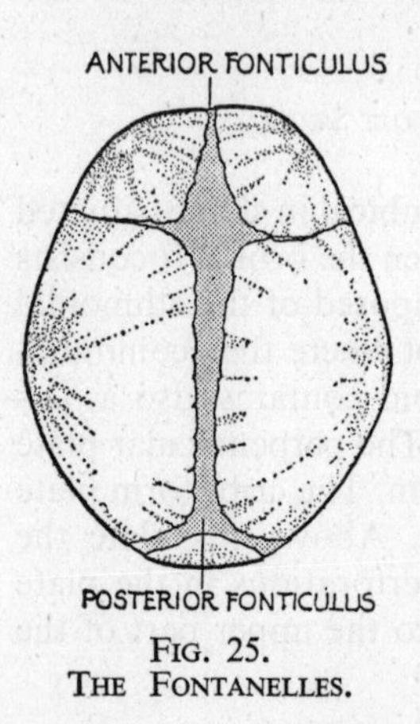

FIG. 25.
THE FONTANELLES.

is important to remember that this fontanelle normally closes at the age of eighteen months.

The *posterior fontanelle* lies at the back, at the junction of the two parietal and the occipital bones. It closes soon after birth.

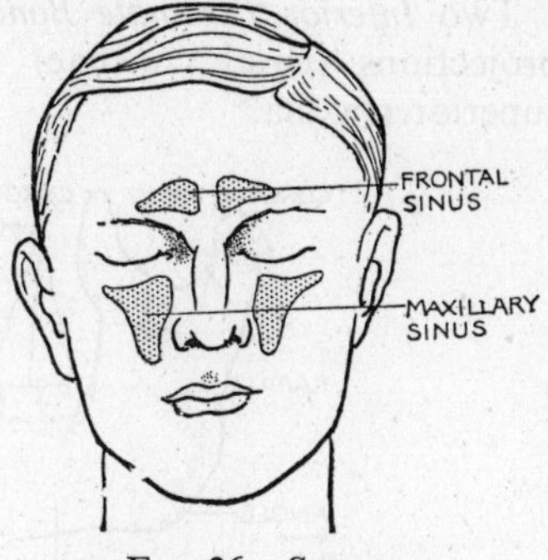

FIG. 26.—SINUSES.

The Sinuses of the Skull. Several cavities or chambers are contained in the bones of the skull. The *frontal*, *maxillary*, *ethmoid*, and *sphenoid sinuses* communicate with the nose. The *mastoid antrum* communicates with the tympanic cavity.

The *frontal sinuses* lie in the frontal bone, one on each side at the root of the nose above the inner angle of the eye. The *maxillary sinuses*, sometimes known as the *antra of Highmore*, lie one on each side of the nose in the superior maxillary bones. A number of small spaces known as the *mastoid cells* lie in the temporal bones; the *mastoid antrum* is the largest of these and lies in the mastoid process.

Bones of the Face. There are fourteen facial bones, all except the lower maxilla being united by sutures and immovable.

Two *Nasal Bones* form the bridge of the nose.

Two *Palate Bones* form the roof of the mouth and the floor of the nose.

Two *Lacrimal Bones* form the tear ducts and part of the orbit at the inner angle of the eye, through which the fluid from the eye is carried to the nasal cavity.

Two *Malar* form the cheek bones. Processes from these bones unite with the zygomatic processes of the temporal bones to form the *zygomatic arch*.

One *Vomer* forms the lower part of the bony partition in the nose. (The upper part of the nasal septum is formed by the perpendicular plate of the ethmoid.)

Two *Inferior Turbinate Bones* are the two larger of three projections (nasal conchae) from the lateral wall of the superior maxilla.

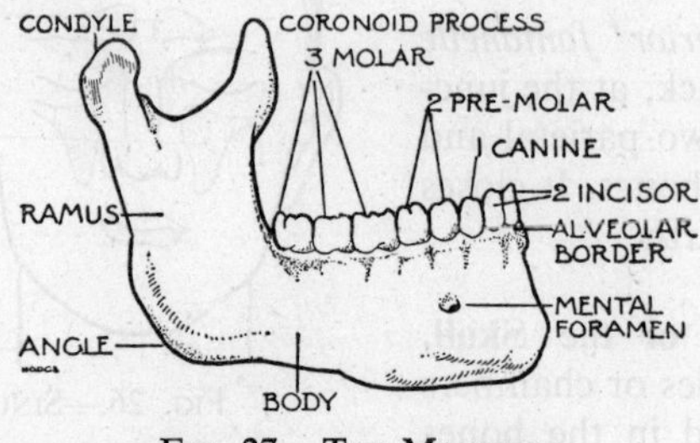

FIG. 27.—THE MANDIBLE.

Two *Superior Maxillae* form the upper jaw and contain the upper teeth. The body of the maxilla contains a large cavity, the maxillary sinus, or antrum of Highmore which communicates with the nasal cavity by two small openings.

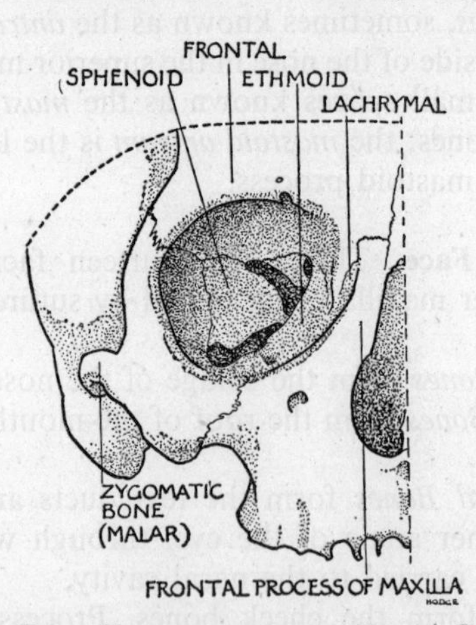

FIG. 28.—THE BONY FORMATION OF THE RIGHT ORBITAL CAVITY.

One *Inferior Maxilla* or *Mandible* forms the lower jaw. It is the only movable bone in the skull. It consists of a *body* which is the central curved horizontal part containing the lower teeth and for ming the chin, and two upright portions called *rami*, one at each side. Where the ramus joins the body of the mandible at each side is the *angle of the jaw*.

The ramus terminates above in two processes, the *coronoid process* in front and the *condyle of the jaw*, or as it is sometimes called, the *head* of the mandible which lies behind. This mandibular head or condyle articulates with the temporal bone to form the *temporo-mandibular joint*.

The Formation of the Orbit. The orbits are two deep cavities in the upper part of the face, for the protection of the eyes. The roof of the orbit is formed by the frontal bone and the floor by the superior maxillary bone. At the back lies the sphenoid. The margins of the orbit are formed by the frontal bone above, the malar to the outer side, and the superior maxillary bone to the inner side. The optic nerve enters the orbit through the optic foramen of the sphenoid.

The Formation of the Nose. The bony framework of the nose, or the nasal fossae, is composed of two cavities about the middle of the face, separated from each other by a thin partition, which extends from the palate up to the frontal bone.

The nasal cavities are bounded by the cribriform plate of the ethmoid bone which forms the roof, the superior maxilla and the palate bones the floor and the superior maxillary bones the outer walls. The inferior turbinate bones project inwards from the outer walls formed by the superior maxillary bones. The nasal bones form the bridge of the nose, and the partition between the two cavities is formed by the vomer, which is the bony foundation of the nasal septum. The nasal cavity communicates with the sinuses of the frontal, ethmoid, maxillary and sphenoid bones. Infection may spread from the nasal cavity to these sinuses.

For the bony formation of the mouth, *see* page 189.

THE THORAX

The skeleton of the thorax is made up of bone and cartilage. The thorax is a cone-shaped cavity, broader below than above, and longer behind than in front.

It is formed by the twelve thoracic vertebrae at the back, the sternum in front, and the twelve pairs of ribs at the sides, which encircle the trunk from the vertebral column behind to the sternum in front. (*See* Thoracic cavity, page 227).

The Sternum. The sternum or breast-bone is a flat bone divided into three parts.

The Manubrium Sterni is a triangular-shaped piece of bone placed abovc the body of the sternum. It articulates with the clavicles at its upper and outer aspect on each side by means of the *clavicular notch.* These articulations are separated by the *suprasternal* or *jugular notch.*

The first pair of ribs articulates with the sides of the manubrium, and the second pair at the junction of the manubrium and the body of the sternum. The joint between the manubrium sterni and the *gladiolus* or body of the sternum is a symphysis; a pad of cartilage separates the joint surfaces. This junction is called the *angle of Ludwig.* It corresponds in position to the level of the second rib.

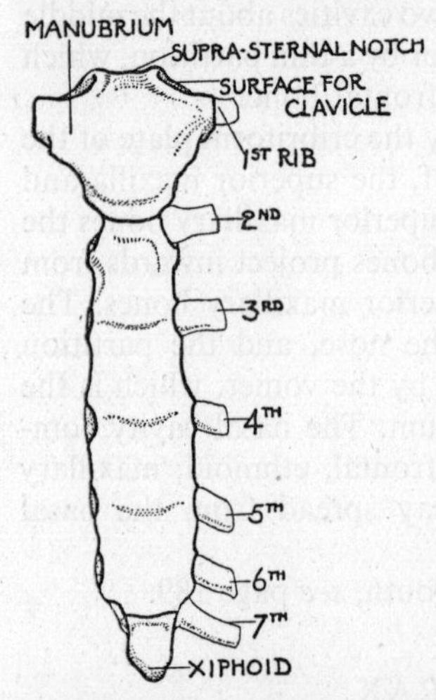

FIG. 29.—THE ANTERIOR ASPECT OF THE STERNUM, SHOWING THE ARTICULATING SURFACES FOR THE CLAVICLE AND THE UPPER SEVEN PAIRS OF RIBS.

The Body of the Sternum is long and narrow and notched on each side for the attachment of the costal cartilages of the third, fourth, fifth, sixth, and seventh ribs.

The Ensiform Process or *Xiphoid Bone* is the lowest part of the sternum. It is cartilaginous in youth but ossifies in older subjects. The diaphragm, the linea alba, and the rectus abdominis are attached to the ensiform process.

The Ribs. There are twelve pairs of ribs. They are attached behind to the thoracic vertebrae, articulating with them by means of facets on the sides of the bodies of the vertebrae, and on the transverse processes, which correspond with similar facets on the head of each rib.

The upper seven pairs of ribs are attached to the sternum anteriorly by means of their costal cartilages. Of the lower five pairs of ribs, the eighth, ninth, and tenth are attached indirectly to the sternum by means of the attachment of their costal cartilages to the cartilage of the rib above. The last two pairs of ribs are unattached in front. *See* fig. of skeleton.

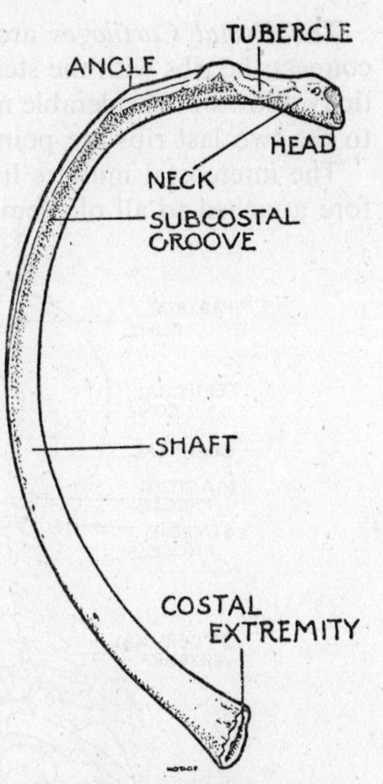

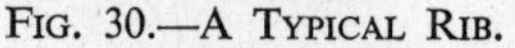
Fig. 30.—A Typical Rib.

The ribs are named according to their anterior attachments. The upper seven pairs are the *true ribs* because they are attached directly to the sternum. The lower five pairs are *false ribs*, so-called because they are only indirectly attached to the sternum. The two lowermost pairs of false ribs being unattached in front, are called *floating ribs*.

A rib is described as a long bone. It has two extremities, anterior and posterior, and a shaft. The vertebral or posterior extremity of the rib presents a head, a neck, and a tubercle. The anterior or sternal end has a depression for the attachment of the costal cartilage. The shaft is thin and flat, it has an inner and an outer surface and an upper and lower border; the internal surface is smooth and is marked by a groove, the *subcostal groove* in which lie the intercostal vessels and nerve.

The ribs slope downwards from back to front. The posterior extremity of the rib is the more fixed point and the anterior end the more movable. By reason of the elasticity of the costal cartilages the movements of the ribs in respiration are very free.

The *Costal Cartilages* are bars of hyaline cartilage which connect the ribs with the sternum, and by means of their elasticity allow of considerable movement. The cartilages attached to the two last ribs are pointed.

The intercostal muscles lie between the ribs and are therefore attached to all of them.

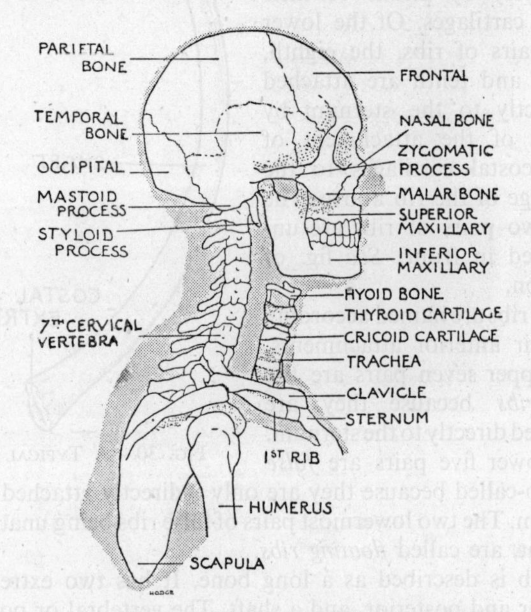

FIG. 31.—SHOWING POSITION OF DIFFERENT PARTS OF THE SKELETON IN RELATION TO THE CERVICAL VERTEBRAE.

THE VERTEBRAL COLUMN

The vertebral or spinal column is a flexible structure formed by a number of bones called vertebrae. Between each two bones the column is supplemented by pads of cartilage. The adult column measures 24 to 28 inches in length. There are 33 vertebral bones, 24 of these are separate bones and the remaining 9 vertebrae are fused to form 2 bones.

The vertebrae are grouped and named according to the region they occupy.

Seven *cervical vertebrae* form the neck or cervical region.

Twelve *thoracic* or *dorsal vertebrae* form the back of the thorax or chest.

Five *lumbar vertebrae* form the lumbar region or loins.

Five *sacral vertebrae* form the sacrum.

Four *coccygeal vertebrae* form the coccyx or tail.

The vertebrae in the three upper regions remain separate or distinct throughout life, and are called *movable vertebrae.* Those in the two lower regions, the sacrum and coccyx, are united in the adult to form two bones. These are called the *fixed vertebrae.*

With the exception of the first two cervical vertebrae, all the movable vertebrae have similar characteristics.

Characteristics of a Typical Movable Vertebra. A typical vertebra consists of two parts, an anterior part called the *body*, and a posterior part called the *neutral arch.*

In the articulated skeleton the bodies of the vertebrae lie one on top of the other like a column of bricks, forming a pillar to support the head. The body of the vertebra lies in front, and passing backwards from it is the neural arch, which in the articulated column forms the *neural canal* or *vertebral foramen* and serves for the passage and protection of the spinal cord. At each side between every two articulated vertebrae is an opening for the passage of nerves to and from the spinal cord. These openings are called the *intervertebral foramina.*

The body of the vertebra is the largest part of the bone. The upper and lower surfaces of it are roughened for the attachment of the intervertebral discs of cartilage. In front it is perforated by small holes, *foramina*, for the passage of the nutrient vessels to the bone. From the back of the body springs the neural arch.

The *neural arch* begins by the projection backwards of two thick processes of bone from the body. These are called *pedicles.* The pedicles are notched above and below, and in the articulated column the lower notch of the pedicle above forms the top, and the upper notch of the pedicle below the bottom, of the intervertebral foramina previously mentioned. Directed backwards from the pedicles on each side are plates of bone called *laminae*. Each pair of laminae unite in the middle line at the back and complete the neural arch.

Several processes of bone arise from the neural arch:

The *spinous process* which is directed backwards at the junction of the laminae behind,

The *transverse processes* which arise one on each side at the point where the pedicles and laminae meet, and

The *articular processes* which project upwards and downwards. In addition two superior articular processes and two

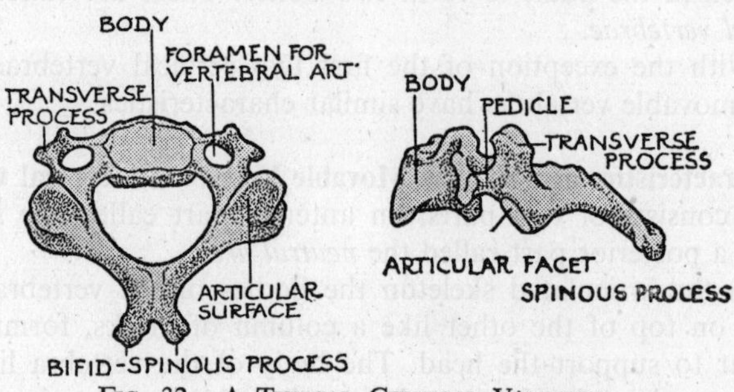

FIG. 32.—A TYPICAL CERVICAL VERTEBRA.

inferior processes arise from each vertebra. The inferior articular processes of the bone above, articulating with the superior articular processes of the bone below, form joints posteriorly between the vertebra.

The body of the vertebra is composed of cancellous bone tissue, covered by a thin layer of compact tissue. The neural arch and the processes arising from it have a thick covering of compact tissue.

The movable vertebrae in the different regions of the column vary in the characteristics common to a vertebra.

The Cervical Vertebrae are the smallest of the bones, and except the first and second, which are peculiar in shape, the cervical vertebrae possess the following characters in common. The bodies are small and oblong in shape, broader from side to side than from before backwards. The neural arch is large. The spinous processes are divided or bifid. The transverse processes are perforated by foramina for the passage of the vertebral arteries.

Special Cervical Vertebrae. The *first cervical vertebra* or *atlas* supports the head and consists of a complete ring of bone

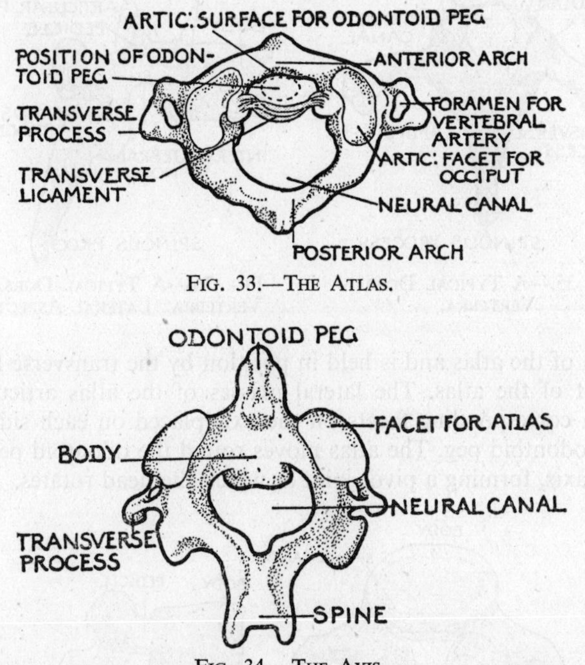

FIG. 33.—THE ATLAS.

FIG. 34.—THE AXIS.

composed of two lateral masses united by an anterior and a posterior arch. On its upper surface it presents kidney-shaped facets for articulation with the condyles of the occipital bone, forming a condyloid joint, the *atlanto-occipital joint*, at which the nodding movements of the head take place. Below, the atlas articulates with the second cervical vertebra.

The *second cervical vertebra* or *axis* is the pivot on which the atlas turns in the rotary movements of the head. From the body of the axis a process of bone rises which is called the *odontoid peg*, this peg articulates with the back of the anterior

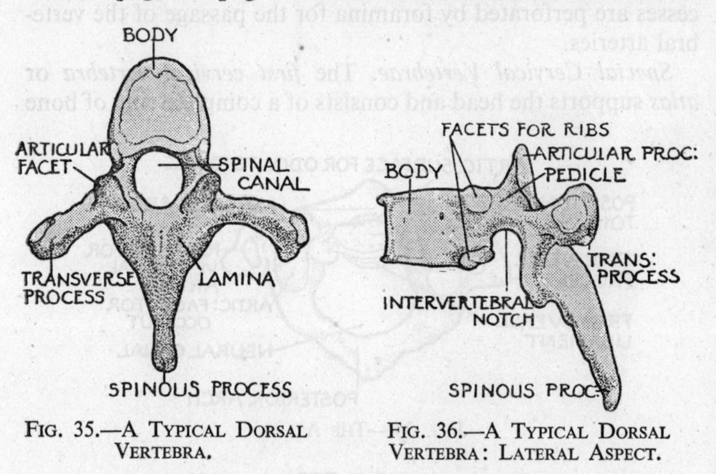

FIG. 35.—A TYPICAL DORSAL VERTEBRA.

FIG. 36.—A TYPICAL DORSAL VERTEBRA: LATERAL ASPECT.

arch of the atlas and is held in position by the transverse ligament of the atlas. The lateral masses of the atlas articulate with corresponding facets on the axis placed on each side of the odontoid peg. The atlas moves round the odontoid peg of the axis, forming a pivot joint at which the head rotates.

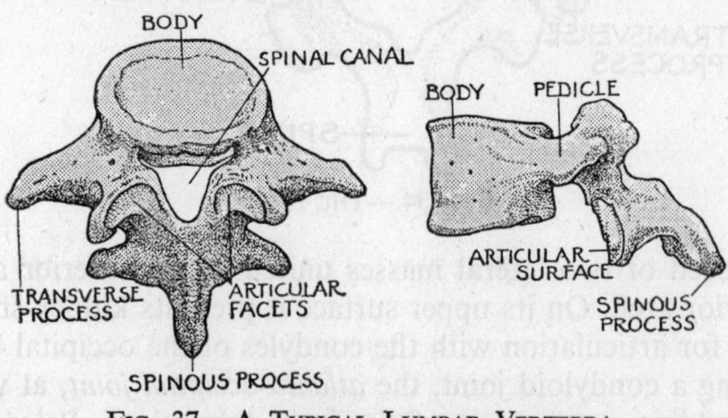

FIG. 37.—A TYPICAL LUMBAR VERTEBRA.

The *seventh cervical vertebra* is the first vertebra with an undivided spinous process. This process has a tubercle at its tip. It forms a distinct projection in the neck and can be seen at the lower part of the back of the neck. Because of this characteristic the bone is called the *vertebra prominens.*

The Dorsal or Thoracic Vertebrae are larger than the cervical and they increase in size as they extend downwards. A typical dorsal vertebra presents the following characteristics. The body is heart-shaped, with facets on each side for attachment of the ribs, the neural arch is relatively small, the spinous process

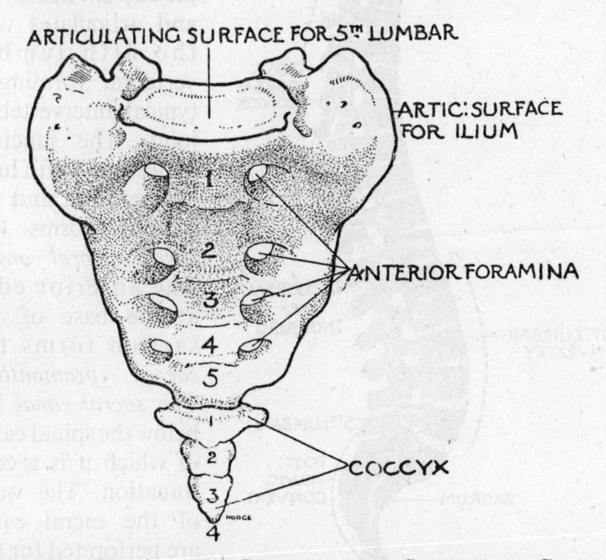

FIG. 38.—THE ANTERIOR SURFACE OF THE SACRUM AND COCCYX.

is long and is directed downwards, and the transverse processes which help to support the ribs are thick and strong.

The Lumbar Vertebrae are the largest. The body is very large compared with the bodies of the other vertebrae. The spinous process is broad and hatchet-shaped. The transverse processes are long and slender. The fifth lumbar vertebra articulates with the sacrum at the lumbo-sacral joint.

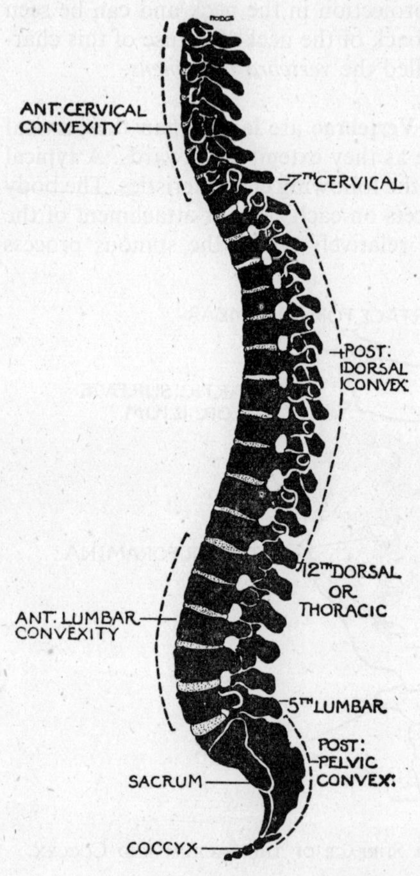

FIG. 39.—THE CURVES OF THE VERTEBRAL COLUMN.

The Sacrum is a triangular bone situated at the lower part of the vertebral column, wedged in between the two innominate bones, and forming the back of the pelvic cavity. The *base of the sacrum* lies above and articulates with the fifth lumbar vertebra, forming a typical intervertebral joint. The junction between the fifth lumbar vertebra and the sacrum forms the *sacrovertebral angle*. The anterior edge at the base of the sacrum forms the *sacral promontory*. The *sacral canal* lies below the spinal canal of which it is a continuation. The walls of the sacral canal are perforated for the passage of the sacral nerves. Rudimentary spinous processes can be seen on the posterior aspect of the sacrum. The *anterior surface of the sacrum* is concave and shows four transverse ridges, which mark the points of union of the five sacral vertebrae. At the extremities of these ridges, on each side, are holes for the passage of nerves. These are called the *sacral foramina*. The *apex of the sacrum* articulates with the coccyx. At the sides the sacrum articulates with the innominate bones, forming the right and left sacro-iliac joints.

The Coccyx is composed of four or five rudimentary vertebrae, fused to form one bone. It articulates above with the sacrum.

The Curves of the Vertebral Column. Looked at from the side, the vertebral column presents four antero-posterior curves: the *cervical curve* in the neck which is convex forwards, the *thoracic* or *dorsal curve*, convex backwards, the *lumbar curve*, convex forwards, and the *pelvic curve*, convex backwards.

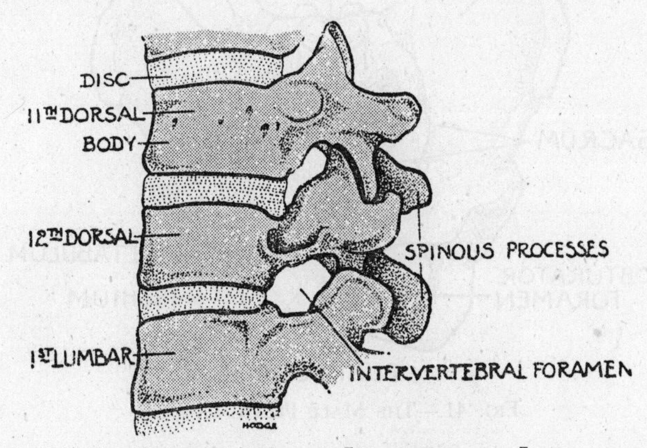

FIG. 40.—THE LATERAL ASPECT OF INTERVERTEBRAL JOINTS OF THE DORSAL-LUMBAR REGIONS.

The two posterior curves are called *primary curves*, and are present before birth (the dorsal and pelvic curves). The two anterior curves are the *secondary curves*.

The cervical curve develops as the infant begins to control the movements of its head, and the lumbar curve develops later when the child begins to learn to walk.

The Joints of the Vertebral Column. These are cartilaginous joints formed by pads of fibro-cartilage placed between each two vertebrae, strengthened slightly by ligaments running in front and behind the vertebral bodies throughout the entire length of the column. Masses of muscle on each side materially aid in the stability of the spine.

The Intervertebral Discs are thick pads of cartilage between the bodies of the vertebrae from the first cervical vertebra to the sacrum. These discs vary in shape and thickness in the different parts of the column, and thereby help in the formation of the curves.

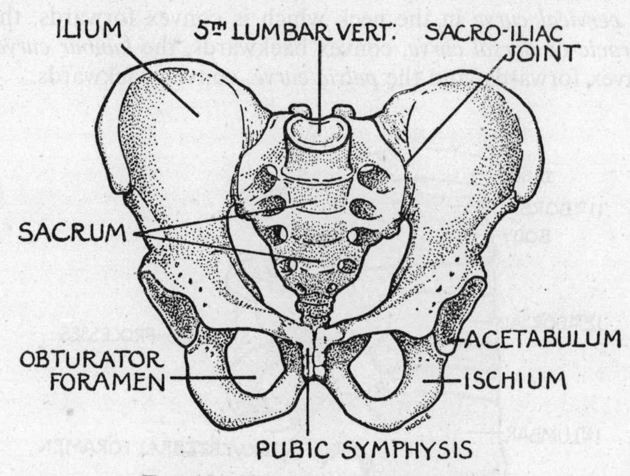

FIG. 41.—THE MALE PELVIC GIRDLE.

The *ligamenta flava* connect together the laminae of the vertebral arches. This ligament contains elastic tissue and by its extensibility assists muscular action in maintaining the erect position of the trunk.

The joints formed between the discs and the vertebrae are only slightly movable joints of the symphysis variety. But the great number of these joints, each permitting slight movement, gives considerable flexibility to the column as a whole.

The Functions of the Vertebral Column. The vertebral column acts as a rigid support to the body, yet at the same time, by means of its intervertebral discs of cartilage which act as buffers and its curves which give flexibility, the spine serves to absorb shock set up when moving the weight of the body as in running and jumping, much in the same way as the curved springs and spring links of a vehicle absorb the direct shocks from the road. In this way the brain and spinal cord are protected from shocks and jars, which is one of the most important functions of the vertebral column.

The vertebral column also supports the weight of the body, affords surfaces for the attachment of muscles, and forms a strong posterior boundary for the cavities of the trunk.

THE PELVIC GIRDLE

The pelvic girdle is the means of connexion between the trunk and lower extremities. This girdle is formed by part of the axial skeleton—the *sacrum* and *coccyx* being wedged in between the *two innominate bones* which form part of the lower extremity.

The pelvis is divided into the *true pelvis* or pelvic basin which lies below the brim, and the *false pelvis* formed by the ilaic bones extending above the brim. The *inlet* of the true pelvis is the brim, formed by the promontory of the sacrum, the ilio-pectineal line (on each side), and the crest of the pubic bones. The *outlet* is bounded by the coccyx and the ischial tuberosities.

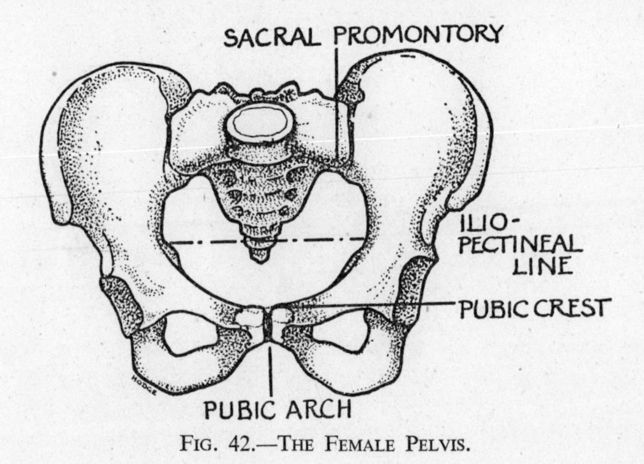

FIG. 42.—THE FEMALE PELVIS.

The *female pelvis* is wider and consequently shallower than the male pelvis, as it is adapted for the passage of the foetal head in childbirth. The inlet is larger and more circular, the cavity wider and shallower, the symphysis pubis is less deep and the pubic arch is wider. The ischial tuberosities are further apart and the coccyx is more movable.

Joints of the pelvis. The *sacro-iliac joint* is an articulation between the auricular surfaces of the ilium and the sides of the sacrum. Only slight movement is possible at this joint as very strong ligaments unite the articulating surfaces of this joint limiting movement in all directions.

The *symphysis pubis* is a cartilaginous joint between the pubic bones, which are separated by a pad of cartilage.

Chapter 3

THE SKELETON OF THE UPPER LIMB

The skeleton of the upper limb is attached to the skeleton of the trunk by means of the shoulder girdle, which consists of the *clavicle* and *scapula.*

Below this the following bones form the skeleton of arm, forearm, and hand, making altogether thirty-two bones:

Humerus	5 Metacarpals
Ulna and Radius	14 Phalanges
8 Carpal bones	

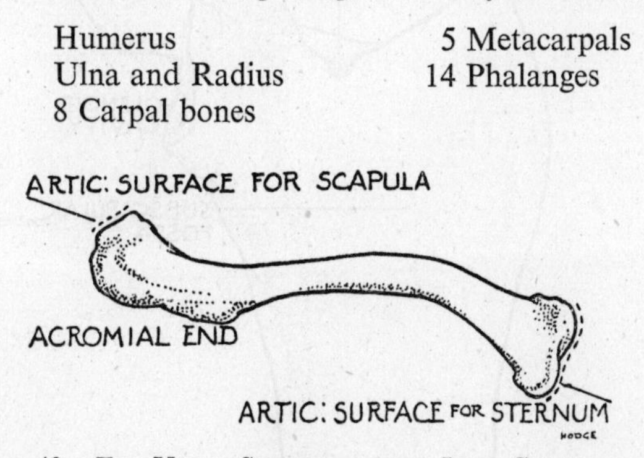

FIG. 43.—THE UPPER SURFACE OF THE LEFT CLAVICLE.

The Clavicle or collar bone is a long curved bone forming the anterior part of the shoulder girdle. It presents for examination a shaft and two extremities. The medial extremity is called the *sternal extremity* and articulates with the sternum. The lateral, the *acromial extremity*, articulates with the acromion process of the scapula. The clavicle also presents superior and inferior surfaces and anterior and posterior borders.

Muscle attachments: Pectoralis major, sterno-cleido-mastoid, deltoid, trapezius.

SCAPULA

The scapula forms the posterior part of the shoulder girdle and lies at the back of the thorax superficially to the ribs.

It is a triangular flat bone presenting for examination two surfaces, three angles, and three borders.

The Surfaces of the Scapula. The anterior or costal surface is called the *subscapular fossa*, and lies nearest the ribs. It gives attachment to the subscapularis muscle. The posterior or dorsal surface is divided by a prominent ridge of bone, called the

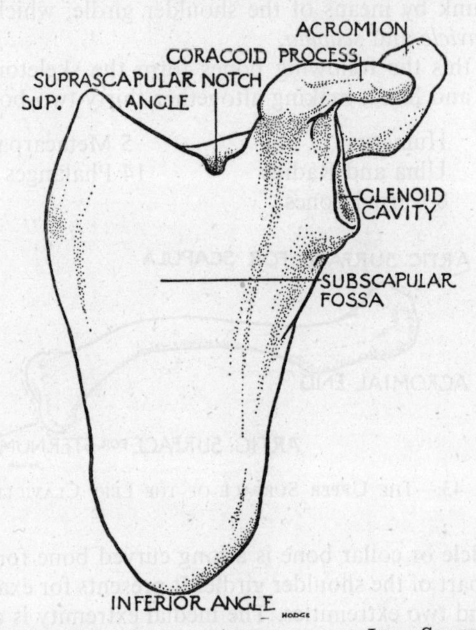

FIG. 44.—THE ANTERIOR ASPECT OF THE LEFT SCAPULA.

spine of the scapula, which passes across it to end in the *acromion process*, which overhangs the shoulder joint. The surface above the spine is the *supraspinous fossa*, which gives attachment to the supraspinatus muscle; that below the spine the *infraspinous fossa*, to which the infraspinatus muscle is attached.

The spine of the scapula gives attachment on its upper border to the trapezius muscle, and on the lower border, including the acromion process, to the deltoid.

The Borders of the Scapula. The *superior border*, which is at the upper part, extends from the superior angle to the base of the *coracoid process*. At the inner extremity of this border is the *suprascapular notch*, through which the scapular vessels pass.

The *vertebral* or *medial border* is that nearest the vertebral column, extending from the superior to the inferior angle.

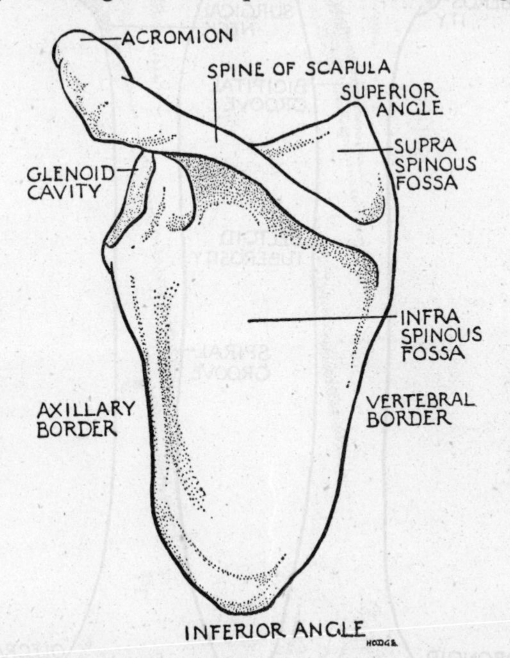

FIG. 45.—THE POSTERIOR ASPECT OF THE LEFT SCAPULA.

The *axillary* or *lateral border* is that nearest the axilla. It is also called the external border. It lies between the inferior angle and the glenoid cavity of the scapula.

The Angles of the Scapula. The *superior angle* lies at the junction of the superior and the vertebral borders. The *inferior angle* is the lowest point of the scapula, at the junction of the axillary and vertebral borders. The *external* or *lateral angle* or the head

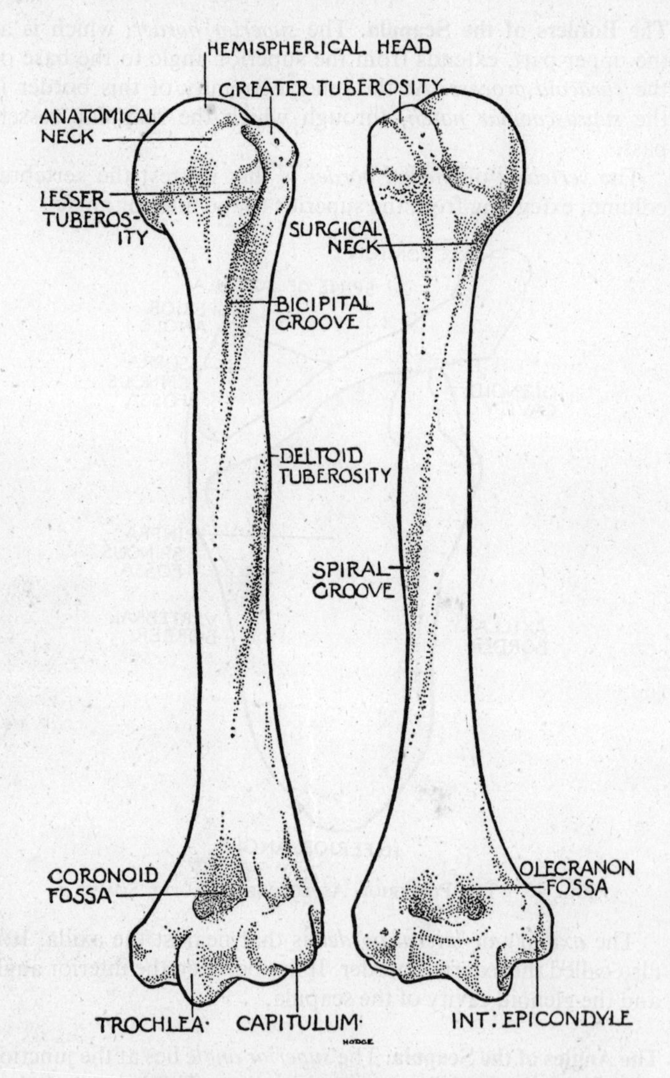

FIG. 46.—THE ANTERIOR AND POSTERIOR ASPECTS OF THE LEFT HUMERUS.

of the scapula is thick and strong. It presents the *glenoid cavity*, which is a shallow cavity directed outwards to receive the head of the humerus in the formation of the shoulder joint (humero-scapular joint). The long head of biceps brachii comes from above the glenoid cavity.

The *coracoid process* of the scapula arises internal to the glenoid cavity and projects forward. It gives attachment to the short head of biceps and to the coraco-brachialis.

HUMERUS

The humerus is a long bone, the longest bone of the upper limb. It presents a shaft and two extremities.

The Upper Extremity of the Humerus consists of a *hemispherical head*, which articulates with the glenoid cavity of the scapula in the formation of the shoulder joint. Immediately below the head is a slightly constricted part called the *anatomical neck*. To the outer side of the upper extremity, below the anatomical neck, is a rough prominence, the *greater tuberosity*, and at the front is a smaller prominence, the *lesser tuberosity* (*tubercle*). Between these tuberosities is a groove, the *bicipital groove* or *intertubercular sulcus*, in which the tendon of the biceps muscle lies. The bone becomes narrower below the tuberosities, and at this point it is called the *surgical neck*, because of the liability of fracture at that part.

The Shaft is rounded in its upper part, but becomes flattened from side to side as it approaches the lower extremity. A rough tubercle on the lateral aspect of the shaft, just above the middle, is called the *deltoid tuberosity* or *tubercle*. It receives the insertion of the deltoid muscle. A groove runs obliquely across the back of the shaft, from the medial to the lateral aspect. It gives passage to the radial or musculo-spiral nerve and is called the *spiral* or *radial groove*.

The Lower Extremity is broad and flat. At its lowest part the articulating surfaces for the bones of the forearm lie. The *trochlea* on the inner side is a pulley-shaped surface for articulation with the ulna and the *capitulum* on the outer side for the radius. Above the articulating surface for the ulna is a depression in front called the *coronoid fossa* of the humerus, into which the coronoid process of the ulna is received, when the elbow is flexed or bent. A large cavity, the *olecranon fossa*, lies in a similar position at the back of the bone, which receives the olecranon process of the ulna, when the elbow is extended or straight.

On each side of the articulating surfaces of the lower extremity are two *epicondyles*, the lateral or external epicondyle to the outer side, and the medial or internal epicondyle to the inner side. The lateral gives attachment to the extensor and supinator muscles of the forearm, the medial epicondyle to the flexors and the pronators. The medial epicondyle is larger than the lateral and is grooved by the ulna nerve.

ULNA

The ulna is a long bone having a shaft and two extremities. It is the innermost bone of the forearm, and is longer than the radius. The head of the ulna is at the lower end.

The Upper Extremity of the Ulna is strong and thick, and enters into the formation of the elbow joint. The *olecranon process* projects upwards at the back, and fits into the olecranon fossa of the humerus, when the elbow is straight.

The *coronoid process* of the ulna projects in front. It is smaller than the olecranon process, and it fits into the coronoid fossa of the humerus, when the elbow is bent.

The *greater sigmoid cavity* or *trochlear notch* of the ulna is formed by these two processes; it articulates with the trochlear surface of the humerus in the formation of the elbow joint. The *lesser sigmoid cavity* or *radial notch* is on the outer or lateral aspect of the upper extremity of the bone, near the coronoid process. The side of the head of the radius articulates with the lesser sigmoid cavity (radial notch) as the radius rotates round the ulna, thus forming the superior radio-ulnar articulation.

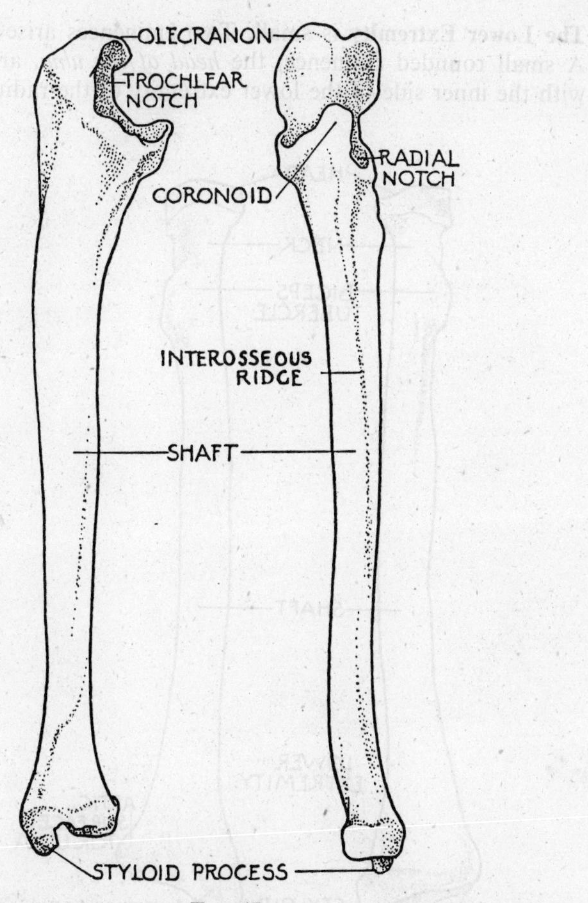

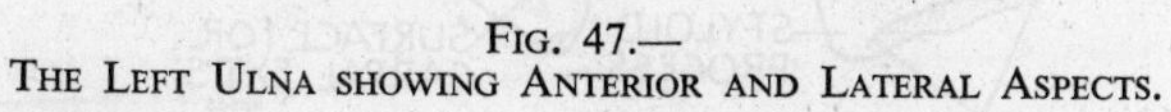

FIG. 47.—
THE LEFT ULNA SHOWING ANTERIOR AND LATERAL ASPECTS.

The Shaft of the Ulna tapers towards its lower end. The shaft is marked off into surfaces by borders. It gives attachment to muscles controlling movement of the wrist and fingers, the flexors coming from the anterior and the extensors from the posterior surface. The muscles pronating and supinating the forearm are also attached to the shaft.

The Lower Extremity is small. Two eminences arise from it. A small rounded eminence, the *head of the ulna*, articulates with the inner side of the lower extremity of the radius in the

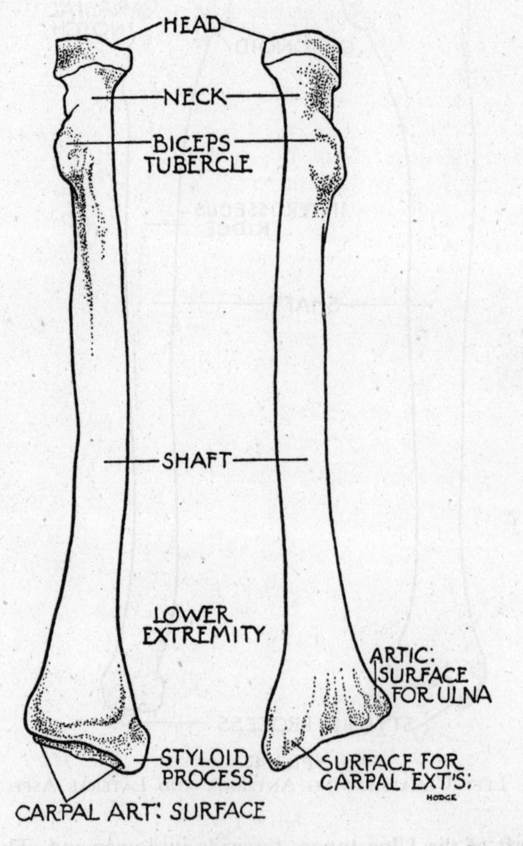

FIG. 48.—THE LEFT RADIUS SHOWING ANTERIOR AND POSTERIOR ASPECTS.

formation of the inferior radio-ulnar joint. A pointed process, the *styloid process*, projects downwards from the back of the lower extremity.

RADIUS

The radius is the lateral or outermost bone of the forearm. It is a long bone with a shaft and two extremities. It is shorter than the ulna.

The Upper Extremity of the radius is small, and presents a button-shaped head with a shallow upper surface for articulation with the *capitulum* of the humerus; the sides of the head articulate with the *radial notch* or *lesser sigmoid cavity* of the ulna. Below the head lies the neck, and below and to the medial side of the neck lies the *biceps tubercle* or *radial tuberosity*, to which the tendon of insertion of the biceps muscle is attached.

The Shaft is narrower above than below, widening as it nears the lower end. The shaft is curved outwards, and it is marked off into surfaces which, as in the ulna, give attachment anteriorly to the deep flexors and pronators, and posteriorly to the deep extensors and supinators of the forearm and hand. The interosseous ligament passes from radius to ulna and separates the muscles on the back from those on the front of the forearm.

The Lower Extremity is rather square in shape, and enters into the formation of two joints. The inferior articulating surfaces of the lower extremity of the radius articulate with the scaphoid and semilunar (lunate) bones in the formation of the wrist joint. An articulating surface at the inner or medial aspect of the lower extremity articulates with the head of the ulna in the formation of the inferior radio-ulnar joint. Towards the outer or lateral aspect the lower extremity is prolonged downwards into the *styloid process* of the radius.

BONES OF WRIST AND HAND

The bones of the hand are arranged in groups. The carpus, or the bones which enter into the formation of the palm of the hand, are long bones. The phalanges, or bones of the fingers, also are long bones.

The carpus is composed of eight bones arranged in two rows, four bones in each row. The upper row is arranged from without inwards.

The scaphoid, is a boat-shaped bone, sometimes called the *navicular*, the *semilunar* or *lunate* is crescentic like a halfmoon—

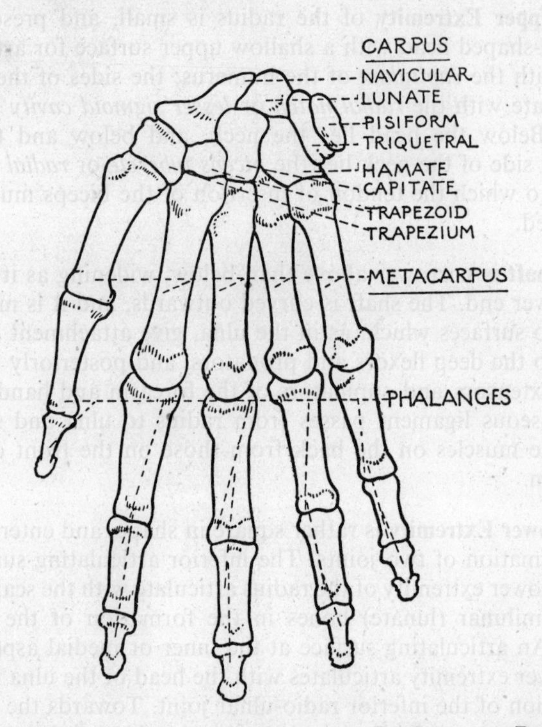

FIG. 49.—THE ANTERIOR ASPECT OF THE BONES OF THE RIGHT WRIST AND HAND.

these two bones articulate above with the lower extremity of the radius in the formation of the wrist joint, and below they articulate with some of the carpal bones of the second row.

The triquetral or *cuneiform* is a wedge-shaped bone which lies internal to the semilunar; the *pisiform*, which is shaped like a pea, lies in front of the cuneiform.

In the lower row the bones, arranged from the outer (lateral) to the inner (medial) aspect, are: The *trapezium*, with which the metacarpal bone of the thumb articulates, the *trapezoid*, a small, wedge-shaped bone, the *capitate* or *os magnum*, which is the largest of the carpal bones, and the *hamate* or *unciform*, which is characterized by a hook-like process arising from the front of the bone.

The metacarpus. There are five metacarpal bones. Each bone has a shaft and two extremities. The extremity articulating with the carpal bones is called the *carpal extremity*, and the joint so formed is the *carpo-metacarpal joint*. The *distal extremity* articulates with the phalanges and is called the head, or the *phalangeal extremity*. The shafts of these bones are prismoidal, and have their broadest surface directed posteriorly (towards the back of the hand). The interosseous muscles are attached to the sides of the shafts.

The phalanges are also long bones, having a shaft and two extremities. The shaft tapers towards the distal end. There are fourteen phalanges, three in each finger and two in the thumb.

Chapter 4

THE SKELETON OF THE LOWER LIMB

The bones of the lower extremity are connected with the trunk by means of the pelvic girdle, which is described on page 61.

The lower extremity consists of thirty-one bones:

1 Innominate bone	1 Patella
1 Femur	7 Tarsal bones
1 Tibia	5 Metatarsal bones
1 Fibula	14 Phalanges

THE INNOMINATE BONE

The innominate bone or *os innominatum* helps to form the pelvic girdle. Situated one on each side, uniting in front at the symphysis pubis, the two bones form a considerable part of the bony pelvis.

The innominate bone is an irregularly flat bone formed by the union of three bones at the acetabulum, which is a cup-shaped cavity on the external surface of the bone which receives the head of the femur in the formation of the hip joint.

The uppermost of the three bones which unite here is the *ilium*, the front one the *pubis*, and the most posterior the *ischium*.

The Ilium presents two surfaces, a crest, two processes, anterior and posterior, and an articulating surface for the sacrum.

The *external* or *gluteal surface* is marked by three ridges, the *gluteal ridges*, superior, middle, and inferior. The gluteal muscles are attached to this part of the bone, the *gluteal maximus* arising from the surface above the superior ridges, and the *gluteus minimus* from the surface between the middle and inferior ridges.

The *internal surface* of the bone is concave and forms the *iliac fossa*, which gives attachment to the iliacus muscle. Below this fossa is a prominent line called the *ilio-pectineal line* which forms the upper boundary of the pelvic cavity.

The *crest of the ilium* is curved and surmounts the bone. It gives attachment to many muscles, including the abdominal muscles and latissimus dorsi. It terminates in front at a point

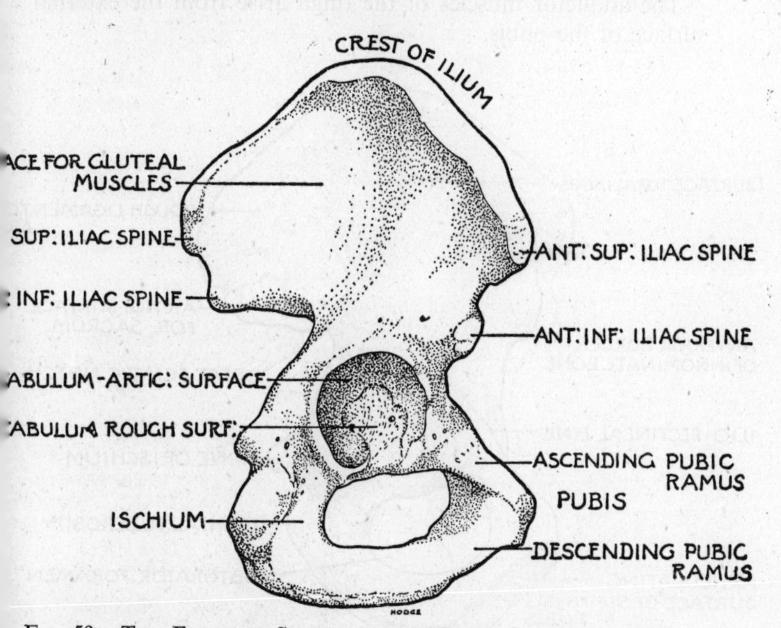

FIG. 50.—THE EXTERNAL SURFACE OF THE RIGHT INNOMINATE BONE.

called the *anterior superior iliac spine*, to which Poupart's ligament, the *inguinal ligament*, is attached, and posteriorly in the *posterior superior iliac spine*. Below these spines are two other prominences, the anterior and posterior inferior spines. The surface between the two posterior spines forms the articulating surface for the sacrum. Below this articulation lies the *great sciatic notch*, through which the great sciatic nerve passes from the pelvis to the thigh.

The Pubis consists of a *body* and two *rami*. The body is square in shape and is surmounted by the *crest of the pubis*. The pubic bones unite in front at the *symphysis pubis*. The rami pass backwards from the body, one upwards, the *ascending ramus*, towards the acetabulum, and one downwards, the *descending ramus*, to join the ramus of the ischium, and together they form part of the boundary of the obturator foramen.

The adductor muscles of the thigh arise from the external surface of the pubis.

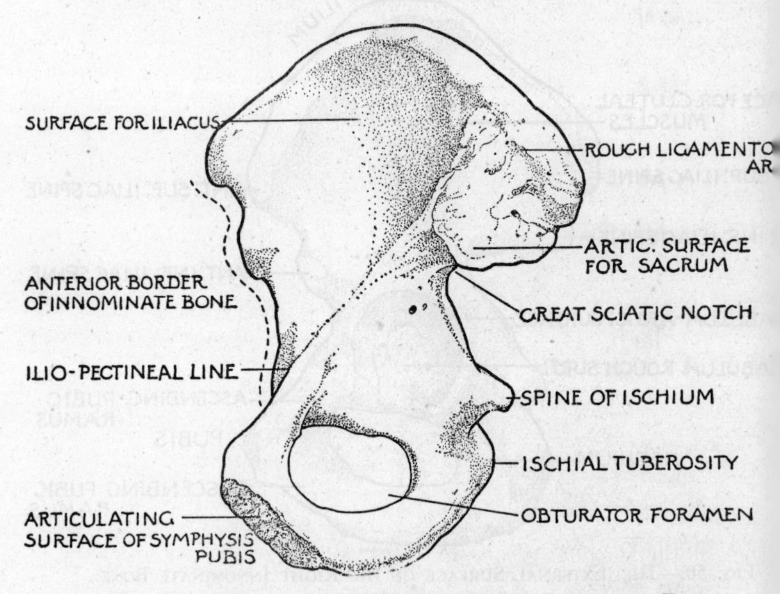

FIG. 51.—THE INTERNAL SURFACE OF RIGHT INNOMINATE BONE.

The Ischium is the thickest and strongest portion of the bone. The *tuberosity of the ischium* lies at its lowest point, and on this the trunk rests when sitting. The tuberosity is marked by two facets which give attachment to the hamstring muscles. A pointed eminence, the *spine of the ischium*, arises from the back of the bone and marks the lowest part of the sciatic notch. The body of this ischium forms the posterior boundary of the obturator foramen; from this the ramus passes forwards, to join the descending ramus of the pubis in forming the inferior boundary.

The Obturator Foramen is a large oval foramen lying below the acetabulum and bounded, as described, by the pubis and ischium. It is filled in with membrane, and at its upper part transmits the obturator vessels and nerves from the pelvis into the thigh.

The Acetabulum is a deep, cup-shaped cavity formed by the union of the three bones; the *pubis* forms the front part, the *ilium* the upper part, and the *ischium* the back part. The acetabulum articulates with the femur in the formation of the hip joint. The articulating surface is shaped like a horse-shoe interrupted at its lowest point by a notch, the *acetabular notch*, permitting the passage of vessels into the joint. A roughened non-articular surface at the bottom—*the acetabular fossa*—is filled in with a pad of fat, its lower margins give attachment to the *ligamentum teres* of the hip joint.

FEMUR

The femur is the longest bone in the body. It articulates with the acetabulum in the formation of the hip joint, and from here the bone inclines inwards to the knee, where it articulates with the tibia. It is a long bone with a shaft and two extremities.

The Upper Extremity presents a spherical head; at the summit of this is an ovoid depression, a roughened pit, for the attachment of the ligamentum teres. Below the head is the neck, which is long and flattened. Where the neck joins the shaft the *greater trochanter* lies to the outer side, and the *lesser trochanter* to the back and inner side. The great trochanter is a prominent process of bone which gives attachment to several muscles, including the gluteal muscles. At the inner side of this is a small, deep fossa, *the digital* or *trochanteric fossa.*

At the base of the neck of the bone, two lines unite the greater and lesser trochanters, the *anterior intertrochanteric line* in front, and the *posterior intertrochanteric line* or *trochanteric crest* at the back. The latter is marked by a tubercle of bone, the *quadrate tubercle.*

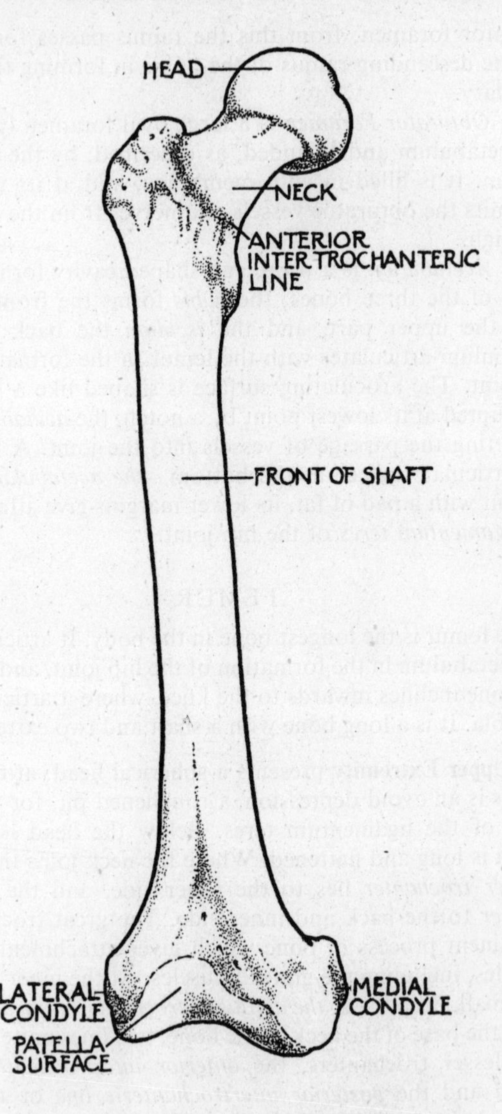

FIG. 52.—THE ANTERIOR ASPECT OF THE RIGHT FEMUR.

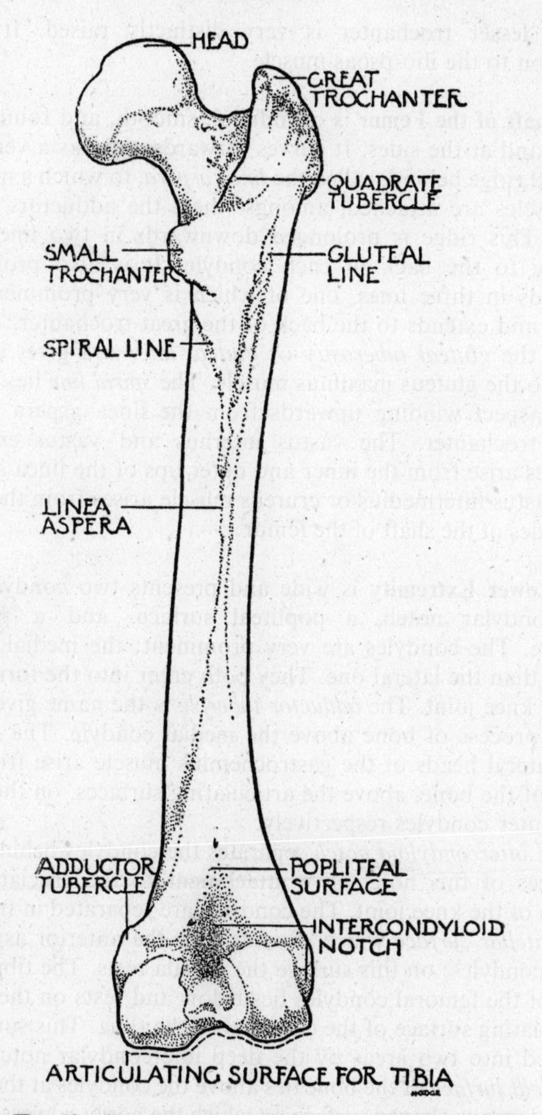

FIG. 53.—THE POSTERIOR ASPECT OF THE RIGHT FEMUR.

The lesser trochanter is very distinctly raised. It gives insertion to the ilio-psoas muscle.

The Shaft of the Femur is cylindrical, smooth, and rounded in front, and at the sides. It curves forwards and has a very well marked ridge behind, called the *linea aspera*, to which a number of muscles are attached, amongst them the adductors of the thigh. This ridge is prolonged downwards in two lines, one passing to the back of each condyle. It is also prolonged upwards in three lines, one of which is very prominent and rough and extends to the back of the great trochanter. This is called the *gluteal tuberosity* or *gluteal line*, and gives attachment to the gluteus maximus muscle. The *spiral line* lies on the inner aspect winding upwards from the linea aspera to the small trochanter. The vastus internus and vastus externus muscles arise from the inner and outer lips of the linea aspera. The vastus intermedius or crureus muscle arises from the front and sides of the shaft of the femur.

The Lower Extremity is wide and presents two condyles, an intercondylar notch, a popliteal surface, and a patellar surface. The condyles are very prominent; the medial one is lower than the lateral one. They both enter into the formation of the knee joint. The *adductor tubercle* is the name given to a small process of bone above the medial condyle. The medial and lateral heads of the gastrocnemius muscle arise from the back of the bone, above the articulating surfaces, on the inner and outer condyles respectively.

The *intercondyloid notch* separates the condyles behind. The surfaces of this notch give attachment to the cruciate ligaments of the knee joint. The condyles are separated in front by the *patellar surface* which extends over the anterior aspect of both condyles; on this surface the patella rests. The tibial surface of the femoral condyles lies below and rests on the upper articulating surface of the condyles of the tibia. This surface is divided into two areas by the deep intercondylar notch. The *popliteal surface* of the bone lies above the condyles at the back. It is a lozenge-shaped surface on which the popliteal vessels and nerves lie. It forms the floor of the *popliteal space*.

The femur articulates with three bones, the innominate bone, the tibia, and the patella, but it does *not* articulate with the fibula.

PATELLA

The patella is a *sesamoid bone* developed in the tendon of the quadriceps extensor muscle. The *apex of the patella* points

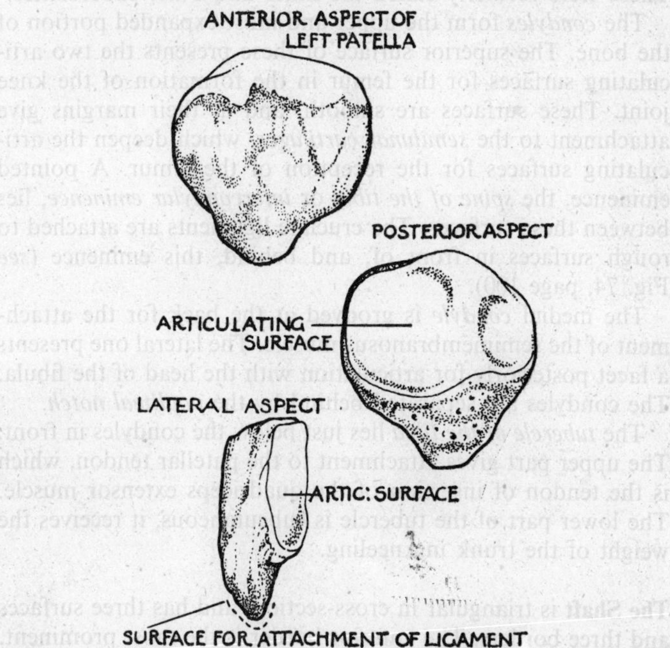

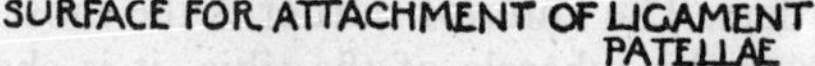

FIG. 54.—THE ANTERIOR, LATERAL AND POSTERIOR ASPECTS OF THE PATELLA.

downwards. The anterior surface of the bone is rough and is covered with a bursa. The posterior surface is smooth and articulates with the patellar surface of the lower extremity of the femur. This articulating surface is divided by a line into two facets. The outer of these is the larger; it rests on the larger part of the patellar surface of the external condyle of the femur.

The *ligamentum patellae* is attached to the apex of the bone.

TIBIA

The tibia is the innermost bone of the leg; it is a long bone with a shaft and two extremities.

The Upper Extremity presents medial and lateral condyles. These were formerly called the inner and outer tuberosities.

The *condyles* form the upper and most expanded portion of the bone. The superior surface of these presents the two articulating surfaces for the femur in the formation of the knee joint. These surfaces are smooth, and at their margins give attachment to the *semilunar cartilages*, which deepen the articulating surfaces for the reception of the femur. A pointed eminence, the *spine of the tibia* or *intercondylar eminence*, lies between these surfaces. The cruciate ligaments are attached to rough surfaces in front of, and behind, this eminence (*see* Fig. 74, page 100).

The medial *condyle* is grooved at the back for the attachment of the semimembranosus muscle. The lateral one presents a facet posteriorly for articulation with the head of the fibula. The condyles are separated behind by the *popliteal notch.*

The *tubercle of the tibia* lies just below the condyles in front. The upper part gives attachment to the patellar tendon, which is the tendon of insertion of the quadriceps extensor muscle. The lower part of the tubercle is subcutaneous, it receives the weight of the trunk in kneeling.

The Shaft is triangular in cross-section, and has three surfaces and three borders. The anterior border is the most prominent. It commences at the tubercle of the tibia, it is sharp and lies subcutaneous in its middle third, where it forms the *crest of the tibia.* It diverges at the lower third towards the medial malleolus. The medial surface is subcutaneous in most of its extent. The lateral surface is grooved for the attachment of the tibialis anterior muscle. The posterior surface is marked by the *soleal line* which is a strong ridge of bone running downwards and inwards. The popliteus muscle is attached above this line, and below it the posterior surface of the tibia is covered by the tibialis posterior and the flexor muscles of the toes.

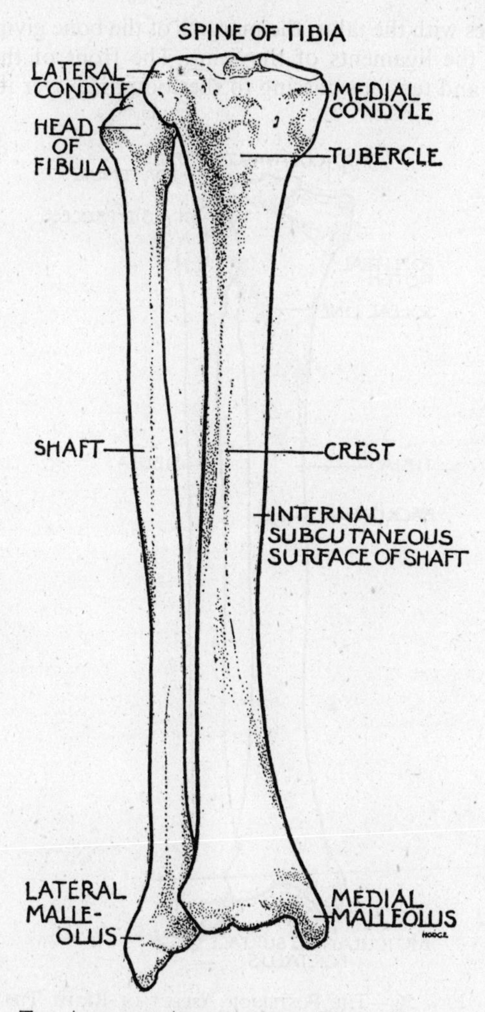

FIG. 55.—THE ANTERIOR ASPECT OF THE RIGHT TIBIA AND FIBULA.

The Lower Extremity enters into the formation of the ankle joint. It is slightly expanded, and is prolonged downwards on the inner side as the *medial malleolus*. The lower extremity articulates with the talus, the margins of the bone giving attachment to the ligaments of the joint. The front of the tibia is smooth, and tendons passing to the foot glide over it.

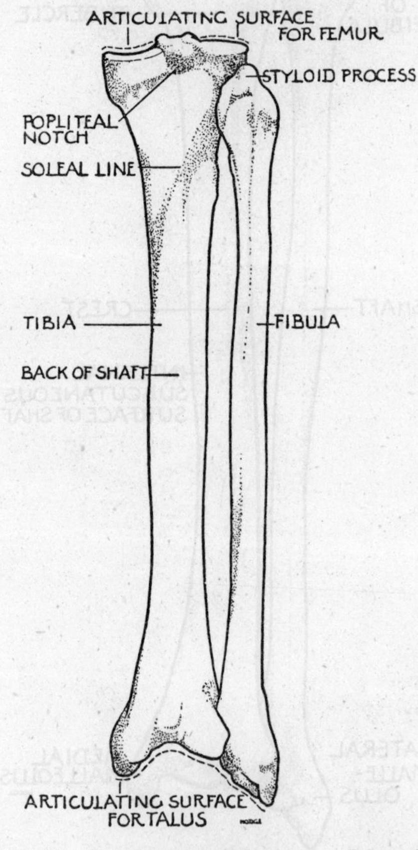

FIG. 56.—THE POSTERIOR ASPECT OF RIGHT TIBIA AND FIBULA.

The lateral surface of the lower extremity articulates with the fibula. The tibia articulates with three bones, the femur, fibula, and talus.

FIBULA

The fibula is the lateral or outermost bone of the leg. It is a long bone with a shaft and two extremities.

The Upper Extremity forms the *head*, and articulates with the back of the outer condyle of the tibia, but does not enter into the formation of the knee joint. It presents an apex termed the *styloid process*, to which one of the ligaments of the knee joint is attached. The head also gives attachment to the biceps femoris muscle.

The Shaft is slender and deeply embedded in the muscles of the leg, to which it gives numerous attachments.

The Lower Extremity is prolonged downwards as the *lateral malleolus*. A rough depression which lies behind the lateral malleolus called the *malleolar fossa* provides a surface for the attachment of some of the powerful ligaments of the ankle joint. The *lateral malleolus* extends lower than the medial malleolus of the tibia. Its lateral surface is subcutaneous and its medial surface articulates with the lateral surface of the talus in the formation of the ankle joint.

BONES OF THE FOOT

The Tarsal Bones. There are seven tarsal bones. They are short bones, made up of cancellous bone tissue, with a covering of compact tissue. These bones support the weight of the body in standing. The cancellous tissue of which they are formed is arranged in such a way that the weight is divided, part being directed backwards on to the calcaneum, and part forwards to be borne by the heads of the metatarsus.

The Calcaneum or *Os Calcis* is the largest bone of the foot. It lies at the back of the foot, transmitting the weight of the body to the ground posteriorly. It gives attachment to the large muscles of the calf through the *tendon of Achilles* or *tendo calcaneus*. Above, it articulates with the talus and in front with the cuboid. A flat process arising from the medial aspect of the calcaneum is known as the *sustentaculum tali*. This helps to support the talus, and it also gives attachment to the spring ligament, which is important in maintaining the medial arch of the foot.

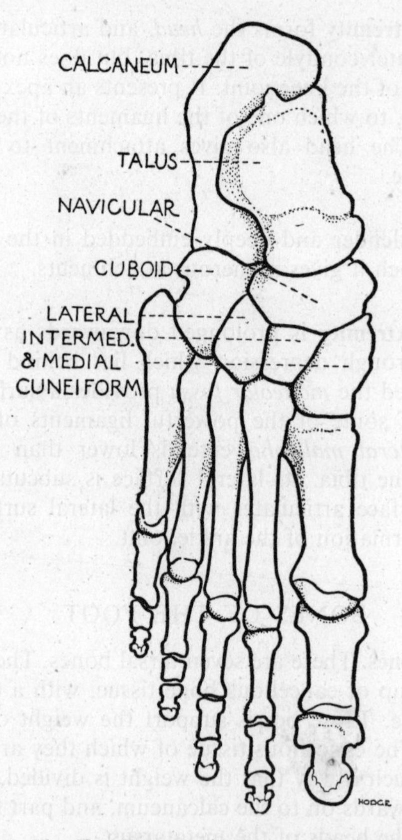

FIG. 57.—THE DORSAL ASPECT OF THE BONES OF THE RIGHT FOOT.

The Talus or *Astragalus* forms the central and highest point of the foot. It supports the tibia and articulates with the malleoli at each side, and with the calcaneum below. It is

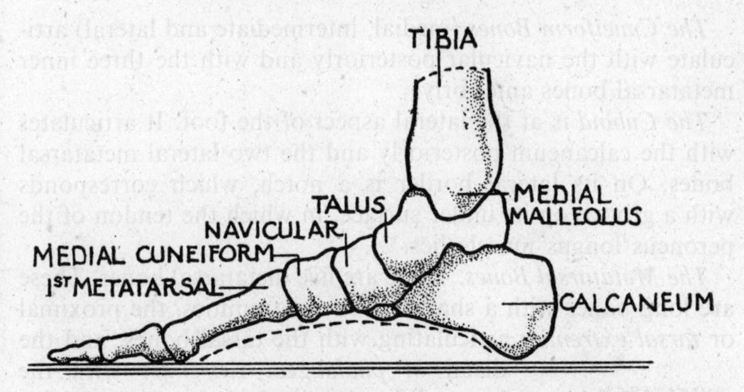

FIG. 58.—THE BONES OF THE RIGHT FOOT SHOWING THE MEDIAL OR INNER LONGITUDINAL ARCH.

divided into a *body*, a *neck*, and a *head*. The head is connected to the body by the neck. The head of the talus articulates with the navicular anteriorly and is partly supported by the spring ligament which passes from the sustentaculum tali to the under surface of the navicular.

The Navicular or *Scaphoid* is on the medial aspect of the foot, between the talus at the back and the three cuneiform bones in front. A rounded prominence on the medial border is known as the tubercle of the navicular.

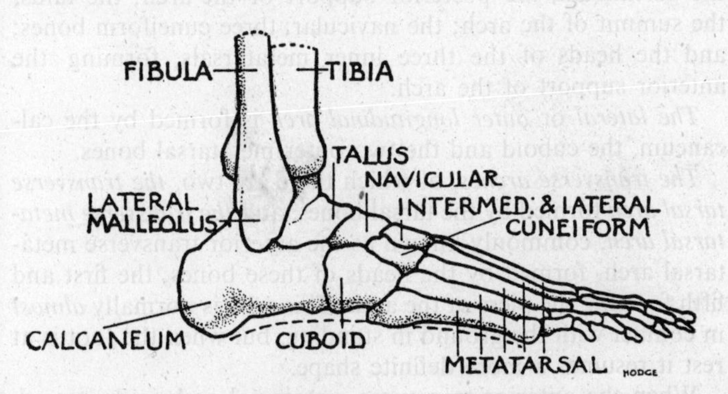

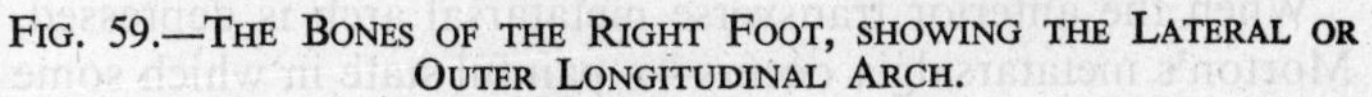
FIG. 59.—THE BONES OF THE RIGHT FOOT, SHOWING THE LATERAL OR OUTER LONGITUDINAL ARCH.

The Cuneiform Bones (medial, intermediate and lateral) articulate with the navicular posteriorly and with the three inner metatarsal bones anteriorly.

The Cuboid is at the lateral aspect of the foot. It articulates with the calcaneum posteriorly and the two lateral metatarsal bones. On its lateral border is a notch, which corresponds with a groove on its under surface, in which the tendon of the peroneus longus muscle lies.

The Metatarsal Bones. There are five metatarsal bones. These are long bones with a shaft and two extremities, the proximal or *tarsal extremity* articulating with the tarsal bones, and the distal or *phalangeal extremity* with the base of the proximal phalanges.

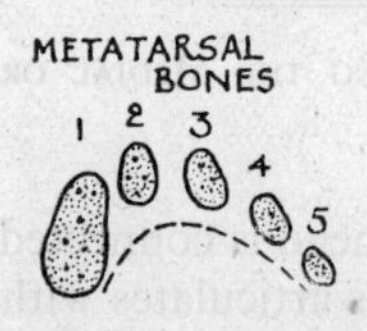

FIG. 60.—SECTION THROUGH THE HEADS OF THE METATARSAL BONES, SHOWING FORMATION OF ANTERIOR TRANSVERSE ARCH.

The first metatarsal is thick and short. The second metatarsal is the longest, and the fifth is marked by a process on the outer side of the tarsal extremity.

The Phalanges are similar to those of the fingers but much shorter.

The Arches of the Foot. Four arches are present in the foot.

The medial or internal longitudinal arch, which is formed from back to front by the calcaneum, the posterior support of the arch; the talus, the summit of the arch; the navicular; three cuneiform bones; and the heads of the three inner metatarsals, forming the anterior support of the arch.

The lateral or *outer longitudinal arch* is formed by the calcaneum, the cuboid and the two outer metatarsal bones.

The transverse arches, of which there are two, *the transverse tarsal arch* formed by the tarsal bones, and *the transverse metatarsal arch*, commonly known as the anterior transverse metatarsal arch, formed by the heads of these bones, the first and fifth forming the piers of the arch. This arch is normally *almost* in contact with the ground in standing, but when the foot is at rest it resumes a more definite shape.

When the anterior transverse metatarsal arch is depressed, Morton's metatarsalgia occurs—a painful state in which some of the digital nerves of the toes are compressed by the third and fourth metatarsal bones.

The bones of the arches of the foot are held together by ligaments and supported by muscles. The medial longitudinal arch is depressed in flat foot. When the muscles are overstrained, or weakened as happens in a prolonged illness, they fail to support the arch. Flat foot may be contributed to by having the foot in a bad position, as by being pressed down under tight bedclothing.

Chapter 5

THE JOINTS OF THE SKELETON

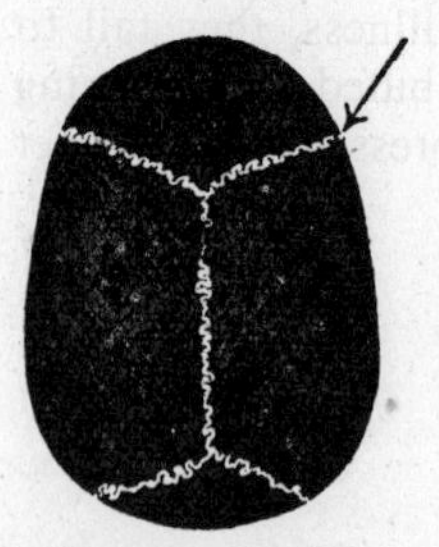

FIG. 61.—TYPICAL IMMOVABLE JOINT SUTURES OF SKULL.

A *joint* or *articulation* is the term used to describe any connection between the bones of the skeleton, the term *arthrology* is applied to the study of joints, there are three main classes fibrous, cartilaginous and synovial joints.

Fibrous Joints or *synarthroses*, are immovable or fixed joints in which no movement between the bones is possible:

Sutures or joints of the flat skull bones,

Peg and socket joints (gomphosis)—the teeth in their sockets, and

Syndesmosis, a joint where the articulating surfaces are connected by membrane as in the inferior tibio-fibular joint.

Cartilaginous Joints or *amphiarthroses* are slightly movable joints in which the joint surfaces are separated by some intervening substance and slight movement only is possible: e.g.

The *pubic symphysis*, where a pad of cartilage unites the two pubic bones. The *intervertebral joints* with their intervertebral discs of cartilage.

The joint between the *manubrium* and the *body of the sternum*.

(A *symphysis* is the term used to describe a partly movable joint, where the bone ends are separated by a pad of cartilage.)

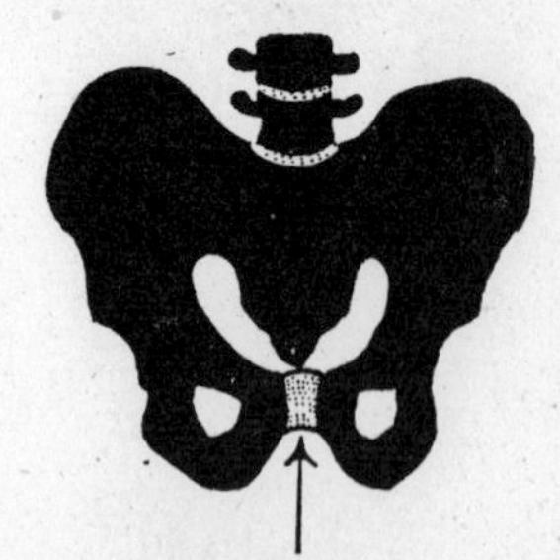

FIG. 62.—TYPICAL CARTILAGINOUS JOINTS—SYMPHYSIS PUBIS AND INTERVERTEBRAL JOINTS.

Temporary cartilaginous joints are found between the diaphysis and epiphyses of the long bones before full growth is complete (*see* page 37).

FIG. 63.—A TYPICAL SYNOVIAL JOINT.

Synovial Joints or *diarthroses* are *freely movable joints* of which there are several varieties, all having similar characteristics (*see* below).

Characters of a Freely Movable Joint. The *ends of the bones* which enter into the formation of the joint are covered by *hyaline cartilage*.

Ligaments are required to bind the bones together.

A joint cavity: the cavity is enclosed by ligaments which form a capsule to the joint.

Synovial membrane covers all the surfaces in the interior of the joint cavity. It becomes continuous with the hyaline cartilage on the ends of the bones, entering into the formation of the joint. *Synovial fluid*, a serous fluid, is secreted by this membrane, and lubricates the joint structures.

Varieties of Synovial Joints. There are six varieties. *Gliding joint* or *plane joint*, in which two flat surfaces of bone glide on each other, e.g. the joints of the carpus and the tarsus.

Ball and socket joint, in which one rounded extremity fits into a cavity in another bone, permitting movement in all directions, as in a ball within a socket or cup-shaped cavity, e.g. the hip joint and the shoulder joint.

Ginglymus or *hinge joint*, in this variety one rounded surface is received into another in such a way that movement is only possible in one plane, as occurs

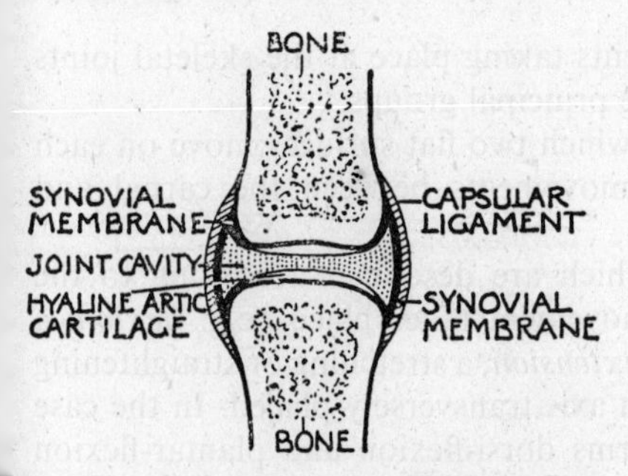

FIG. 64.—A SECTION OF A TYPICAL SYNOVIAL JOINT, SHOWING THE DIFFERENT PARTS WHICH ENTER INTO THE FORMATION OF A MOVABLE JOINT.

in the movements of a hinge. The best examples are the elbow joint and the interphalangeal joints of the fingers and toes.

Condyloid joint: this is similar to a hinge joint, but it is so adapted as to permit movement in two planes, lateral as well as backward and forward so that flexion and extension, and abduction and adduction and slight circumduction are possible, as in the wrist joint, but not rotation.

Trochoid or *pivot joint:* this is one in which rotation only is possible, as in the movements of the head, where the ring-like atlas rotates round the peg-shaped process of the axis; another example is seen in the movements of the radius on the ulna in pronation and supination of the forearm (*see* page 96).

Saddle joint, or a joint of reciprocal reception, e.g. the joint between the trapezium and the first metacarpal bone of the thumb. This permits great freedom of movement, one concave-convex surface is received by another convex-concave surface, so that both in the vertical and the transverse directions the bones are closely adapted to one another. The result of the bones being so adapted gives the free movements to the thumb, those of flexion and extension, abduction and adduction, a combination of these movements results in circumduction, i.e. circular movement of the thumb. The thumb can also be opposed, i.e. brought to face the fingers in the palm of the hand.

Movements. The movements taking place at the skeletal joints may be divided into three principal groups.

Gliding movements, in which two flat surfaces move on each other as occurs in the movements between the carpal and tarsal bones.

Angular movements, which are described according to the direction in which the movement takes place—e.g. *flexion*, a bending or doubling up; *extension*, a stretching or straightening out—take place round an axis transversely placed. In the case of the ankle joint the terms dorsi-flexion and plantar-flexion are employed (*see* page 102). *Adduction*, that is movement towards the medial aspect of the body, and *abduction*, in a direction away from the medial aspect of the body, take place round an axis running in an antero-posterior direction—from front to back.

Rotation movements are those in which one bone moves around or within another bone as in the pivot joints, e.g. the rotation of radius on ulna. It also occurs at the shoulder and to a more limited extent at the hip joint. *Circumduction* is the term used to describe a combination of rotation and angular movements, a carrying in circles, e.g. the carrying of the arm forward, upward, backward and downward; including flexion, abduction, extension and adduction, and some rotation.

Limitation of joint movement is due in many instances to the shape of the articulating surfaces, for example extension of the elbow is limited by the olecranon process of the ulna impinging against the humerus. In other instances movement is limited by strong bands of ligaments as in the ilio-femoral ligament on the front of the hip joint which limits extension of the thigh. Flexion of the elbow and of the leg on the thigh are limited by the soft parts coming into contact.

JOINTS OF THE UPPER EXTREMITY

The Sterno-Clavicular Joint is a gliding joint formed by the large sternal extremity of the clavicle, articulating with the clavicular facet on the sternum; a pad of fibro-cartilage lies in the joint cavity between these bones which divides the joint cavity into two so that this joint may also be described as a double gliding joint. The bones are united by ligaments, and the joint cavity is lined by synovial membrane.

The *movements* possible at this joint are slight upward, downward, forward, and backward movement of the flat surfaces on each other.

The Acromio-Clavicular Joint is formed by the outer end of the clavicle articulating with the acromion process of the scapula. It is a freely movable joint of the gliding variety but only slight movement is possible.

The Shoulder Joint or the *humero-scapular joint* is a joint of the ball-and-socket variety. The hemispherical head of the humerus

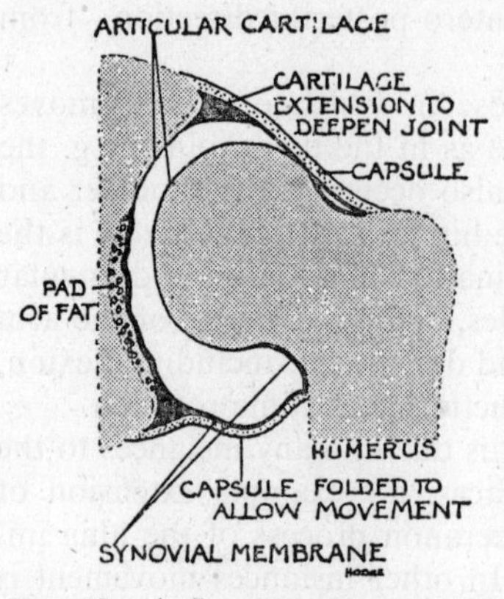

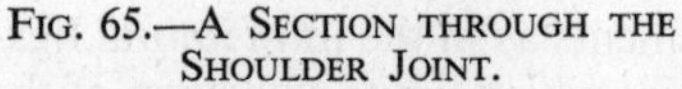
FIG. 65.—A SECTION THROUGH THE SHOULDER JOINT.

articulates within the glenoid cavity of the scapula. The bones are united together by ligaments which form a very loose capsule. The degree and the limitation of movement here is largely dependent on the surrounding muscles, and the pressure of the atmosphere in retaining the bones in position whilst looseness of the capsular ligament allows free joint movement in all directions, abduction, adduction, flexion, extension, internal and external rotation, and circumduction.

The tendon of the long head of the biceps muscle is intimately associated with the shoulder joint. It passes through the cavity of the joint and pierces the capsule where it leaves the joint as it lies in the bicipital groove or intertubercular sulcus.

Movement. Owing to the looseness of the capsular ligament movement is possible in every direction.

Flexion, that is carrying the arm forward and across the chest, is performed by pectoralis major.

Extension is performed by the muscles attached to the axillary border of the scapula, mainly teres major and latissimus dorsi.

Abduction, i.e. raising the arm to right angles with the trunk, is performed by the deltoid.

Adduction is performed partly by the weight of the limb and also by muscles in front and behind, but mainly by the pectoralis major and teres major.

Rotation inwards and outwards and *circumduction* is also possible. The latter consists of carrying the arm in circles, up, out, back, and down.

The Elbow Joint is a hinge joint, between the trochlear surface on the lower extremity of the humerus, and the trochlear notch or greater sigmoid cavity of the ulna. This forms the principal part of the joint, the *humero-ulnar joint*. The head of the radius articulates with the capitulum of the humerus, forming the *humero-radial joint*, and these four articulating surfaces lie within the joint capsule, the radius being carried backwards and forwards with the ulna, in the movements of the joint.

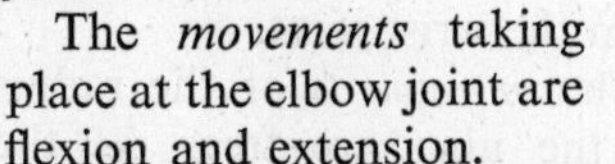

The *movements* taking place at the elbow joint are flexion and extension.

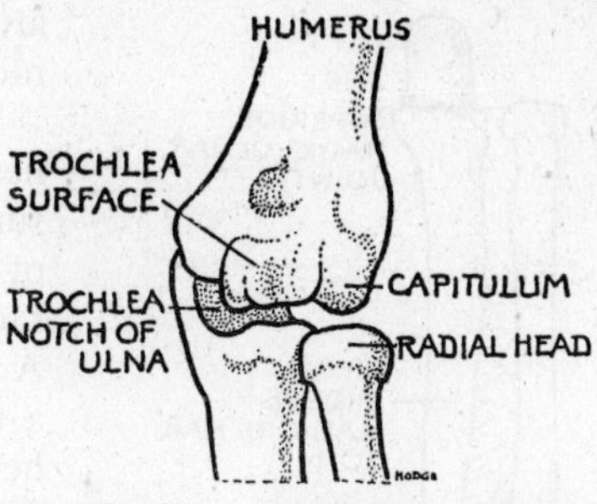

FIG. 66.—THE ANTERIOR ASPECT OF THE BONES FORMING THE LEFT ELBOW JOINT.

Flexion is performed by the brachialis, biceps, and brachioradialis, and *extension* by triceps.

The *carrying angle of the elbow* when the elbow is extended and the forearm and hand supinated is about 170 degrees with the upper arm. This is due to the obliquity of the articulating surfaces between the humerus and ulna. The advantage obtained by this carrying angle is that articles are carried clear of the body.

The Radio-Ulnar Joints. There are two joints between the radius and the ulna, the superior and inferior radio-ulnar joints. In addition to these two joints the bones are united by an interosseous membrane which passes from an attachment on the interosseous border of the radius to a similar border on the ulna. This membrane also separates the muscles on the front from those on the back of the forearm.

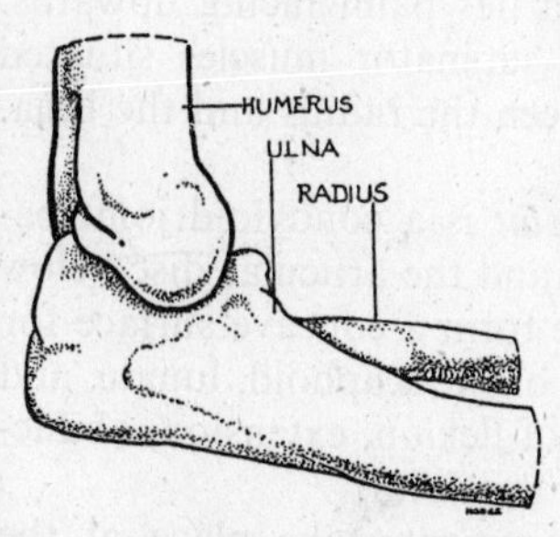

FIG. 67.—THE LEFT ELBOW JOINT IN FLEXION.

The *superior radio-ulnar joint* is formed by the sides of the head of the radius articulating with the radial notch or lesser sigmoid cavity of the ulna. The radial head is held in position by the *annular* or *orbicular ligament* which encircles it, and which is

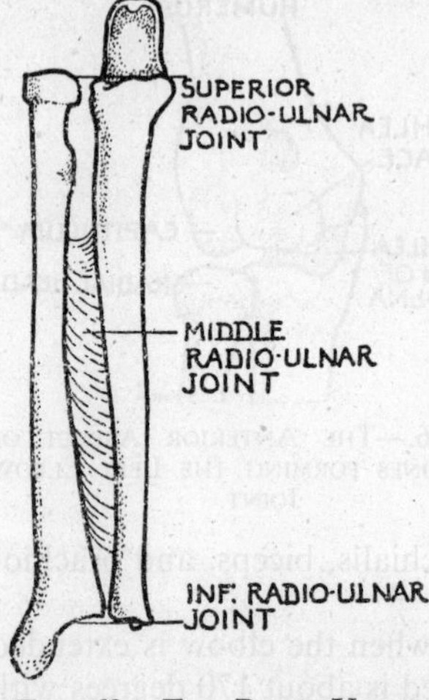

FIG. 68.—THE RADIO-ULNAR JOINTS OF THE RIGHT FOREARM.

attached to the margins of the radial notch of ulna.

The inferior radio-ulnar joint lies between the articulating surface on the medial aspect of the lower extremity of the radius, and the head of the ulna. A pad of fibro-cartilage which is a triangular disc lies below the head of the ulna, separating it from the wrist joint.

The *movements* of the radius on the ulna are free. As the head of the radius rotates within the annular ligament at the superior radio-ulnar joint, the lower end of the radius rotates on the head of the ulna at the inferior radio-ulnar joint, carrying the hand with it in the movements of pronation and supination of the forearm.

Pronation is rotation of the radius on the ulna until the hand lies palm downwards. This movement is performed by a group of muscles called pronators which lie on the front of the forearm between the radius and the ulna.

Supination is the opposite movement. Beginning with the forearm prone, it is rotated from within outwards until the radius and ulna lie parallel and the hand lies palm facing upwards. Supination is performed by two supinator muscles situated on the back of the forearm, between the radius and the ulna.

The Wrist Joint or *radio-carpal joint* is a condyloid joint between the lower end of the radius and the articular disc below the head of the ulna above. These form a concave surface for the reception of the upper aspects of the scaphoid, lunate, and triquetral bones. The movements of flexion, extension, abduction, and adduction take place at this joint.

Movements. Four principal movements take place at the wrist joint:

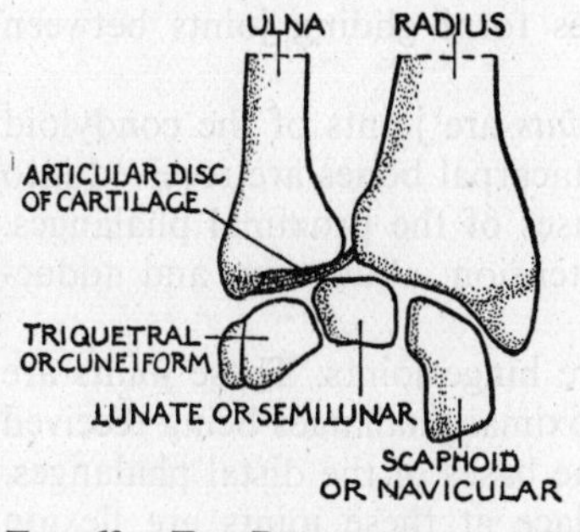

Fig. 69.—The Bones forming the Wrist Joint (left).

Flexion by the flexor muscles on the front of the forearm,

Extension by the extension muscles on the back of the forearm,

Abduction by the flexor and extensor muscles on the radial or thumb side of the wrist acting in unison, and

Adduction by muscles on the ulnar side of the wrist acting together in the same way. (Movement of one's own wrist joint and noting the position of the muscles which contract to perform these movements is the best way to study the movements at this or any other joint.)

JOINTS OF HAND AND FINGERS

The carpal joints. The articulating surfaces between the carpal bones are flat and smooth. These flat surfaces move easily on each other, forming gliding joints between the different bones. The carpal bones are placed closely together, so that only limited gliding movements are possible, but a fairly considerable amount of movement occurs when all the carpal bones move together.

The carpo-metacarpal joints are gliding joints formed between the distal aspect of the lower row of carpal bones and the superior articulating surfaces on each of the five metacarpal bones. The carpo-metacarpal joint of the thumb—saddle-joint—is formed between the base of the first metacarpal and the trapezium (*see* page 92). *Inter-metacarpal joints* are formed between the bases of the metacarpal bones;

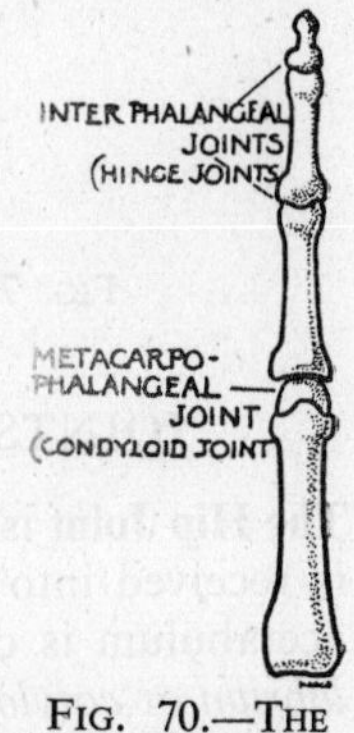

Fig. 70.—The Carpo-metacarpal and Interphalangeal Joints.

the lateral articulating surfaces form gliding joints between these bones.

The metacarpo-phalangeal joints are joints of the condyloid type. The heads of the five metacarpal bones are received into articulating surfaces on the bases of the proximal phalanges. The movements of flexion, extension, abduction, and adduction take place at these joints.

The interphalangeal joints are hinge joints. These joints are formed by the heads of the proximal phalanges being received into articulating surfaces on the bases of the distal phalanges. The movements which take place at these joints are flexion and extension.

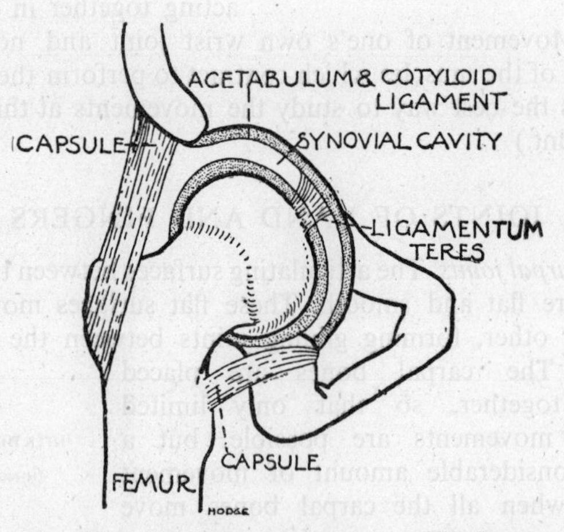

FIG. 71.—A SECTION THROUGH THE HIP JOINT.

JOINTS OF THE LOWER EXTREMITY

The Hip Joint is a ball-and-socket joint. The head of the femur is received into the *acetabulum* of the innominate bone. The acetabulum is deepened by the attachment of the *acetabular labrum* or *cotyloid ligament* to its circumference. This ligament is in the nature of a rim of fibro-cartilage which deepens and increases the adaptability of the surface formed by the acetabulum for the reception of the head of the femur.

The acetabulum is described in two parts. An *articulating surface*, which is horse-shoe shaped, and a *depression* at the bottom of the cavity, which is roughened and filled by a pad of fatty tissue. The gap at the lower part of this non-articular depression is bridged by the *transverse ligament* of the hip-joint, The *ligamentum teres* passes from the ovoid depression on the head of the femur, to the sides of the acetabular notch where it fuses with the transverse ligament. At this point also the vessels and nerves supplying the joint enter.

The capsular ligament of the hip joint is thick and strong and limits the movement of the joint in all directions. The ligament is also specially strengthened by bands of fibres in several parts. One of the most important of these bands lies in front of the joint, the *ilio-femoral ligament*. This ligament limits extension at the joint, and so helps to maintain the erect position in standing.

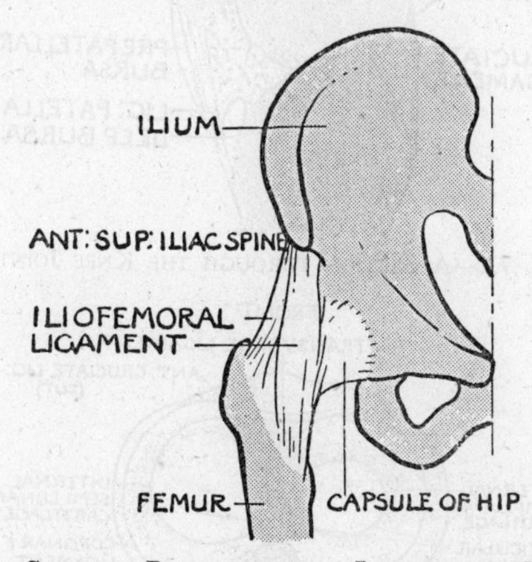

FIG. 72.—SHOWING POSITION OF THE ILIO-FEMORAL LIGAMENT.

The *movements* occurring at the hip joint are flexion, extension, abduction, adduction, internal and external rotation. A combination of all these movements is called circumduction.

Flexion is performed by drawing the thigh up towards the abdomen by contraction of the psoas and iliacus muscles.

Extension is performed by the gluteus maximus which straightens the flexed thigh and carries the thigh backwards.

Abduction, or carrying the leg outwards is performed by gluteus medius and minimus.

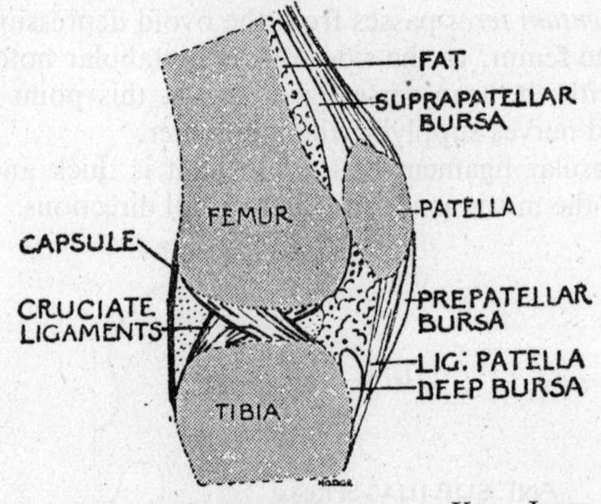

FIG. 73.—A SECTION THROUGH THE KNEE JOINT.

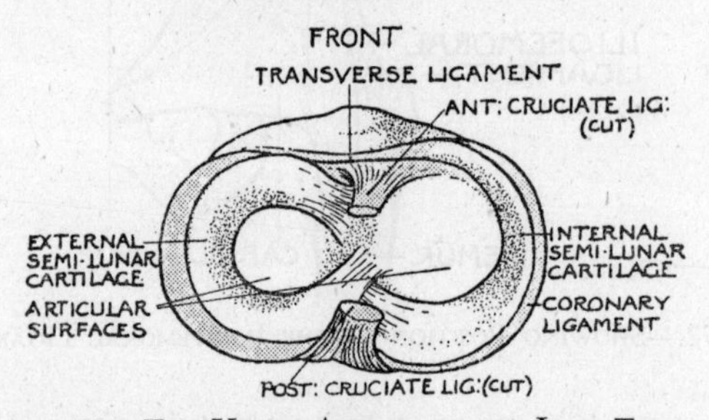

FIG. 74.—THE UPPER ASPECT OF THE LEFT TIBIA.
Showing some of the Interarticular Structures.

Adduction, or drawing the thigh inwards and across the opposite thigh, is performed by the large group of adductor muscles on the inner aspect between the thigh and the pubis.

The Knee Joint is a ginglymus or hinge joint formed by the condyles of the femur articulating with the superior surfaces of the condyles of the tibia. The patella lies on the smooth patellar surface of the femur over which it glides during the movements of the joint. It is not a part of the knee joint but lies in front of it.

Interarticular structures. Several important structures lie within the knee joint. *The semilunar cartilages* are placed on the margins of the articulating surfaces of the tibia, to deepen these for the reception of the condylar surfaces of the femur. *The cruciate ligaments* pass from the top of the tibial condyles, to the rough surfaces on the intercondyloid notch of the femur. These serve to limit the movement of the knee joint.

The capsular ligament is extensive and is considerably strengthened by expansions from the muscles and tendons which surround and pass over the joint.

The synovial membrane of the knee joint is the largest in the body. In addition to lining the joint structures, it extends upwards and downwards beneath the ligaments of the patella, and forms several bursae about the joint.

Movements. Flexion of the leg at the knee is performed by the hamstring muscles situated at the back of the thigh, assisted by the gastrocnemius or calf muscles.

Extension of the knee is performed by the quadriceps extensor group of muscles which forms the front of the thigh.

The Tibio-Fibular Joints. These joints are formed between the upper and lower extremities of the two bones of the leg, the shafts of the bones being united by an interosseous ligament as in the forearm.

The superior tibio-fibular joint is a gliding joint between a facet on the upper extremity of the fibula, articulating with another on the back of the lateral condyle of the tibia. The bones are united by ligaments, and the joint cavity is lined by synovial membrane as in all the diarthrodial joints. The fibula does not enter into the formation of the knee joint.

The inferior tibio-fibular joint is formed between the medial surface of the lower extremity of the fibula, and an articulating surface on the lateral aspect of the lower extremity of the tibia before these bones enter into the formation of the ankle joint. The surfaces are rough and separated by membrane, except for a short distance at the lower edge, where articulating surfaces are smooth.

The Ankle Joint is a ginglymus or hinge joint formed between the lower extremity of the tibia and its medial malleolus, and the lateral malleolus of the fibula which together form a socket to receive the body of the talus. The *capsule* of the joint is strengthened by additional important ligaments. The *deltoid ligament* on the medial aspect passes from the medial malleolus to the adjoining tarsal bones. This ligament is often badly torn in severe sprains of the ankle.

The *movements* of the ankle joint are flexion and extension, or, as more usually expressed, *dorsi-flexion* and *plantar-flexion*. *Dorsi-flexion* is performed by the anterior tibial group of muscles which contract and bend the foot up towards the leg. *Plantar-flexion* is performed by the posterior tibial group, including gastrocnemius, which straighten out the foot as in tip-toe walking.

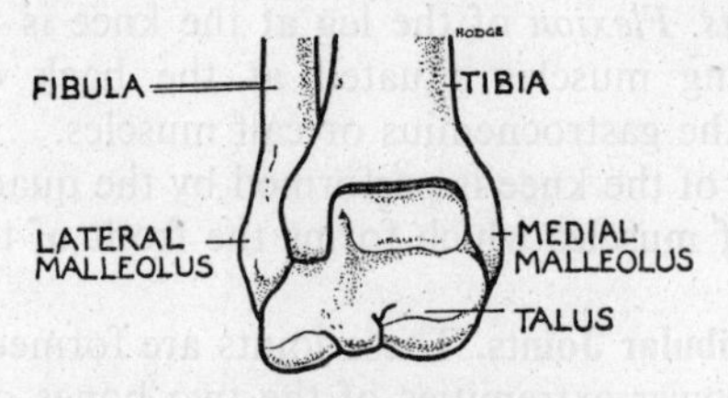

FIG. 75.—THE ANTERIOR ASPECT OF THE BONES FORMING THE ANKLE JOINT (RIGHT).

JOINTS OF THE FOOT

The joints between the tarsal bones are gliding joints. The bones are united by dorsal, plantar, and interosseous ligaments.

The interosseous ligament placed between the under surface of the talus and the upper surface of the calcaneum is thick and strong, and grooves the joint surfaces of both these bones.

Movements. A little rocking occurs at the talo-calcaneal joint, which is similar to adduction and abduction. The joints between the head of the talus and the navicular, and between the calcaneum and the cuboid, are called the *medio-tarsal joints* (*see* Figs. 58 and 59, page 87). It is at these joints that the movements of *inversion* and *eversion* take place.

In inversion the inner border of the foot is raised and the sole is directed inwards. In eversion the outer border of the foot is raised and the sole tends to be directed outwards. In conjunction with these movements, slight adduction and abduction occurs at the talo-calcaneal joint.

The *tarso-metatarsal*, the *metatarso-phalangeal*, and the *inter-phalangeal joints* are similar to those described in the hand (*see* pages 97–8).

Chapter 6

THE MUSCLES OF THE SKELETON

The muscles of the skeleton form part of one of the four groups of elementary tissues (*see* page 28). *Myology* is the term used to describe the study of muscles.

Muscles are attached to bone, cartilage, ligaments, and to the skin. Those placed immediately beneath the skin are flat. The muscles which surround the trunk are broad and flat, and those of the limbs are long.

The skeletal muscles are named according to their *shape*, as the Deltoid which is shaped like an inverted Greek letter D; according to the *direction* of their fibres, as the Rectus Abdominis, Obliquus Abdominis; according to the *position* of the muscle, as Pectoralis Major, Tibialis Anterior; according to their *function*, as Flexors, Extensors, etc.; according to their attachments, as Sterno-Mastoid; and according to the *number* of parts of which the muscle is composed, as Biceps—of two heads, Triceps—of three heads.

Their names also sometimes imply a combination of these features, as *Flexor Profundus Digitorum*, flexor—action, profundus—position, digitorum—point of attachment.

Skeletal muscles are usually attached to two definite points, the more fixed point being named the *origin* and the more movable point the *insertion*. The origin is considered to be the point from which the muscle arises, and the insertion the point to which the muscle passes, the latter point being the structure providing attachment which is to be moved by that particular muscle. With the exception of a very few, each muscle can act on either point; thus the origin and insertion are said to become reversed. For example: Biceps arises from the scapula and passes down the arm to be inserted into the radius; thus the scapula being the more fixed point, the radius is the point moved by the biceps, but if a horizontal bar is grasped by the hands and the body raised to the arms, biceps will contract to assist in this movement, and will then act with the origin

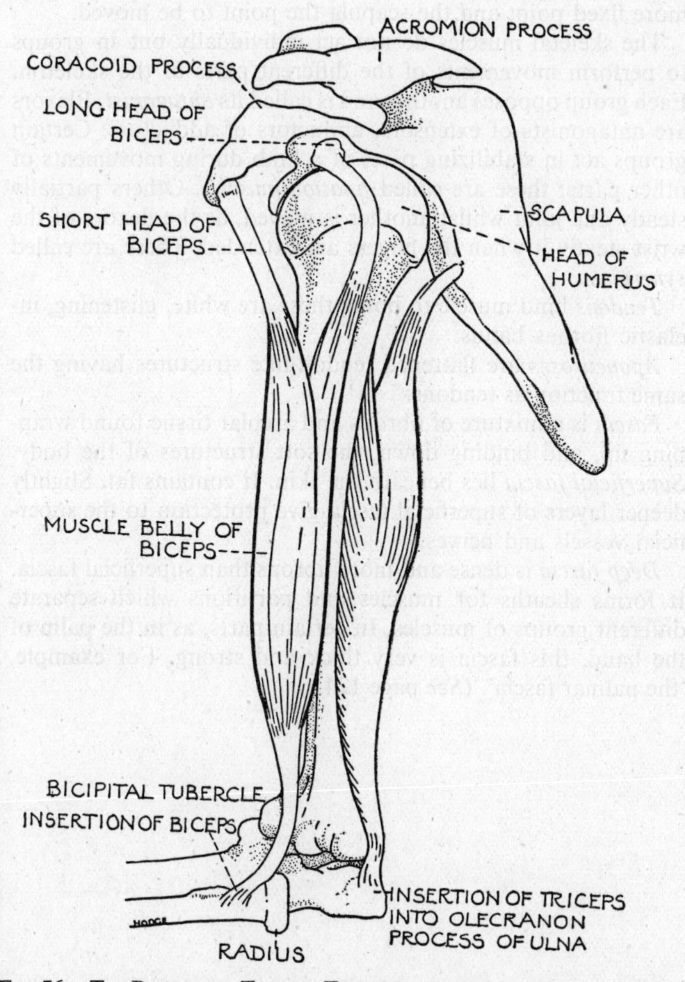

FIG. 76.—THE BICEPS AND TRICEPS. THESE ARE TYPICAL SKELETAL MUSCLES. NOTE THE TENDONS OF ORIGIN AND INSERTION, ALSO THE BELLY OF THE MUSCLE.

and insertion reversed. In this case the radius becomes the more fixed point and the scapula the point to be moved.

The skeletal muscles do not act individually but in groups to perform movements of the different parts of the skeleton. Each group opposes another and is called its *antagonist*. Flexors are antagonists of extensors, abductors of adductors. Certain groups act in stabilizing parts of a limb during movements of other parts; these are called *fixation muscles*. Others partially steady one joint whilst another is moved, as the flexors of the wrist steady it when the fingers are extended. These are called *synergists*.

Tendons bind muscle to bone; these are white, glistening, inelastic fibrous bands.

Aponeuroses are flattened tendon-like structures having the same function as tendons.

Fascia is a mixture of fibrous and areolar tissue found wrapping up, and binding down, the soft structures of the body. *Superficial fascia* lies beneath the skin. It contains fat. Slightly deeper layers of superficial fascia give protection to the superficial vessels and nerves.

Deep fascia is dense and more fibrous than superficial fascia. It forms sheaths for muscles and partitions which separate different groups of muscles. In certain parts, as in the palm of the hand, this fascia is very thick and strong. For example, 'the palmar fascia'. (*See* page 124.)

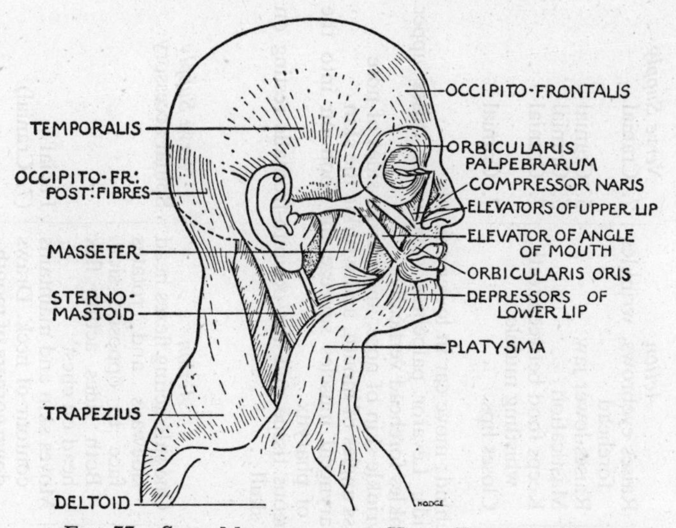

FIG. 77.—SOME MUSCLES OF THE HEAD, FACE AND NECK.

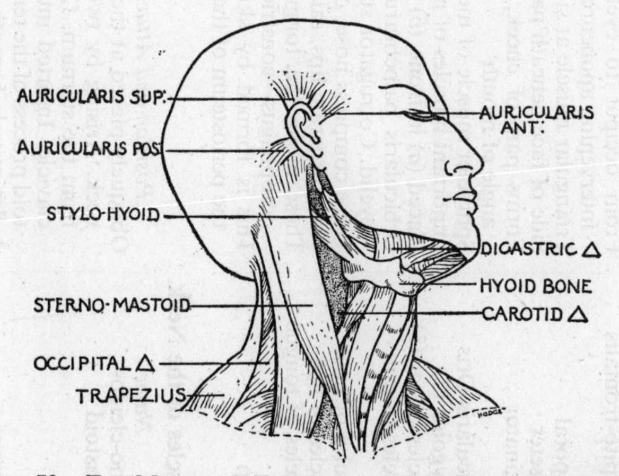

FIG. 78.—THE MUSCULAR FORMATION OF THE TRIANGLES OF THE NECK.

Muscles of the Head and Face

Name	*Position and Attachments*	*Action*	*Nerve Supply*
Occipito-frontalis	From occiput to eyebrow, with intervening aponeurosis	Raises eyebrows, wrinkles forehead	7. Cranial
Temporal	Triangular muscle at side of head	Raises lower jaw	5. Cranial
Masseter	Side of face beneath parotid gland	Mastication	5. Cranial
Buccinator	Forms part of cheek, passing to angle of mouth	Keeps food between teeth, whistling muscle	7. Cranial
Orbicularis Oris	Sphincter muscle of mouth	Closes lips	7. Cranial
Pterygoids (2)	Important muscles of mastication		
Muscles of ear (3)	Placed (*a*) in front, (*b*) above, (*c*) behind; move ear in lower animals		
Muscles of eye	Orbicularis palpebrarum; closes lids. Levator palpebrae superioris: raises upper eyelid. Corrugator supercilii: wrinkles forehead vertically		
Muscles of nose	These compress nose, dilate nose, wrinkle skin of nose, and elevate sides of nose		
Muscles of lips	These separate lips, raise and depress angles of mouth, and wrinkle the skin		
Muscles of tongue	These move the tongue. Four pharyngeal muscles squeeze the food on into the oesophagus—constrictor muscles of pharynx		
Scalp	This is formed by skin, sub-cutaneous tissue and the occipito-frontalis resting on the periosteum of the vault of the skull		

Muscles of the Neck

Name	*Position and Attachments*	*Action*	*Nerve Supply*
Sterno-cleido-mastoid	Obliquely placed at the side of the neck. Arising by two heads (1) from the sternum, (2) from the clavicle. Inserted into the mastoid process of the temporal bone	One side acting flexes head sideways and rotates face to opposite side. Both sides acting flex head on chest	Spinal accessory
Platysma	A flat muscle beneath the skin of the neck	Moves skin and maintains contour of neck. Draws down corners of mouth	Facial (7. Cranial)

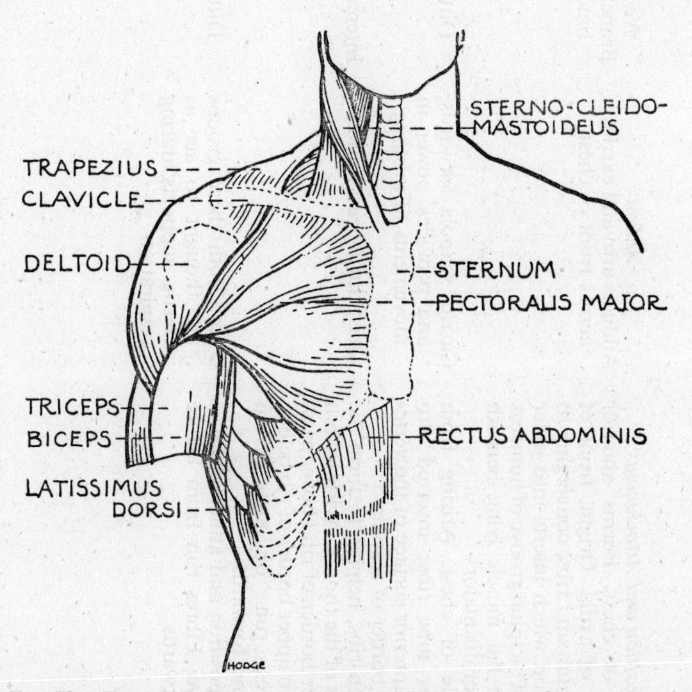

FIG. 79.—THE MUSCLES OF THE ANTERIOR ASPECT OF THE SHOULDER AND CHEST (RIGHT).

The deformity of wry neck or torticollis is due to contraction of the sterno-mastoid muscles.

Muscles of the Chest

Name	*Position and Attachments*	*Action*	*Nerve Supply*
Pectoralis Major .	Front of chest. Forms anterior part of axilla. Origin, front of sternum and ribs, converging to tendon which inserts into outer lip of bicipital groove of humerus	Adducts arm and carries it across front of chest	Branches from the brachial plexus
Pectoralis Minor .	A thin flat muscle lying beneath pectoralis major		
Serratus Magnus (anterior)	At side of chest. Arising from upper nine ribs; inserted into the anterior surface of the vertebral border of scapula	Carries scapula forwards, and provides power in movements of pushing	Ditto
External Intercostals	Between ribs, helping to form the sides of the thorax. Arising from lower border of rib above, passing to upper border of rib below. Fibres run obliquely from behind forwards	Assist during respiration	Intercostals
Internal Intercostals	Same position and attachments as above. Fibres run from before backwards	Ditto. Both these groups are thought to act as elastic supports during respiration	Ditto

The Diaphragm. The diaphragm is a dome-shaped muscle separating the thoracic from the abdominal cavities. It forms the floor of the former and the roof of the latter cavity.

It arises from the lumbar vertebrae by two pillars or crura, from the posterior surface of the ensiform process, from the inner surfaces of the lower six pairs of ribs and converges to form a central tendinous portion.

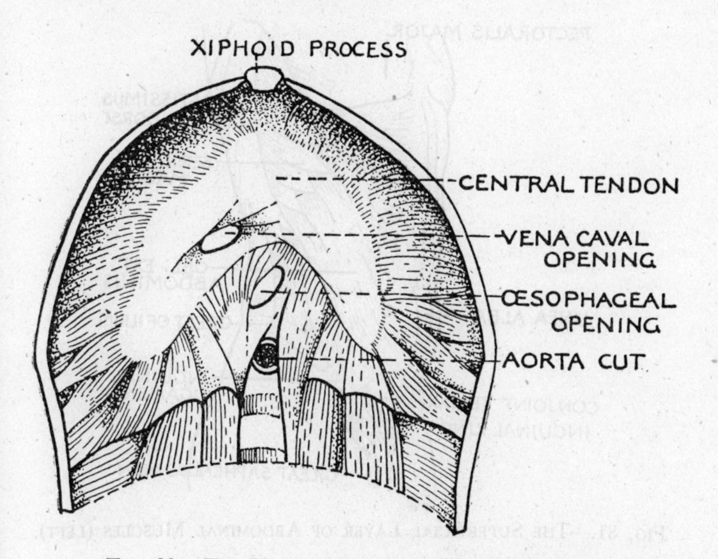

FIG. 80.—THE UNDER SURFACE OF THE DIAPHRAGM.

Contraction of the muscle fibres decreases the height of the dome of the diaphragm, therefore enlarging the vertical diameter of the thoracic cavity; this movement brings about inspiration. In expiration the fibres of the muscle relax and it returns to its former position, so the size of the thorax is again decreased.

The diaphragm is the chief muscle of inspiration. It also compresses the abdominal viscera and assists in the acts of micturition, defaecation, and parturition. The height of the diaphragm changes with posture. It is highest when lying and lowest when erect. It is for this reason that patients suffering from dyspnoea are more comfortable when sitting up.

There are three openings in the diaphragm: the *aortic* opening for the passage of the aorta and thoracic duct, the *oesophageal* opening through which the oesophagus and the vagus nerves pass and the *caval opening* for the passage of the inferior vena cava.

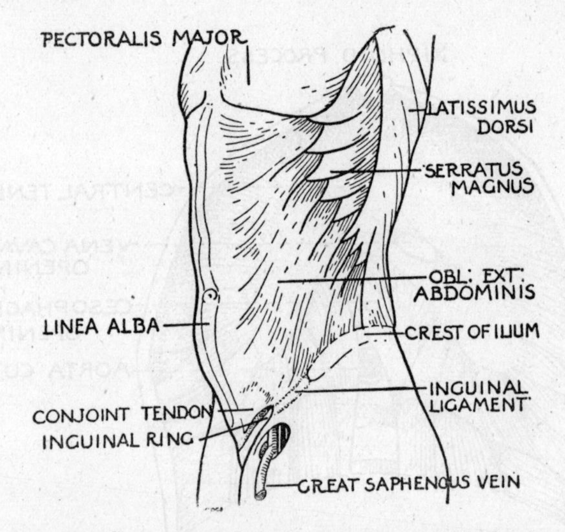

FIG. 81.—THE SUPERFICIAL LAYER OF ABDOMINAL MUSCLES (LEFT).

Relations of the Diaphragm. Above, the apex of the heart and the pericardium, the bases of the lungs and the pleurae.

Below, the liver, stomach, spleen, both suprarenal glands, and both kidneys.

The oesophagus, inferior vena cava, and the vagus nerves pass through the diaphragm, the aorta and thoracic duct pass behind it.

Nerve supply—Phrenic.

Abdominal Muscles

Name	*Position and Attachments*	*Action*	*Nerve Supply*
Rectus Abdominis	A long flat muscle down the front of the abdomen from the sternum to the pubis on either side of the middle line	Flexes spine, as in bowing. Supports viscera	Intercostals
Obliquus Externus Abdominis	With fibres running obliquely from the lower ribs to the iliac crest	Flexes trunk laterally. Rotates trunk, supports viscera	Ditto
Obliquus Internus Abdominis	Position same as above muscle, but fibres run in opposite direction	Assists obliquus externus abdominis	Ditto
Transversalis Abdominis	Beneath two preceding muscles, the fibres running transversely	Assists the oblique muscles	Ditto
Quadratus Lumborum	In the lumbar region, each side of the vertebral column from the last rib to the iliac crest	Assists abdominal muscles	Branches from lumbar plexus

Inguinal Canal. A canal formed in the muscles of the anterior abdominal wall, above Poupart's ligament, directed obliquely from without, inwards and downwards. It contains the spermatic cord in the male, the round ligament in the female; and also transmits nerves and blood vessels.

Poupart's Ligament (the *inguinal ligament*) is formed by a thickened portion of the lower border of the external oblique muscle of the abdomen. It passes from the anterior superior iliac spine to the pubic spine. Beneath it the femoral artery and vein and the anterior crural (*femoral*) nerve pass into the thigh.

Linea Alba, a white line: a line of tendon along the middle of the abdomen from the ensiform cartilage to the pubis. It separates the two recti muscles. It is interrupted by the *umbilicus* in the foetus, the orifice of which closes a few days after birth.

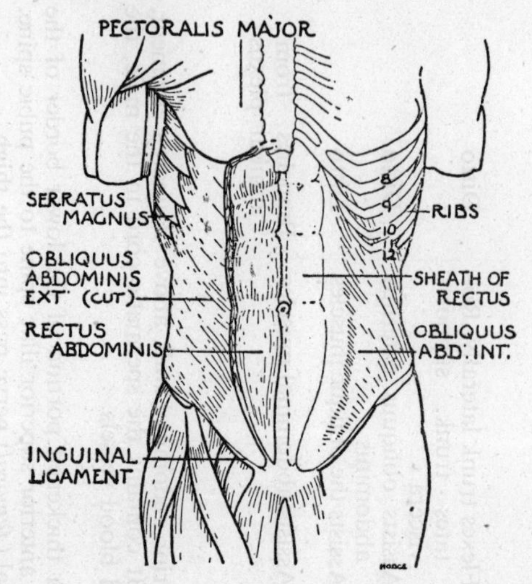

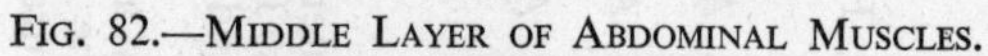
FIG. 82.—MIDDLE LAYER OF ABDOMINAL MUSCLES.

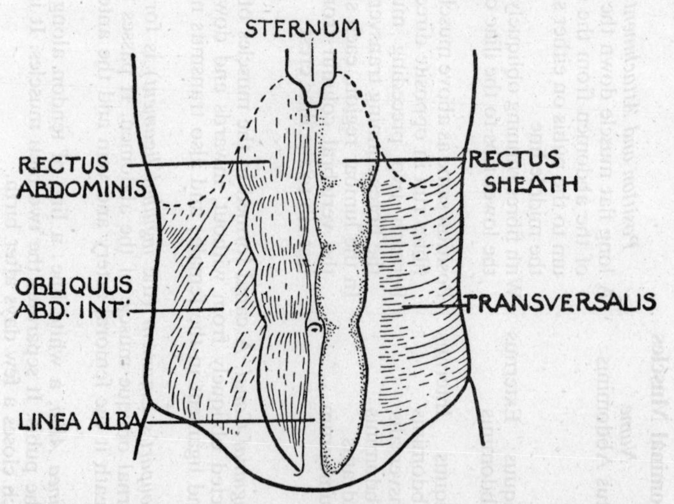

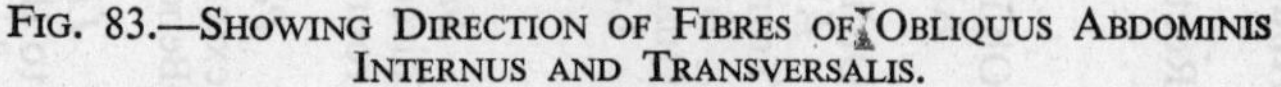
FIG. 83.—SHOWING DIRECTION OF FIBRES OF OBLIQUUS ABDOMINIS INTERNUS AND TRANSVERSALIS.

Muscles of the Back

Name	*Position and Attachments*	*Action*	*Nerve Supply*
Trapezius . .	A broad flat muscle, on back of neck and shoulders. Origin, occipital bone, spines of vertebrae. Insertion: back of clavicle, upper border spine of scapula, and acromion process	Draws head back, draws shoulders together, thus expanding chest. Assists in shrugging shoulders	Spinal accessory and brachial plexus
Latissimus Dorsi .	Broad flat muscle over lower part of chest and loins. Origin: lower dorsal vertebrae, lumbar fascia, crest of ilium. Insertion: converging to tendon attached bicipital groove of humerus	Draws humerus down and back. Rotates arm inwards. When arm is fixed, raises body to arms	Brachial plexus
Erector Spinae .	Deep muscles of back, lying in a groove each side of the vertebral column	Extend spine. Keep trunk erect	Posterior primary divisions. Dorsal nerves

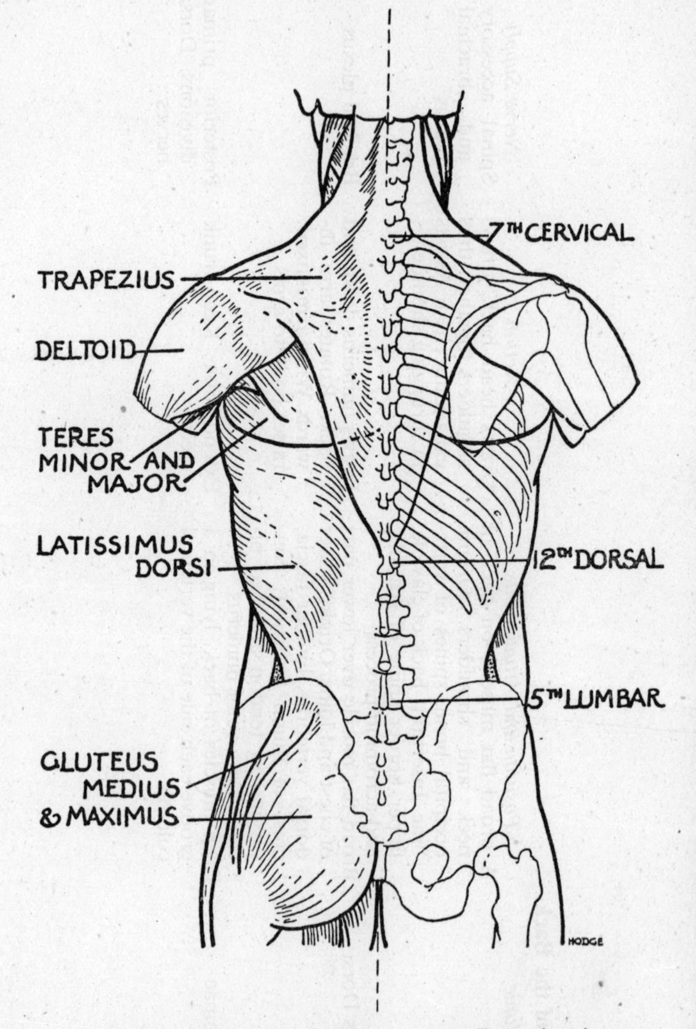

FIG. 84.—SUPERFICIAL MUSCLES OF THE BACK (LEFT).

Muscles of Upper Extremity: Shoulder and Arm

Name	*Position and Attachments*	*Action*	*Nerve Supply*
Deltoid	On point of shoulder as an epaulet. Arises, lateral third clavicle, acromion process, and spine of scapula. Inserted deltoid impression lateral side shaft of humerus	Raises arm at right angles with the body	Circumflex, from brachial plexus
Subscapularis	Subscapular fossa. Passes from fossa to lesser tuberosity of humerus	Internally rotates humerus	Branches from brachial plexus
Supraspinatus	Fills supraspinous fossa of scapula and passes to great tuberosity of humerus	Assists deltoid	Ditto
Infraspinatus	Fills upper part infraspinous fossa, passes to great tuberosity of humerus	Externally rotates humerus	Ditto
Teres Major	A thick muscle arising from impression near inferior angle scapula; inserted into medial lip bicipital groove on humerus	Assists latissimus dorsi in drawing arm down and back	Ditto
Teres Minor	Lies beneath teres major. Passes from axillary border of scapula to humerus		Ditto

Muscles of Upper Extremity: Shoulder and Arm—*continued*

Name	*Position and Attachments*	*Action*	*Nerve Supply*
Biceps . . .	A long muscle, arises by two heads (1) from coracoid process, (2) from scapula above glenoid cavity; the latter tendon passes through shoulder joint, then lies in bicipital groove of humerus. Insertion on tubercle of radius	Supinates forearm, flexes elbow	Musculo-cutaneous from brachial plexus
Coraco-brachialis .	A thin muscle beside biceps; passes from coracoid process scapula, to humerus	Adducts arm	Ditto
Brachialis . .	A broad muscle in front of elbow joint; arises from front shaft of humerus, inserted front coronoid process ulna	Flexes elbow	Ditto and Radial
Triceps . . .	Back of arm, arising by 3 heads (1) from scapula, (2) and (3) from back of shaft of humerus external and internal to musculo-spiral groove. Inserted into olecranon process of ulna	Extends elbow	Radial

Muscles of Upper Extremity: Superficial Flexors and Pronators

Name	*Position and Attachments*	*Action*	*Nerve Supply*
Pronator Radii Teres	From medial epicondyle humerus to lateral surface shaft radius	Pronates hand	Median
Flexor Carpi-radialis	From common tendon of origin on medial epicondyle humerus to front of carpus	Flexes wrist	Ditto
Palmaris Longus .	Ditto	Ditto and makes palmar fascia tense	Ditto
Flexor Carpi-ulnaris	Ditto	Flexes wrist	Ulnar
Flexor Sublimis Digitorum . .	From similar origin and passes to second phalanges of fingers	Flexes wrist and fingers	Median

Deep Flexors and Pronators

Name	*Position and Attachments*	*Action*	*Nerve Supply*
Pronator Quaratus	Flat square muscle passing from ulna to radius anteriorly above wrist joint	Pronates hand	Median
Flexor Profundus Digitorum . .	Front of shaft of ulna to terminal phalanges of fingers	Flexes wrist and fingers	Median and ulnar
Flexor Longus Pollicis . .	Front of shaft of radius to terminal phalange of thumb	Flexes wrist and thumb	Median

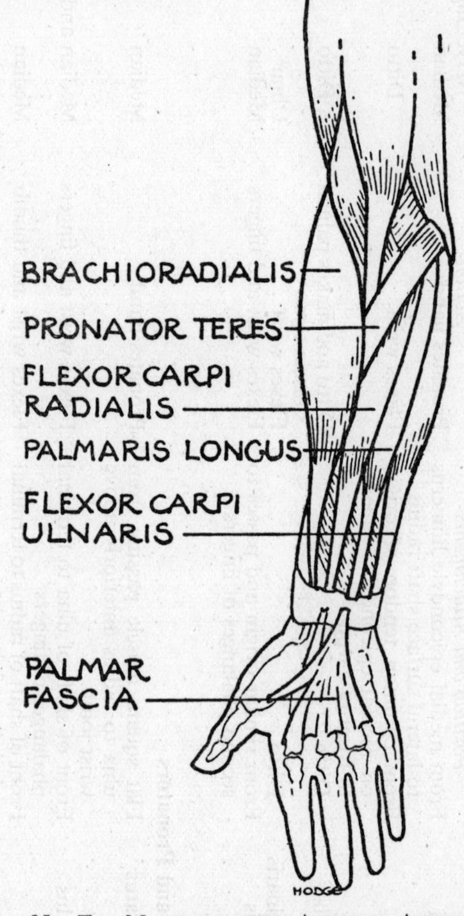

FIG. 85.—THE MUSCLES ON THE ANTERIOR ASPECT OF THE FOREARM (RIGHT).

Muscles of Upper Extremity: Superficial Extensors and Supinators

Name	*Position and Attachments*	*Action*	*Nerve Supply*
Brachioradialis (*supinator longus*)	From ridge above extensor condyle humerus; fleshy for a few inches, then tendinous; inserts base styloid process radius	Supinates forearm, flexes elbow	Radial
*Extensor Carpi Radialis Longus	Arises below supinator longus; inserts base 2nd metacarpal	Extends wrist	Ditto
*Extensor Carpi Radialis Brevis	Extensor epicondyle humerus to base 3rd metacarpal	Ditto	Ditto
*Extensor Communis Digitorum	From extensor epicondyle to split into four tendons which insert 2nd and 3rd phalanges	Extends wrist and fingers	Ditto
*Extensor Minimi Digiti	Same origin and inserts into back proximal phalange little finger	Extends wrist and little finger	Ditto
*Extensor Carpi Ulnaris	Same origin and inserts base 5th metacarpal	Extends wrist	Ditto

Deep Extensors and Supinators

Supinator Brevis	Curves round upper part of radius from below lesser sigmoid cavity of ulna to front of radial shaft	A strong supinator of forearm	Radial

Deep Thumb Extensors. Three in number, passing from back of shaft of radius and ulna to act on (1) the carpo-metacarpal joint, (2) the metacarpo-phalangeal joint, (3) the interphalangeal joint of the thumb.

Extensor Indicis. Passes to index finger to assist common extensor.

* Extensors of wrist, extend or dorsi-flex it; which means they bend it backwards.

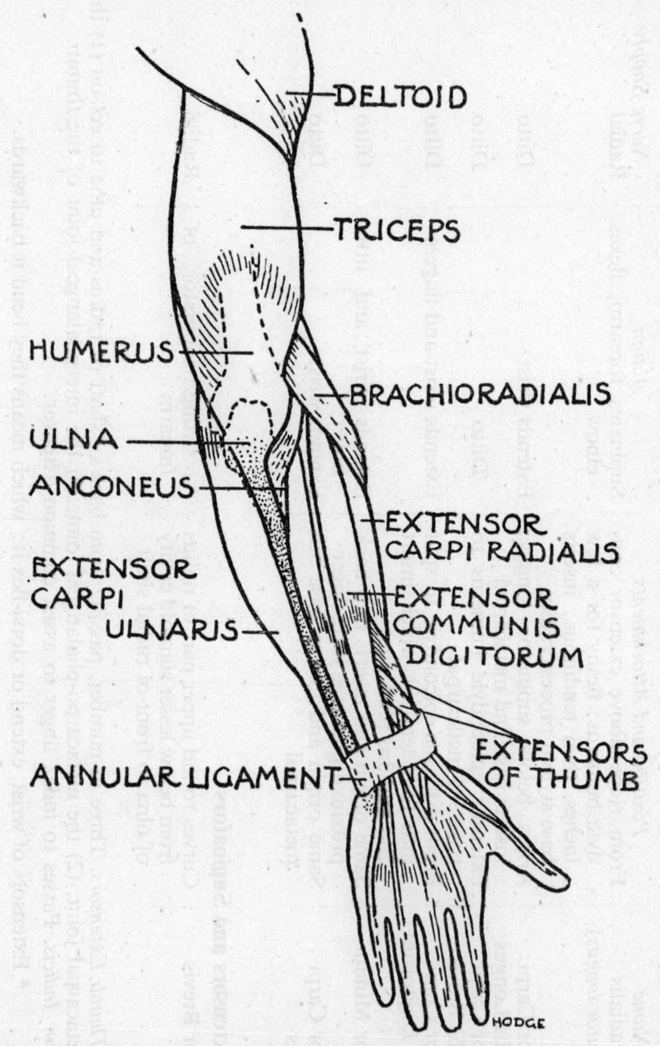

FIG. 86.—THE EXTERIOR MUSCLES ON THE POSTERIOR ASPECT OF THE FOREARM (RIGHT).

Paralysis of the extensor muscles of the wrist and fingers results in 'wrist- drop'. It occurs in lead poisoning.

Other Important Structures of the Wrist and Hand

Palmar Fascia. A specially thickened portion of the deep fascia, spread out over the palm of the hand and binding down the deep structures.

Annular Ligaments. Also thickened portions of deep fascia passing over the front and back of the carpus binding down the tendons which pass to the hands and feet.

Synovial Sheaths. Sheaths of synovial membrane which surround the tendons as they pass beneath the annular ligaments.

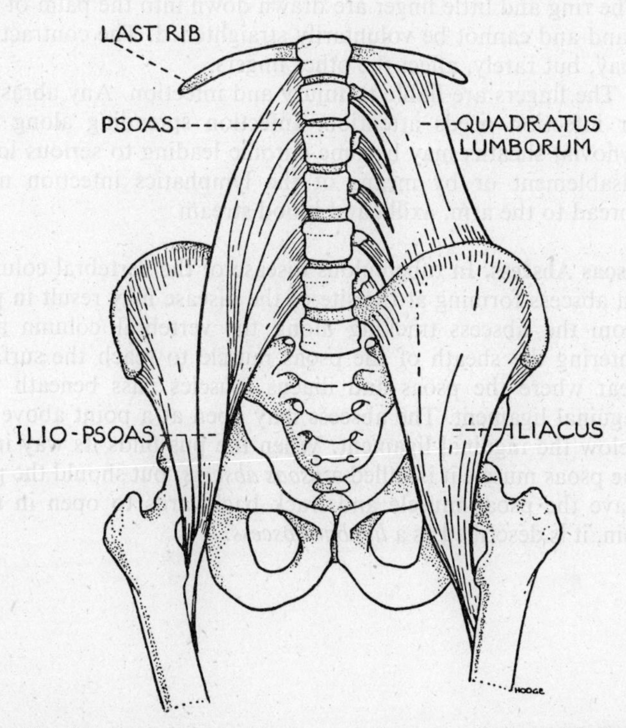

FIG. 87.—SHOWING THE POSITION OF THE PSOAS AND ILIACUS MUSCLES. ON THE RIGHT THE BLENDING OF THE TWO MUSCLES IS SHOWN AS THEY PASS TO THEIR COMMON INSERTION ON THE SMALL TROCHANTER OF THE FEMUR.

Thenar Eminence. A group of five small muscles forming the fleshy part of the ball of the thumb.

Hypothenar Eminence. A group of four small muscles forming the pad of muscle on the outer side of the palm in line with the little finger.

Lumbricales. Small muscles deeply placed in the palm of the hand.

Interossei. Small muscles placed between the metacarpal bones.

The palmar fascia sometimes becomes contracted and this produces a deformity known as 'Dupuytren's Contraction'. The ring and little finger are drawn down into the palm of the hand and cannot be voluntarily straightened. The contraction may, but rarely, affect the other fingers.

The fingers are liable to injury and infection. Any abrasion or infection needs attention. Infection spreading along the synovial sheaths may become chronic leading to serious local disablement or by means of the lymphatics infection may spread to the arm, axilla and blood stream.

Psoas Abscess. In tuberculous disease of the vertebral column an abscess forming at the site of the disease may result in pus from the abscess tracking along the vertebral column and entering the sheath of the psoas muscle to reach the surface near where the psoas and iliacus muscles pass beneath the inguinal ligament. The abscess may open at a point above or below the inguinal ligament. When the pus finds its way into the psoas muscle it is called a *psoas abscess*, but should the pus leave the psoas muscle and track backwards to open in the loin, it is described as a *lumbar abscess*.

Muscles of Lower Extremity: Hip Joint and Thigh

Name	*Position and Attachments*	*Action*	*Nerve Supply*
Ilio-psoas: Psoas	Back of abdominal cavity, arising sides of lumbar vertebrae, passes beneath Poupart's ligament; inserted lesser trochanter of femur	Flexes thigh	Branches from lumbar plexus
Ilio-psoas: Iliacus	Lies in, and arises from, the iliac fossa, unites with psoas to be inserted into lesser trochanter and bone below it	Ditto	Femoral
Quadriceps Femoris (four): Rectus Femoris, Vastus Externus, Vastus Internus, Crureus or Vastus Intermedius	On front of thigh passing from ilium and shaft of femur to unite in a common tendon and be inserted into the upper border of the patella	Extends knee	Ditto
Sartorius	Lies across thigh, from iliac spine to tibia	(Tailor's muscle), aids in action of crossing legs	Ditto
Adductors (four): Pectineus, Adductor Longus, AdductorMagnus, Adductor Brevis	On inner side of thigh, passing from pubis to shaft of femur	Adducts thigh, also externally rotates thigh	Obturator
Hamstrings (three): Biceps (outer), Semi-membranosus, Semi-tendinosus	On back of thigh passing from tuberosity of ischium to tibia and fibula	Flexes knee. Extends thigh	Great sciatic

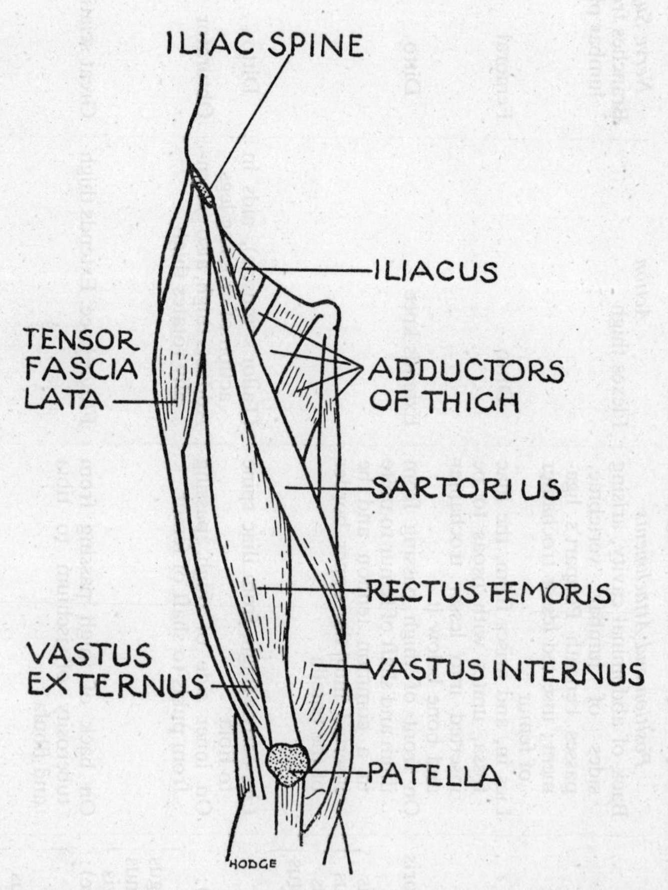

FIG. 88.—THE MUSCLES OF THE ANTERIOR ASPECT OF THE THIGH (RIGHT).

Muscles of Lower Extremity: Hip Joint and Thigh—*continued*

Name	*Position and Attachments*	*Action*	*Nerve Supply*
Gluteal muscles (three) forming the buttock:			
Gluteus Maximus	The largest muscle, forming the prominence of the buttock. Arising from ilium, sacrum, passing to the deep fascia of the thigh and gluteal line of femur	Raises trunk to erect position from stooping. Makes fascia of thigh tense. Also abducts the thigh	Inferior gluteal
Gluteus Medius Gluteus Minimus	Beneath gluteus maximus passing from the ilium to the great trochanter of the femur	Assists gluteus maximus	Superior gluteal

Anterior Tibial Region

Name	*Position and Attachments*	*Action*	*Nerve Supply*
Tibialis Anterior (Anticus)	Front of leg from groove on shaft of tibia to medial aspect of tarsal bones	Dorsi-flexes ankle. Inverts foot	Anterior tibial
Extensor Longus Hallucis	Front of leg from fibula to great toe	Dorsi-flexes ankle. Extends toes	Ditto
Extensor Longus Digitorum	Front of leg from fibula to divide into four tendons for four lesser toes	Dorsi-flexes ankle. Extends toes	Ditto
Peroneal muscles (three):			
Peroneus Longus } Peroneus Brevis }	Passing from fibula to sole of foot. (Tendon of peroneus longus grooves bones of sole of foot)	Evertors of the foot	Musculo-cutaneous
Peroneus Tertius			Anterior tibial

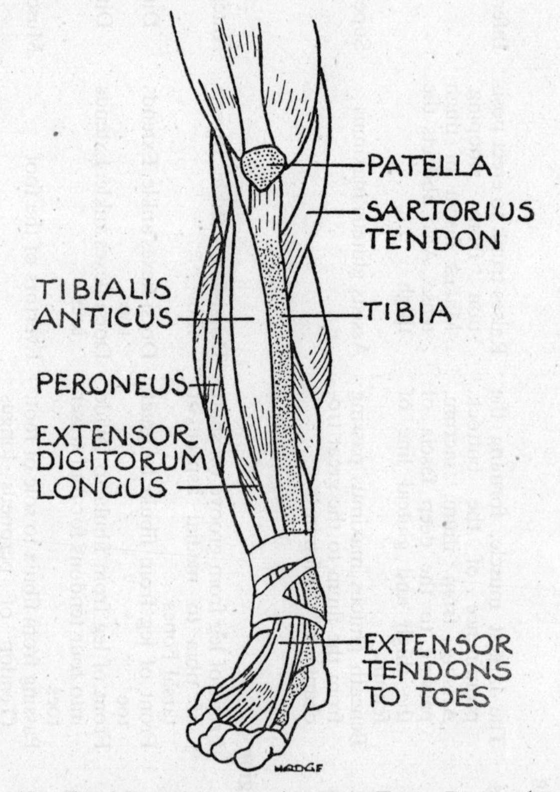

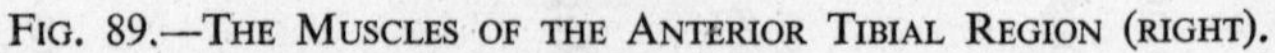
FIG. 89.—THE MUSCLES OF THE ANTERIOR TIBIAL REGION (RIGHT).

Muscles of Lower Extremity: Posterior Tibial Region

Name	*Position and Attachments*	*Action*	*Nerve Supply*
Gastrocnemius	Large muscle of calf of leg. Origin, back of condyles of femur. Inserted by means of tendon of Achilles into calcaneum	Plantar flexes ankle. Raises body on toes. Propels body forwards in walking	Medial popliteal
Soleus	Beneath gastrocnemius, also germinates in tendon of Achilles	Assists gastrocnemius	Posterior tibial
Plantaris	A long thin muscle beside gastrocnemius		
Popliteus	Deeply placed at back of knee	Flexes knee	Medial popliteal
Flexor Longus Hallucis	Back of fibula to great toe	Plantar flexes ankle. Flexes great toe	Posterior tibial
Flexor Longus Digitorum	Back of fibula to four outer toes	Plantar flexes ankle. Flexes toes	Ditto
Tibialis Posterior (Posticus)	Deeply placed at back of leg, passing to plantar surface of the tarsal bones	Inverts foot. Supports arch of foot	Posterior tibial

Tensor Fasciae Femoris. A small muscle on the lateral aspect of the thigh inserted into the deep fascia of this region and on contraction makes the deep fascia tense.

Annular Ligaments. Similar to those of the wrist and having the same function.

Plantar Fascia. Similar in structure to that of the hand. It is arranged in three portions, a central and two lateral.

Tendon of Achilles. A strong tendon by which gastrocnemius is attached to the calcaneum, it lies behind the ankle joint (*see* Fig. 90).

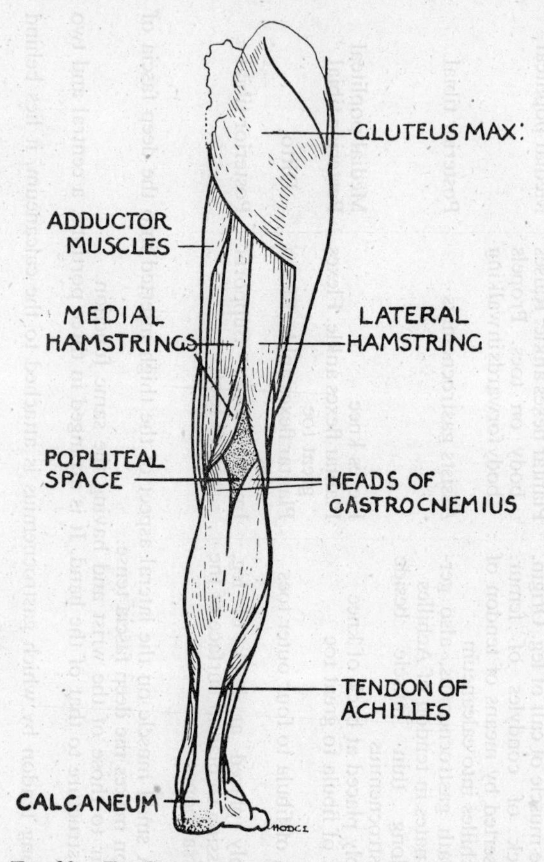

FIG. 90.—THE SUPERFICIAL MUSCLES OF THE BACK OF THE THIGH AND LEG.

Contraction of the hamstring muscles often complicates knee-joint disease, giving rise to the deformity of flexion at the knee joint. Contraction of the tendon of Achilles occurs in drop foot.

Anatomical Spaces.

The Axilla is a pyramidal-shaped space between the arm and the wall of the chest. It is bounded medially by the chest wall

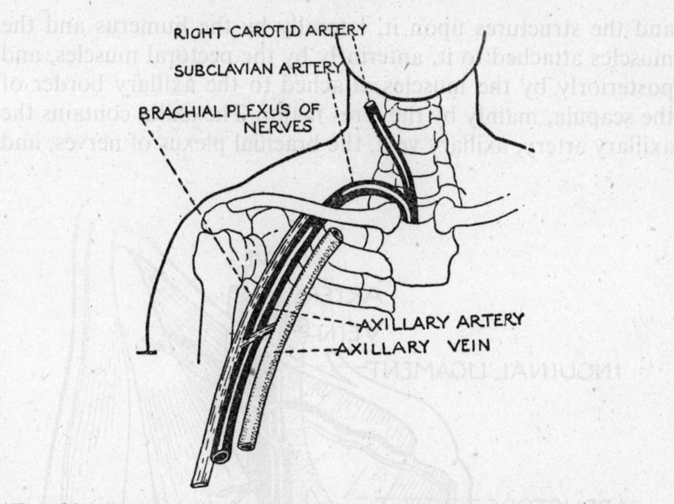

FIG. 91.—POSITION OF THE STRUCTURES CONTAINED IN THE AXILLA—AXILLARY ARTERY AND VEIN, AND THE BRACHIAL PLEXUS.

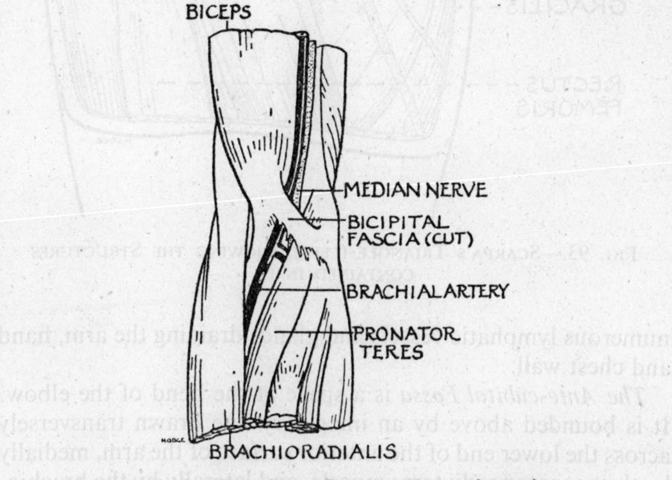

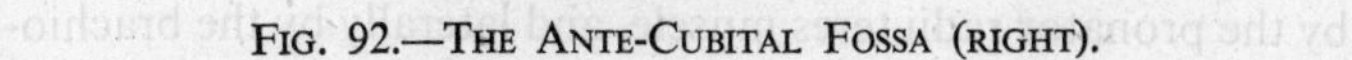

FIG. 92.—THE ANTE-CUBITAL FOSSA (RIGHT).

and the structures upon it, laterally by the humerus and the muscles attached to it, anteriorly by the pectoral muscles, and posteriorly by the muscles attached to the axillary border of the scapula, mainly by the teres major. The axilla contains the axillary artery, axillary vein, the brachial plexus of nerves, and

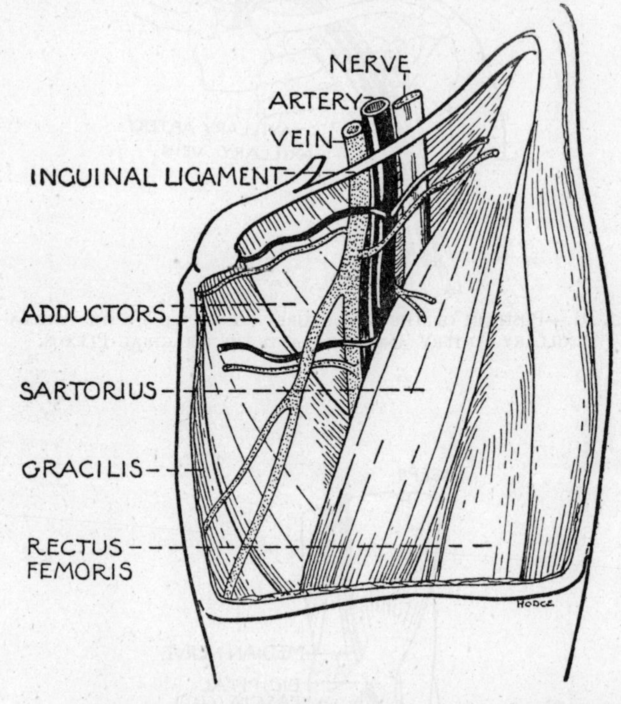

FIG. 93.—SCARPA'S TRIANGLE (LEFT), SHOWING THE STRUCTURES CONTAINED IN IT.

numerous lymphatic vessels and glands draining the arm, hand and chest wall.

The Ante-cubital Fossa is a space at the bend of the elbow. It is bounded above by an imaginary line drawn transversely across the lower end of the anterior surface of the arm, medially by the pronator radii teres muscle, and laterally by the brachioradialis. The floor of this cavity is formed by the brachialis anticus muscle. It contains the brachial artery, median nerve, and the tendon of the biceps muscle.

The Ischio-Rectal Fossa is a space between the ischium and the rectum. It is filled with connective tissue and fat. An ischio-rectal abscess may arise by infection spreading from the rectum as in a case of infected haemorrhoids.

Scarpa's Triangle is placed immediately below the inguinal (Poupart's) ligament which forms the base of the triangle; it is then bounded laterally by the sartorius muscle and medially by the adductors of the thigh. The floor is formed by the deep muscles of the thigh. It contains the femoral artery, femoral vein, femoral nerve, and lymphatic vessels and glands.

Hunter's Canal is a passage running along the front and medial aspect of the thigh to reach the back. It extends from Scarpa's triangle to the popliteal space. The femoral artery and deep femoral vein pass through this canal.

The Popliteal Space lies at the back of the knee joint, the posterior surface of which forms the floor of the space. It is a lozenge-shaped space bounded above by the medial and lateral hamstring muscles and below by the medial and lateral heads of gastrocnemius. It contains the popliteal artery and vein, the medial popliteal nerve, and several small lymphatic glands (*see* Fig. 90).

Chapter 7

THE CIRCULATORY SYSTEM

The circulatory system consists of the blood and the organs concerned in the circulation:

The *Heart*, which is the great pumping organ maintaining the circulation throughout the body,

Arteries carrying blood *from* the heart,

Veins carrying blood *to* the heart,

Capillaries uniting the arteries and the veins and forming the 'capillary lake' where the traffic between nourishment and waste matter proceeds and the interchange of gases takes place, and

Lymphatics which collect, filter, and pass back to the blood stream, the lymph which has exuded through the minute capillary walls to bathe the tissues may also be regarded as part of the circulatory system (*see* Chapter 10).

HEART

The heart is a cone-shaped, hollow, muscular organ, having the base above and the apex below. The apex inclines towards the left side.

Position of the Heart. The heart lies in the thorax, between the lungs and behind the sternum, and directed more to the left than the right side. The exact position may be marked on the body.

A line drawn from the third right costal cartilage half an inch from the sternum, upwards to the second left costal cartilage three-quarters of an inch from the sternum, marks the position of the *base of the heart*.

A point marked on the left side between the fifth and sixth left ribs or in the fifth left intercostal space half an inch internal to a vertical line drawn through the nipple, gives the position of the *apex of the heart*. (This line is known as the nipple line.)

By uniting these two markings by lines, as shown in the accompanying diagram, the position of the heart may be indicated.

Structure of the Heart. The heart is about the size of the closed fist. The adult heart weighs from eight to nine ounces. It is divided by a septum into two sides, right and left. There is no communication between these two sides after birth. Each side of the heart is further subdivided into two chambers, an upper

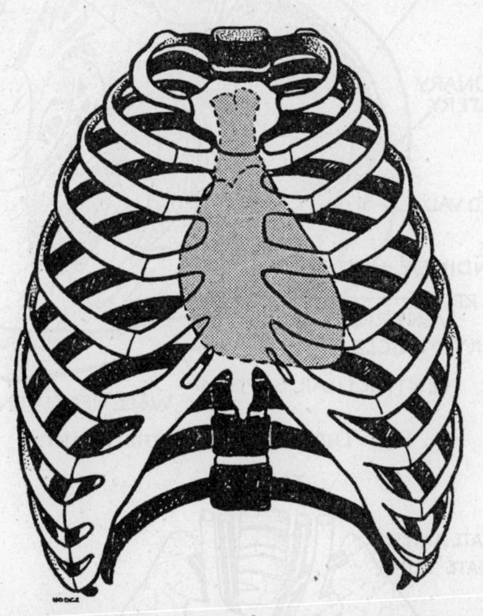

FIG. 94.—THE POSITION OF THE HEART IN RELATION TO THE STERNUM, RIBS AND COSTAL CARTILAGES.

chamber called an *atrium* or receiving chamber, and a lower chamber, a *ventricle* or distributing chamber. There are two atria, right and left, and two ventricles. The atria and ventricles of each side communicate with one another by means of the *atrio-ventricular openings*, which are guarded by valves, on the right side by the *tricuspid valve* and on the left the *mitral valve*. When closed the valves form the floor of the auricles. A small conical muscular pouch which projects from each atrium, is called the *auricle*.

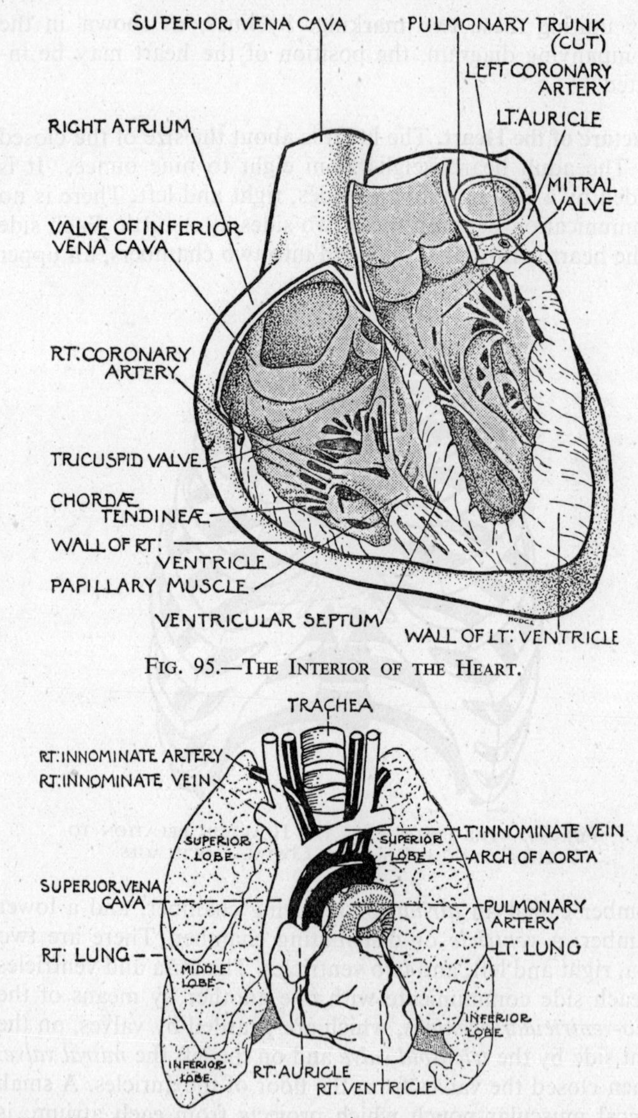

FIG. 95.—THE INTERIOR OF THE HEART.

FIG. 96.—THE HEART, LUNGS, AND GREAT BLOOD VESSELS, FROM THE FRONT.

The atrio-ventricular valves permit of the passage of blood in one direction only, i.e. from above downwards, from atrium to ventricle; and they prevent the blood flowing upwards from ventricle to atrium. The tricuspid valve is composed of three flaps or cusps, and the mitral of two flaps, which gives it some resemblance to a bishop's mitre, hence the name.

The heart is surrounded by a serous membrane called the *pericardium.* There are two layers, the *visceral pericardium* which is closely adherent to the heart, and the *parietal pericardium* which is reflected back from the base of the heart, and surrounds it like a loose sac. By this arrangement the heart lies in a double sac of pericardium with serous fluid between the two layers. The parietal pericardium is firm and inelastic and limits the distension of the organ.

The heart is lined by endothelium; this layer is called the *endocardium.* The valves are simply thickened portions of this membrane.

The thickness of the heart wall is composed of a network of heart muscle fibres, and is known as the *myocardium.*

The heart may thus be described as consisting of three layers:
The *Pericardium*, or outer covering,
The *Myocardium*, the middle muscular layer, and
The *Endocardium*, the inner lining.

The muscular walls of the heart vary in thickness: the ventricles being the distributing chambers have the thickest walls; the walls of the left are thicker than those of the right ventricle. The walls of the atria (auricles) are thin and fibrous.

The interior of each of the ventricular walls is marked by thickened columns of muscle. Some of these project as papillae, the *papillary muscles*, and to the lower borders of these are attached thin tendinous cords, the *chordae tendineae.* These cords have a second attachment to the lower borders of the atrio-ventricular valves, and this attachment prevents the flaps of the valves from being forced up into the atria, when the ventricles contract. Each ventricle holds about three ounces of blood, the atrium slightly less.

The Blood Vessels attached to the Heart. The *superior and inferior venae cavae* empty their blood into the right atrium.

The opening of the latter is guarded by the semilunar valve of Eustachius.

The *pulmonary artery* carries blood away from the right ventricle. The *four pulmonary veins* bring blood from the lungs to the left atrium.

The *aorta* carries blood away from the left ventricle.

The openings of the aorta and the pulmonary artery are guarded by the *semilunar valves.*

Blood Supply and Nerve Supply of the Heart. The right and left *coronary arteries* are the first to leave the aorta, these then divide into smaller arteries which encircle the heart and supply blood to all parts of the organ. The return blood from the heart is collected mainly by the *coronary sinus* and returned directly into the right auricle.

Nerve supply. The heart is supplied by the sympathetic and vagus nerves. Branches from these nerves pass to the sino-auricular node. Control from the sympathetic proper accelerates the rate of the heart beat, and control by the vagus, which is part of the para-sympathetic or autonomic system (*see* page 310), causes the action of the heart to be slowed or inhibited. An exact adjustment between cardiac acceleration and cardiac inhibition results in the heart beating at its normal rate. Emotion, by interfering with the action of the vagus, will cause the heart to beat more rapidly.

THE CARDIAC CYCLE

The events which occur in the heart during the circulation of the blood are spoken of as the *cardiac cycle.*

This is divided into two parts, contraction or *systole* and relaxation or *diastole.* Contraction of the auricles occurs simultaneously and is called the auricular systole; their relaxation, the auricular diastole. Similarly the contraction and relaxation of the ventricles are the ventricular systole and diastole respectively.

The pulse is this action of the heart felt at the arteries; therefore if the pulse count is 70, the cardiac cycle will occur 70 times per minute.

The contraction of the auricles is short and sharp, that of the ventricles is longer and more forcible, and that of the left ventricle the most forcible of any, as it has to force the blood throughout the body, overcoming great resistance, whilst the right ventricle has only to force the blood through the lungs.

The Heart Sounds. Two sounds may be heard during the action of the heart. These are best heard by placing an ear over the precordial region.

The first sound is called the *systolic*, and the second the *diastolic*. The systolic is said to be due to the closing of the

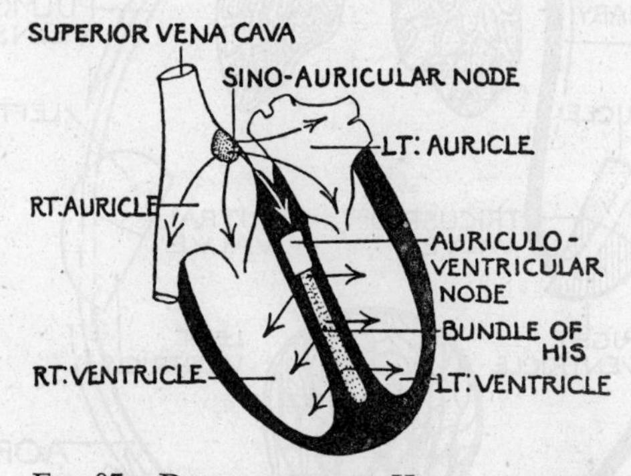

FIG. 97.—DIAGRAM OF THE HEART, SHOWING THE SINO-AURICULAR NODE AND INDICATING THE WAY IN WHICH THE CARDIAC IMPULSE IS CONDUCTED

auriculo-ventricular valves, and the contraction of the ventricles; the diastolic to the closing of the semilunar valves, after the contraction of the ventricles. These sounds are described as 'Lūbb' and 'Dŭp'. The first is long and dull, and the second short and sharp.

The cardiac impulse or apex beat is the impact of the left ventricle against the anterior wall of the chest, occurring during the contraction of the ventricles. This impulse can be felt, and often seen, in the fifth intercostal space, about three and a half inches from the middle line of the sternum, internal to the nipple line.

Properties of Heart Muscle. Cardiac muscle has certain characteristics.

Contractility. By contracting the muscle of the heart pumps out of its chambers the blood which enters during diastole.

Conductivity. The contraction is conveyed (conducted) along every individual fibre of the heart muscle with perfect smoothness. This property is very marked in the bundle of His.

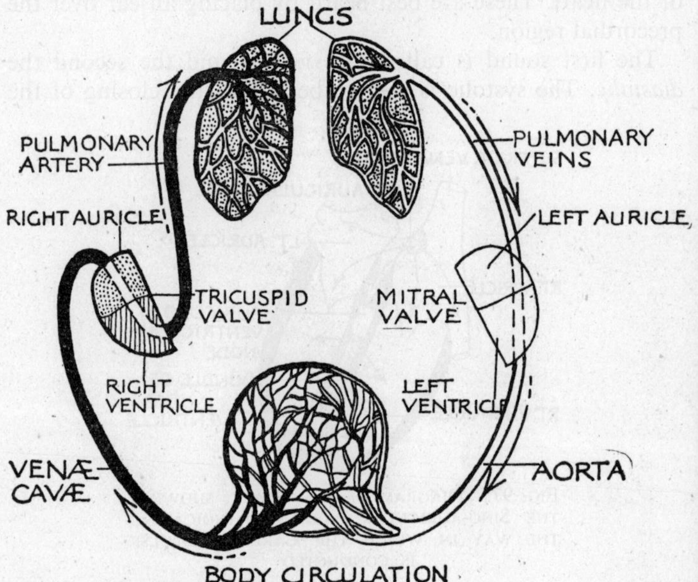

FIG. 98.—A DIAGRAM OF THE CIRCULATION.
The Heart is shown separated into right and left sides. The arrows indicate the direction in which the blood flows.

Rhythm. Cardiac muscle possesses the inherent power of rhythmic contraction. The cardiac impulse starts at the *sino-auricular node* or *sinus*, which is a collection of highly specialized nerve tissue, placed near where the superior vena cava opens into the right auricle. This node is often spoken of as the 'pace-maker of the heart'. It is stimulated by the vagus and sympathetic nerves. The heart beat starts here and passes over both auricles and also passes to the *atrio-ventricular* or *auri-*

culo-ventricular node which lies at the upper part of the inter-ventricular septum. From this node the impulse passes to a special bundle of nerve and muscle tissue known as the bundle of His which passes on the cardiac impulse and spreads it over all parts of the ventricles.

In a condition known as heart-block the bundle of His fails to transmit the impulses started at the sino-auricular node or sinus, so that only one in two or one in three impulses reach the arteries, with the result that the pulse is abnormally slow.

The pulse is the beat of the heart felt at the arteries. It may be felt at any point where an artery crosses a bone and lies superficially, as in the radial pulse and over the temporal artery.

The pulse pressure is the degree of pressure produced by the contraction of the ventricles, i.e. during systole. It is estimated as being below 50 m.m.Hg. and anything over this figure is considered abnormal.

In adult life the pulse rate varies from 65 to 80 beats a minute. It varies with temperature, conditions of living, of work, of food intake and according to the age of the subject as the following table suggests:

Normal Pulse Rate Range. (*Number of beats per minute.*)

In the newly born	140	At the age of 5 years	96–100
During the first year .	120	At the age of 10 years	85–90
During the second year	110	In adult age	65–80

In old age about 60

THE CIRCULATION OF THE BLOOD

The heart is the chief organ of the circulation of the blood. The course of the blood from the left ventricle to the right auricle is called the greater or *systemic circulation.* The course from the right ventricle to the left auricle is the *pulmonary circulation.*

The Systemic Circulation. The blood leaves the *left ventricle* of the heart by the *aorta,* the largest artery in the body. This breaks up into numerous smaller arteries which carry the blood to the different parts of the body. These arterioles divide and sub-divide until finally very minute vessels called capillaries are formed (it is through the thin walls of the capillary blood vessels that the blood gives up oxygen to the tissues, and receives carbonic acid gas in exchange). These capillaries then unite and form larger vessels called venules which in turn become veins, and carry the blood back to the heart. The veins unite and unite again until finally two large venous trunks are formed, the *inferior vena cava* which collects the blood from

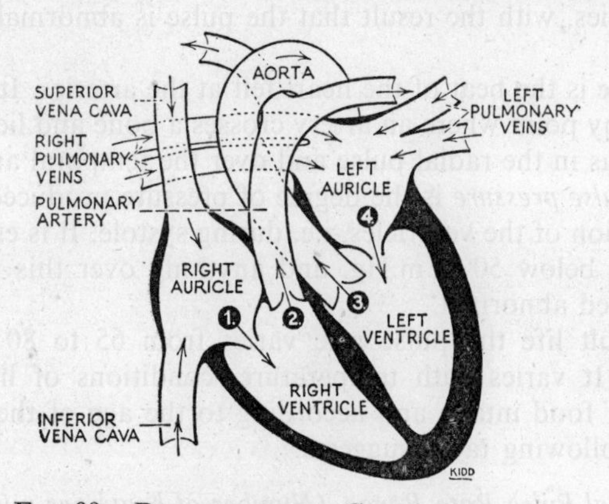

FIG. 99.—DIAGRAM OF THE CIRCULATION OF BLOOD THROUGH THE HEART.

The figures given indicate the situation of the different valves and the arrows indicate the direction in which the blood is flowing through the valvular opening.
1. Tricuspid valve. 3. Aortic valve.
2. Pulmonary valve. 4. Mitral valve.

the trunk and lower extremities and the *superior vena cava* which collects blood from the head and upper extremities. Both these vessels empty their contents into the *right auricle* of the heart.

The blood then passes through the auriculo-ventricular opening to reach the *right ventricle*. The ventricle contracts and pumps the blood into the *pulmonary artery* which divides and carries it to the *right and left lungs*. In the lungs each pulmonary artery branches into numerous arteries, which finally break up into capillaries; these surround the air cells in the lung tissue, and here the blood gives up the impurities received in the tissues of the body, and receives oxygen in exchange.

The capillaries then unite until veins are formed and the blood is carried back to the heart by *four pulmonary veins.* These empty the blood into the *left auricle* of the heart. The blood then passes through the auriculo-ventricular opening into the *left ventricle,* which contracts and pumps the blood into the aorta to begin its circulation around the body again.

The Pulmonary Circulation is that part of the circulation dealing with the purification of the blood in the lungs.

The *impure venous blood* is pumped by the *right ventricle* into the *pulmonary artery* and taken to the *lungs,* where it is purified. The oxygenated arterial blood is then collected by the *four pulmonary veins* and returned to the *left auricle* of the heart.

The Portal Circulation is the circulation of the blood through the liver (*see* Fig. 100).

The blood which has circulated through the stomach, intestines, pancreas, and spleen is collected by the *portal vein* and taken to the liver. In the liver this vein breaks up into smaller veins and capillaries, and these unite with capillaries of the *hepatic artery* and transverse the substance of the liver. This *dual blood supply* is then collected by a system of veins which unite to form several *hepatic veins.* These convey the blood from the liver to the *inferior vena cava,* which lies in a deep groove on the posterior surface of the liver.

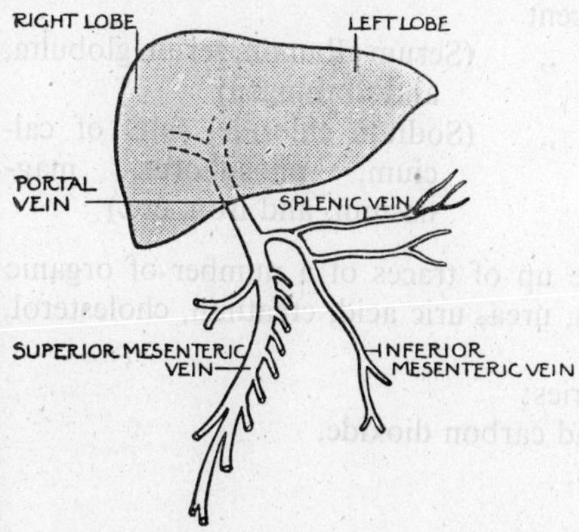

FIG. 100.—A DIAGRAM OF THE PORTAL VEIN AND ITS BRANCHES.

The Liver is shown divided into right and left lobes, the Portal Vein dividing to enter both lobes.

The coronary circulation supplies the heart (*see* page 138).

Chapter 8

THE BLOOD

Blood is a fluid tissue composed of two parts. The intercellular substance is a fluid called plasma, in which float formed elements—the blood cells or corpuscles. The *total volume* of blood forms about one-twelfth of the weight of the body. About 55 per cent, a little over half the volume, is fluid, the remaining 45 per cent of the weight being made up of the blood cells. The volume of blood is constant in health, being regulated to a great extent by the osmotic pressure in the vessels and in the tissues.

The *specific gravity* of whole blood is about 1055, and of blood plasma about 1030.

Composition of Blood. *Blood fluid* or *plasma* is made up as follows:

Water	91 per cent	
Protein	7 ,, ,,	(Serum albumin, serum globulin, and fibrinogen)
Salts	0·9 ,, ,,	(Sodium chloride, salts of calcium, phosphorus, magnesium, and iron, etc.)

The balance is made up of traces of a number of organic materials: glucose, fats, urea, uric acid, creatinin, cholesterol, and amino-acids.

The plasma also carries:

Gases—oxygen and carbon dioxide,
Internal secretions,
Enzymes, and
Antigens.

Blood cells. There are three varieties:

Erythrocytes or red cells,
Leucocytes or white cells, and
Platelets or thrombocytes.

The Red Cells or Erythrocytes are small circular bi-concave discs, so-called because they are concave on both sides, so that when looked at from the side they appear like two crescents placed back to back. There are 5,000,000 red cells in each cubic millimetre of blood. They are a pale buff colour when seen singly, but in masses appear red and give the colour to the blood. In structure they consist of an outer envelope or stroma which encloses a mass of *haemoglobin.*

The red blood cells originate in bone marrow, especially in that of the short, flat, and irregular bones, in the cancellous tissue at the ends of the long bones and in the marrow in the shafts of the ribs. In process of development in the bone marrow the red cells pass through several stages, at first they are large, and contain a nucleus but no haemoglobin; they are next charged with haemoglobin and finally lose their nucleus and are then passed out for circulation in the blood.

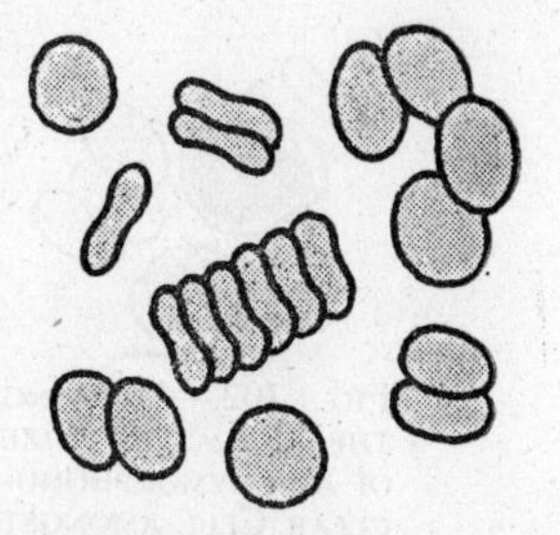

FIG. 101.—RED BLOOD CELLS, SOME ARE IN ROULEAU FORMATION, SHOWING THAT THESE CELLS ARE BI-CONCAVE DISCS.

The red cells live for from twenty-one days to a month and then die and break up in the blood stream. They are retained in the spleen where the stroma is destroyed and the haemoglobin thus liberated reaches the liver by the portal vein. The pigment becomes the colouring matter of bile, and the iron is stored in the liver. Eventually the iron reaches the blood stream again to be used for the formation of new red blood cells.

Haemoglobin is a complex protein which contains a pigment *haematin* rich in iron. It has an affinity for oxygen, and combines with it forming *oxy-haemoglobin.* In this way oxygen is distributed to the tissues.

The amount of haemoglobin present in normal blood is reckoned as 100 per cent, but few people have this ideal amount especially if they live in cities, so that anything over 90 per cent is considered normal. The 100 per cent indicates that there are 15 grammes of haemoglobin in 100 cubic centimetres of blood.

In many forms of anaemia the amount of haemoglobin present in the blood is diminished. In some severe forms it may fall below 30 per cent. As haemoglobin contains the iron necessary to combine with oxygen, it will readily be understood that these patients present symptoms of deficient oxygen such as dyspnoea which is often one of the first indications of anaemia.

Laking of blood is the escape of haemoglobin into the blood fluid as the result of rupture of the cell stroma, sometimes due to toxins or poisons and sometimes due to drugs.

FIG. 102.—SHOWING THE RELATIVE SIZE OF A POLYMORPHONUCLEAR CELL AMONGST RED CELLS.

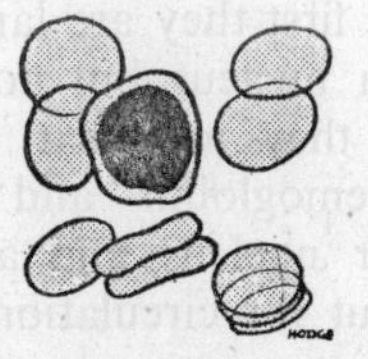

FIG. 103.—SHOWING THE RELATIVE SIZE OF A MONOCYTE AMONGST RED BLOOD CELLS.

White Blood Cells are larger and fewer than the reds. There are from 7,000 to 10,000 (with an average of 8,000) in each cubic millimetre of blood. They are classified as follows.

Granulocytes or *polymorphonuclear cells* form almost 75 per cent of the total white cell count; they are formed in the red marrow of bone. These cells contain a many-lobed nucleus and the protoplasm of the cells is granular, hence the term granular cell or granulocyte. When a drop of blood is placed on a slide and two stains are added in order to make a blood count, cells in this group are typed according to their manner of staining.

Neutrophile cells form the majority; these stain with neutral dyes, or a mixture of the acid and alkaline stains, and appear *purple*.

Eosinophile cells. A very few cells form this group; they take the acid (eosin) stain and appear *red*.

Basophile cells take the basic dyes and stain *blue*.

Lymphocytes form about 25 per cent of the total white cell count (*see* below). These cells are developed in the lymph glands, the spleen, liver, and lymphatic tissue. They are non-granular cells and have no power of amoeboid movements. They are subdivided into small and large lymphocytes. In addition a few larger cells are described as *monocytes*, these cells are capable of amoeboid movement and their function is similar to that of the granulocytes.

Function of the White Cells. The *granulocytes* and *monocytes* play a very important part in protecting the body from micro-organisms. By *phagocytic action* (*phago*—I eat) they ingest living bacteria. As many as 10 to 20 micro-organisms may be seen in a granulocyte under microscopic examination. When performing this function they are called *phagocytes*. By their power of amoeboid movement they can move freely in and out of the blood vessels and wander about in all parts of the body. In this way they can:

Surround any area which is infected or injured,
Take in living organisms and destroy them (ingestion),
Remove other materials, such as bits of dirt, splinters of wood, catgut sutures, etc., by a similar process, and
In addition, the granulocytes possess a protein-splitting ferment which enables them to act on living tissue, break it down, and remove it. In this way diseased or injured tissue can be removed and healing promoted.

As the result of the phagocytic action of the white blood cells inflammation may be entirely arrested. When the activity does not proceed to complete resolution, pus may be formed. *Pus* consists of the dead bodies of friends and foes—phagocytes killed in the battle against the invading germs are called *pus cells*. Many dead germs also are present in pus and in addition there is a considerable amount of liquefied tissue. As the fight proceeds, if the white cells overcome the invading organisms, eventually all signs of destruction will be removed, living and dead bacteria, pus cells and liquefied tissue all being removed by the healthy granulocytes acting as phagocytes.

Of the *function of the lymphocytes* less is known. They have no power of amoeboid movement, they float in the blood stream and are also found in lymphatic tissue in all parts of the body. They do not ingest bacteria, but it is thought that they make valuable antibodies to protect the body against chronic infection and to maintain some degree of immunity to all infections.

Leucocytosis is the term used to describe increase in the total number of white cells in the blood when the increase exceeds 10,000 per cubic millimetre.

Leucopenia means decrease in the white count to fewer than 6,000.

Lymphocytosis—increase in the number of lymphocytes.

Agranulocytosis—a marked decrease in the number of granulocytes or polymorphonuclear cells.

Blood Platelets or Thrombocytes are small cells about one-third the size of a red blood cell. There are 300,000 of them in each cubic millimetre of blood. They are thought to be concerned in the clotting of blood.

Summary of the Number of Blood Cells in each cubic millimetre of Blood

The *normal blood count* or the number of cells per cubic millimetre of blood is approximately:

Red Cells	4,500,000 to 5,500,000	Average	5,000,000
White cells	6,000 to 10,000	Average	8,000

Made up as follows:

	per cent	*Average* per cent
Granulocytes:		
Neutrophile cells . . .	60 to 70	66
Eosinophile cells . . .	1 to 4	3
Basophile cells . . .	$\frac{1}{2}$ to 1.5	1
Lymphocytes (large and small) .	20 to 30	25
Monocytes	4 to 8	5
Total		100

Platelets	250,000 to 500,000	Average	350,000

Blood Plasma is a yellowish fluid, alkaline in reaction, having a specific gravity of about 1030. The composition of plasma and the list of substances contained in it is given on page 144.

Functions of plasma. Plasma acts as the medium for the transmission of nutriment, fats, glucose, amino-acids, and valuable salts to the tissues, and as the medium for carrying away waste materials—urea, uric acid, and some of the carbon dioxide.

Plasma proteins have special functions—they are thought to manufacture protective substances which are then carried by the plasma.

Fibrinogen, one of the proteins in plasma, is essential for the clotting of blood.

By the viscosity of the plasma proteins, the passage of lymph into the tissues is regulated and the volume of the blood is maintained.

The reaction of blood plasma. Blood is always alkaline, the degree of alkalinity depends on the hydrogen-ion concentration and this is expressed as the *p*H of blood.

The *p*H of 7 —— represents a neutral solution
The *p*H from 7 to 1 —— an acid solution
The *p*H from 7 to 14 —— an alkaline solution

It will be seen that the figure *p*H 7 is a neutral solution. Blood is always slightly alkaline—the *p*H of blood is given by different authorities as varying between *p*H 7·45 and 7·25. This figure is constantly maintained, only very slight variation on either side is compatible with life. The maintenance of the constant degree of alkalinity of the blood therefore is most important and this is controlled by the following factors:

The *elimination of carbon dioxide* (which is an acid gas) from the lungs.

The *excretion of acids* in the urine.

The *alkaline reserve* property of the blood, which depends on the presence of sodium bicarbonate in the plasma acting as what is described as a *buffer substance* and preventing reduction of the alkalinity of the blood by acids resulting from metabolism.

The Coagulation of Blood. When blood has been shed, it quickly becomes sticky and soon sets as a red jelly. This jelly or clot contracts or shrinks, and a straw-coloured fluid called *serum* is squeezed out from it.

If shed blood is microscopically examined, very fine threads will be seen, these are the fibrin threads formed from the fibrinogen in the blood plasma *by the action of a ferment thrombin*. These threads entangle the blood cells and together with them form the clot. If shed blood is collected in a test tube, the clot will eventually float in the serum.

The clotting of blood is a complicated process, and several factors are necessary to bring it about. As already stated the ferment *thrombin* is instrumental in converting *fibrinogen* into *fibrin threads*. *Thrombin* is not present in normal unshed blood, but its precursor *prothrombin* or *thrombogen* is present and is converted into the active ferment thrombin by the action of thrombokinase. *Thrombokinase* or *thromboplastin* is an activating agent liberated on injury to the blood cells, it is thought largely by injury to the blood platelets, which, provided that *calcium salts* are present in the blood, will convert thrombogen into thrombin so that clotting can take place.

To produce a clot therefore four factors are necessary:

Calcium salts, normally present in blood,

Cell injury which liberates thrombokinase,

Thrombin formed from thrombogen in the presence of thrombokinase, and

Fibrin formed from fibrinogen in the presence of thrombin.

The *process of clotting* may be expressed by the formula:

Prothrombin+calcium+thrombokinase	=*Thrombin*
Thrombin+fibrinogen	=*Fibrin*
Fibrin+blood cells	=*Clot*

Coagulation is hastened (*a*) by heat a little higher than the body temperature, (*b*) contact with a rough material, such as the roughened edge of a damaged blood vessel or a surgical dressing. It is retarded (*a*) by cold, (*b*) by being kept in a vessel coated with paraffin wax because blood needs to be in contact with a surface that can be wet by water before it will clot, and paraffin is not a water-wetting surface, (*c*) by the addition of potassium citrate or sodium citrate, which removes the calcium salts normally present.

Coagulation time is investigated before large operations are undertaken. A small cut is made in the lobe of the ear with a fairly large needle and drops of blood are collected on blotting paper. Normally bleeding should have ceased in from one to five minutes.

Summary of the Functions of Blood

(1) To act as the transport system of the body conveying all chemical substances required for the nourishment of the body in order that its normal functions may be fulfilled.

(2) The red cells convey oxygen to the tissues and remove some of the carbon dioxide.

(3) The white cells provide many of the protective substances and by phagocytic action some of the cells protect the body against bacteria.

(4) The plasma distributes proteins needed for tissue formation; it provides the tissue fluid by which all cells receive nourishment and forms the vehicle by which waste matter is conveyed to the various excretory organs for elimination.

(5) The internal secretions, hormones, and enzymes are conveyed from organ to organ by means of the blood.

BLOOD PRESSURE

Arterial Blood Pressure is the force of pressure which the blood is exerting against the walls of the blood vessels, in which it is contained. A sphygmomanometer is used to determine the blood pressure. Roughly speaking the normal pressure of blood in the large arteries is reckoned as 100 plus age, so that in a person of 20 years the blood pressure would be 120 m.m.Hg. but this is not invariable as even in advanced years a normal systolic pressure does not exceed 140 to 150 m.m.Hg.

In measuring arterial blood pressure an instrument is used. The upper arm is encircled by an inflatable rubber bag contained in a cuff which is connected to a pressure pump and manometer. By pumping, the pressure in the bag is rapidly raised to 200 m.m.Hg. which is sufficient to obliterate completely the brachial artery so that no blood comes through, and the radial pulse is obliterated also. The pressure is then lowered to a point where the pulse can be felt. At this point the pressure shown on the column of mercury in the manometer is considered to be the *systolic pressure*. The pressure on the brachial artery is then gradually reduced until the heart sounds or pulse beats can be distinctly heard or felt, and the point at which the sounds begin to fade is generally accepted as the *diastolic pressure*.

Normally the difference in pressure between systole and diastole is from 40 to 50 m.m.Hg. The lower limit of systolic pressure in the normal adult is estimated at approximately 105 m.m.Hg., and the upper limit at 150. In women the blood pressure is from 5 to 10 m.m.Hg. lower than in men.

Normal Blood Pressure Range. (In m.m.Hg.)

	Diastolic	*Systolic*
In infancy the blood pressure is .	50	70 to 90
In childhood	60	80 to 100
During the adolescent period .	60	90 to 110
In the young adult . . .	60 to 70	110 to 125
As age advances it is increased .	80 to 90	130 to 150

Blood pressure is produced by the contractible power of the heart muscle which drives the contents of the ventricle into the already over-filled arteries. It changes slightly in physiological variations of exertion as in exercise, with mental changes of anxiety and emotion, in sleep and when eating. For this reason the blood pressure is always taken when a person is relaxed, resting and preferably recumbent.

Factors Maintaining Blood Pressure

The pumping force of the heart. The blood pressure is highest in the blood vessels nearest to the heart, and lowest in the vessels most distant from the heart. By means of cardiac contraction the heart exercises its muscular force on the blood contained in it. The output of the heart beat is spoken of as the *systolic discharge*. The quantity of blood ejected by each ventricle is 60-70 c.c.—a total of 120-140 c.c. for each beat of the heart. The contents of the left ventricle are ejected against much greater resistance than that of the right—hence the powerful muscular walls of the left ventricle.

The quantity of circulating blood. It is necessary to fill any system of tubes to capacity in order to develop pressure. As the blood vessel walls are elastic and distensible these must be over filled before any degree of pressure can be effected. Loss of blood, as in haemorrhage, will result in a fall of pressure. The administration of fluid such as blood plasma or saline will cause the pressure to rise again.

The viscosity of blood. Blood derives its viscosity from plasma proteins and from the number of corpuscles contained in the blood stream. Any change in these two factors will alter the blood pressure. For example in anaemia the blood corpuscles are decreased in number and consequently the pressure is lower whilst in any condition where the number of blood cells is increased, as in leukaemia, the pressure is increased.

The amount of friction exerted by fluid on the walls of tubes through which it is flowing varies according to the viscosity of the fluid. The more concentrated the fluid the greater will be the force required to drive it through the vessels.

The elasticity of the walls of the blood vessels. The pressure is greater in arteries than in veins because the muscular coat of the arteries is more elastic than that of the veins. In the arteries and arterioles pulsation exists but beyond this, in the capillaries and veins the flow is even and continuous.

The Peripheral resistance. This is the resistence offered by the friction of the blood flowing in the vessels. Resistance is highest in the arterioles because the resistance to friction is proportionate to the number of separate vessels through which blood is flowing. There is considerable elasticity in the coats of the arterioles and therefore more energy is expended in forcing the blood from the arterioles onwards into the capillaries and veins towards the right side of the heart.

The velocity of the blood. By velocity we understand the rate at which the blood flows through the different blood vessels. This depends on the size of the bed provided by the vessels or groups of vessels and differs from the blood pressure. The blood in the aorta is moving rapidly. It slows down in the arteries and becomes very slow in the capillaries.

In the capillary bed, or capillary 'lake' as it is sometimes called, the blood is flowing through a very great number of extremely minute vessels but the actual cross section of the area provided by these vessels is about 600 times that of the aorta. This widening of the area through which the same amount of blood flows results in a marked slowing of the stream. It is here, in this very slow stream, that the interchange of gases, absorbed food substances, and waste products takes place between the red blood corpuscles and plasma in the capillaries and the tissue fluids and tissue cells outside the blood vessels. As the blood is collected by veins the rate of flow is increased again and the blood flowing through the lumin of inferior and superior venae cavae together is as rapid as the stream in the aorta. In order to maintain the circulation the blood reaching the heart must be of the same volume as the blood leaving the heart.

Because of the extremely low pressure in the veins other factors assist the flow of blood back to the heart. These include:

The movement of the skeletal muscles exerting pressure on the veins.

The movements produced by breathing, in particular by the rise and fall of the diaphragm which acts as a pump.

A *suction action* exerted by the auricles, which are empty during diastole thus attracting the blood outwards from the veins.

Chapter 9

THE PRINCIPAL BLOOD VESSELS

There are several kinds of blood vessels. *Arteries and Arterioles*, which convey blood away from the heart, always carry pure blood, the exception being the pulmonary arteries which carry venous blood.

Venules and Veins, which carry blood towards the heart and, except the pulmonary veins, always carry impure blood.

Capillaries, are very minute blood vessels in which arterioles terminate and venules begin. They form a delicate network of vessels which ramify in most parts of the tissues of the body.

Certain arteries, such as those carrying blood to the brain, and some of the vessels of the lungs, liver, and spleen, do not terminate in capillaries. These vessels are called *end arteries*.

The Structure of Blood Vessels. *Arteries* are composed of three coats:

Outer fibrous and connective tissue coat, *tunica adventitia*,

Middle muscular and elastic coat, *tunica media*, and

Inner endothelial coat, *tunica intima*.

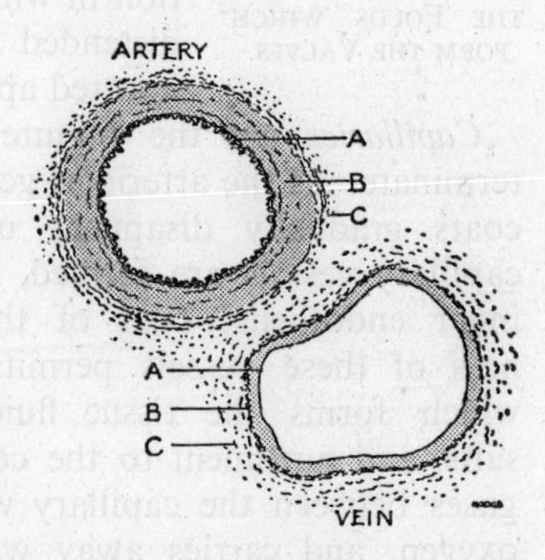

FIG. 104.—STRUCTURE OF ARTERY AND VEIN.
A. Endothelium.
B. Muscular Coat.
C. Fibrous Coat.
Note the thick muscular coat of the artery.

The outer coat is protective. The middle layer is strong; it holds the vessel open and by the state of contraction of the muscle fibres exerts steady pressure on the blood.

The inner endothelial coat is very smooth, being lined by a single layer of flat pavement cells.

The middle coat of the aorta and the larger arteries contains a large quantity of elastic fibres and less muscular tissue, as these require to be very distensible. The smaller arteries and arterioles contain relatively more muscle tissue, as their walls must be readily adapted, by the vaso-motor control, to the needs of the body.

The arteries and arterioles are supplied with blood by a special system of vessels, known as the *vaso-vasorum*; they have also a nerve supply of slender nerve filaments embracing the walls of the vessels.

Veins are composed of the same three layers as the arteries, but the middle muscular layer is thinner, less firm, more collapsible, and much less elastic than the arteries. The veins in the limbs where the blood travels against gravity have valves arranged so as to allow the blood to flow towards the heart, but not in the opposite direction. These valves are crescent-shaped folds composed of the inner lining of the vein, endothelium, strengthened by a little fibrous tissue. The folds are opposite one another, their free edge is in the direction in which the blood is flowing. When distended with blood the valves give a knotted appearance to the vein.

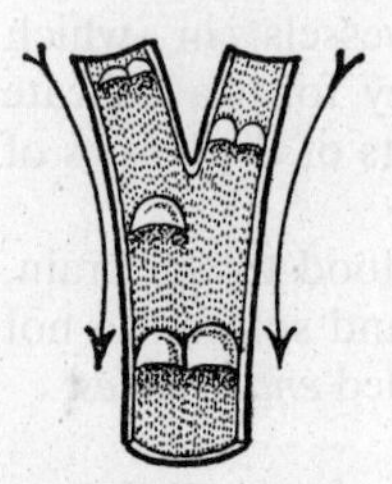

FIG. 105.—A VEIN OPENED TO SHOW THE FOLDS WHICH FORM THE VALVES.

Capillaries are the minute vessels in which the arteries terminate. As the arterioles get smaller and smaller, the three coats gradually disappear until, when the fine hair-like capillary vessels are formed, these consist of one layer, the inner endothelial coat of the arteries. The extreme thinness of these vessels permits the transudation of lymph, which forms the tissue fluid and brings water, valuable salts, and nutriment to the cells, and by the interchange of gases between the capillary vessels and tissue cells, supplies oxygen, and carries away waste matter including carbon dioxide.

The capillaries, therefore, perform a very important function, as they distribute the substances to the tissues which enable the various processes of the body to go on.

The Composition of the Blood Varies in the arteries and veins. *Arterial blood* contains oxygen and is *bright scarlet* in colour because the haemoglobin is combined with oxygen. If an artery is cut across, this bright red blood will be seen to spurt out in jets corresponding with the heart beat.

Venous blood is darker and *purplish* in colour, as much of the oxygen has been given up to the tissues. If a vein is cut across, the blood flows out in an even stream. *Blood in the capillaries* is continually changing in composition and colour, due to the interchange of gases taking place. Capillary bleeding is recognized by the blood oozing smartly on to the surface.

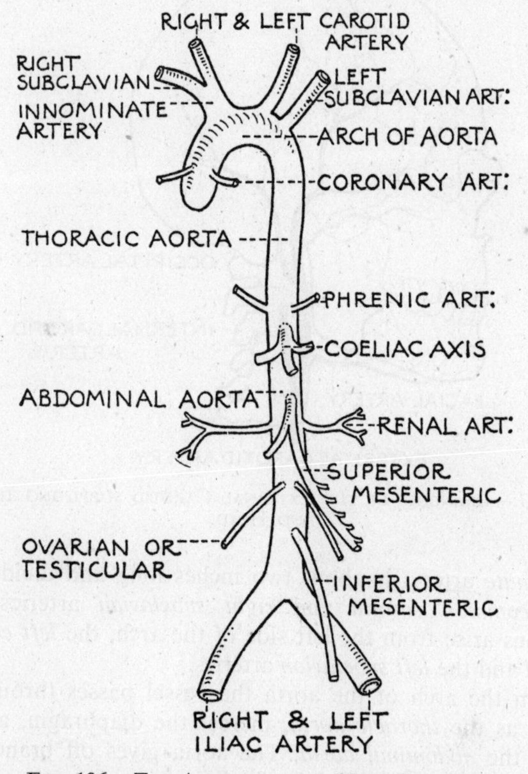

FIG. 106.—THE AORTA AND ITS MAIN BRANCHES.

NAMES AND POSITIONS OF THE CHIEF ARTERIES

The Aorta is the main artery in the body. The part situated in the thorax is known as the *thoracic aorta*. The aorta leaves the left ventricle of the heart where its opening is guarded by a semilunar valve. It then arches over the base of the heart, *as the arch of the aorta*, reaching as high as the manubrium sterni. Three branches arise from this arch. One on the right, the

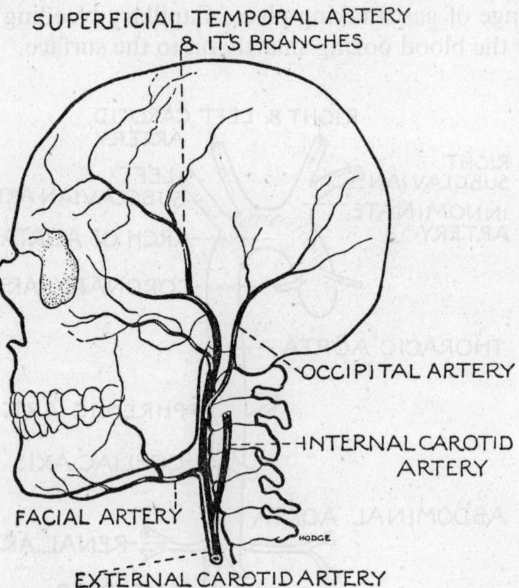

FIG. 107.—BRANCHES OF THE EXTERNAL CAROTID SUPPLYING THE FACE AND HEAD.

innominate artery, is about two inches long and divides into *right common carotid* and *right subclavian* arteries. Two branches arise from the left side of the arch, the *left common carotid* and the *left subclavian* arteries.

From the arch of the aorta the vessel passes through the thorax as the *thoracic aorta*, pierces the diaphragm, and becomes the *abdominal aorta*. The aorta gives off branches to supply the thoracic and abdominal viscera.

The following are the more important branches of the abdominal aorta.

The coeliac axis arises just beneath the diaphragm, and divides into three branches, the *hepatic*, *gastric* (coronary), and *splenic* arteries, to supply the liver, stomach, pancreas, and spleen.

The *mesenteric* arteries, superior and inferior, supply the mesentery and intestines.

The *renal* arteries supply the kidneys.

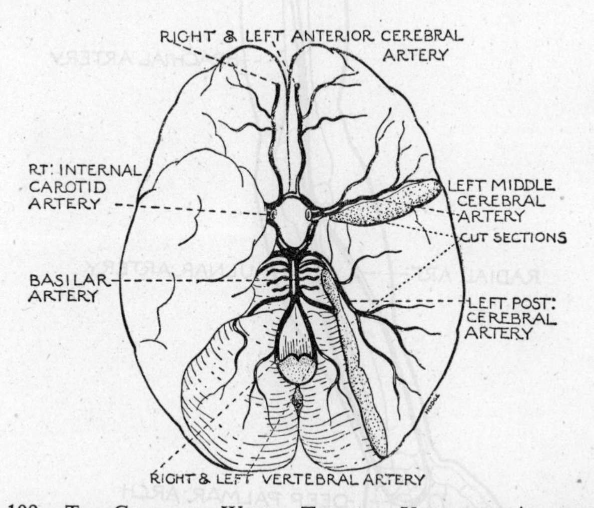

FIG. 108.—THE CIRCLE OF WILLIS. THE TWO VERTEBRAL ARTERIES AT THE BACK AND THE TWO INTERNAL CAROTID ARTERIES IN FRONT UNITE TO FORM THE CIRCLE OF WILLIS, FROM WHICH ARTERIES ARISE TO SUPPLY THE BRAIN. THE CENTRAL LOBE OF THE BRAIN HAS BEEN REMOVED ON THE LEFT SIDE TO SHOW THE MIDDLE AND POSTERIOR CEREBRAL ARTERIES.

The *spermatic* or *testicular* arteries in the male and the *ovarian* in the female supply the testes and the ovaries respectively.

In front of the fourth lumbar vertebra the abdominal aorta divides into the right and left *common iliac* arteries. These then divide into the right and left *internal* and *external iliac* arteries. The internal iliac enters the pelvis to supply the organs there.

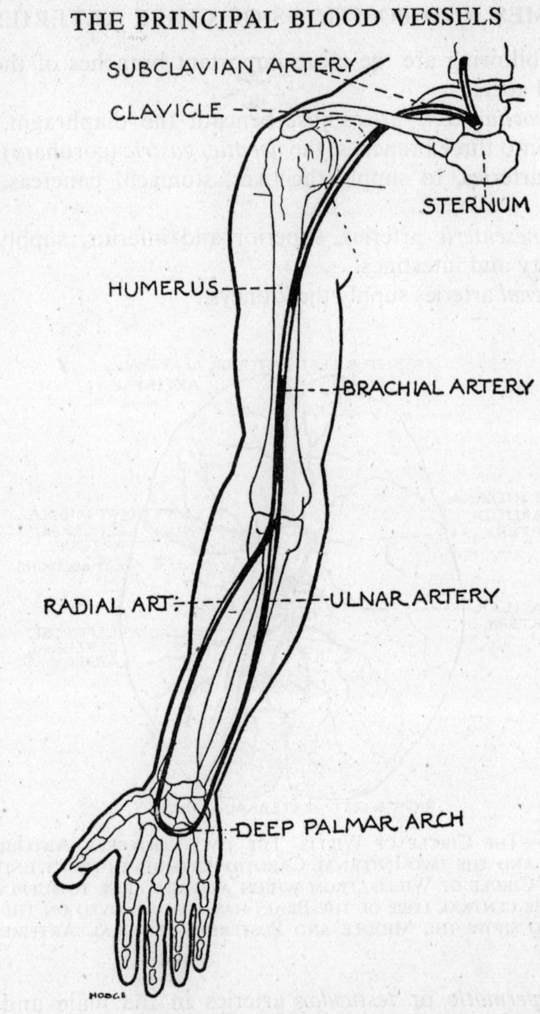

FIG. 109.—THE ARTERIES OF THE RIGHT UPPER LIMB.

The external iliac passes under Poupart's ligament, enters the thigh, and becomes the *femoral* artery.

The Common Carotid Artery. The common carotid artery ascends in the neck and divides into the *internal* and *external carotid* arteries.

The *internal carotid* artery passes through the carotid canal in the temporal bone, enters the skull, and divides into *ophthalmic* and *anterior* and *middle cerebral* arteries.

The *external carotid* artery divides into three main branches to supply the outer side of the cranium and face.

The *facial* artery passes over the inferior maxillary bone, near its angle, crosses the angle of the mouth, and divides into numerous branches at the root of the nose.

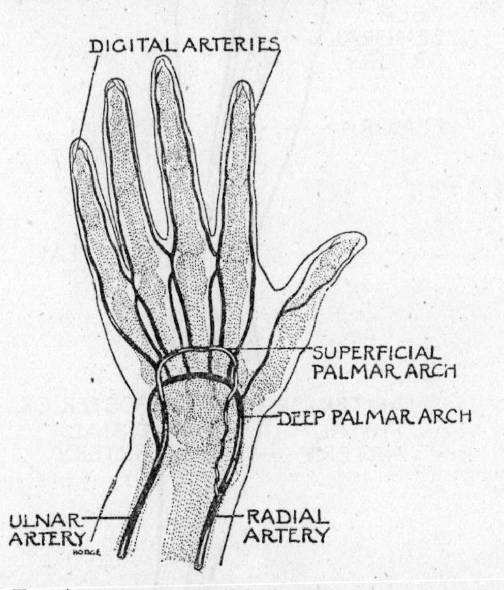

FIG. 110.—THE ARTERIES OF THE HAND. THE DEEP AND SUPERFICIAL PALMAR ARCHES.

The *temporal* artery which ascends at the side of the head can be felt pulsating where it lies superficial to the temporal bone. It gives branches to the side of the head.

The *occipital* artery passes to the back of the head and divides into branches to supply this part.

Circle of Willis. The *vertebral* arteries arise from the subclavian arteries, and, passing up the neck through the foramina in the transverse processes of the cervical vertebrae, enter the skull,

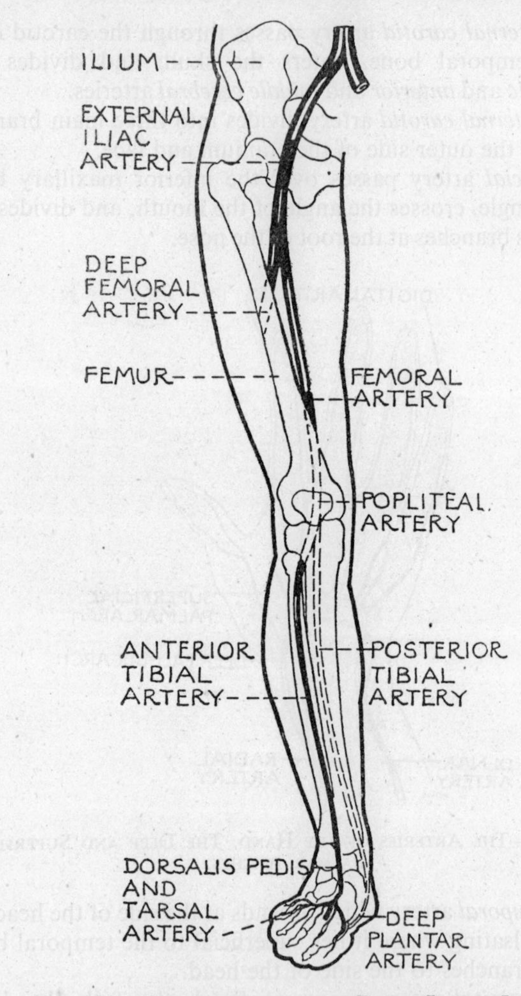

FIG. 111.—THE ARTERIES OF THE RIGHT LOWER LIMB.

uniting to form the *basilar* artery. This gives off the right and left *posterior cerebral* arteries. Branches from these pass forwards and anastomose with the middle and anterior cerebral arteries to form the *circle of Willis*.

The Subclavian Artery and its Terminations. The subclavian artery arising from the aorta passes over the first rib, which it grooves; then passes under the clavicle to enter the axilla, where it becomes the *axillary* artery. At the lower boundary of the axilla it becomes the *brachial* artery, which runs down the arm at the inner side of the biceps muscle, to divide at the bend of the elbow into *radial* and *ulnar* arteries.

The radial artery passes down the radial side and the ulnar artery down the ulnar side of the forearm, supplying blood to the structures of this region. Passing over the front of the wrist, terminations of these arteries form the *deep* and *superficial palmar arches* in the hand. These give off palmar and digital branches to the hand and fingers (*see* Fig. 110).

The Femoral Artery and its Terminations. The femoral artery passes down the medial aspect of the thigh and in the lower third passes behind, where it becomes the *popliteal* artery at the bend of the knee. It divides into two main arteries to supply the leg.

The *anterior tibial* artery which lies in front and to the inner side of the tibia, and passing over the bend of the ankle becomes the *dorsalis pedis* artery. This supplies the structures in the dorsum of the foot and gives branches to the dorsal surface of the toes.

The second division of the popliteal artery is the *posterior tibial*, which passes down behind the tibia, deeply placed in the muscles of the leg. This artery enters the foot by passing behind the medial malleolus under the annular ligament of the ankle. It then divides into lateral and medial *plantar* arteries to supply the structures in the sole of the foot. A branch of the lateral plantar artery unites with the medial plantar artery to form the *plantar arch* (*see* Figs. 111 and 112).

THE PRINCIPAL PRESSURE POINTS IN HAEMORRHAGE

A pressure point of an artery is a point at which the vessel is known to pass over some hard structure such as a bone, so that when pressure is applied the artery is gripped between the

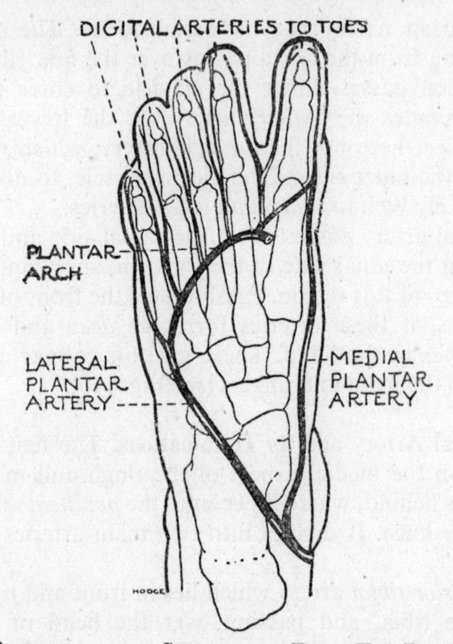

FIG. 112.—ARTERIES OF THE SOLE OF THE FOOT. THE POSTERIOR TIBIAL ARTERY PASSES BEHIND THE INTERNAL MALLEOLUS AND DIVIDES INTO EXTERNAL (LATERAL) AND INTERNAL (MEDIAL) PLANTAR ARTERIES.

finger, or article used to apply the pressure, and the bone beneath. When the fingers are used to apply pressure it is said to be *digital pressure.*

Name of Artery	*Pressure Point*
Common Carotid .	Two inches above clavicle, against vertebrae
Temporal . .	Side of face in front of the ear
Occipital . .	Behind the mastoid process
Subclavian . .	Behind clavicle, by pressure downwards and backwards on to the first rib
Axillary . .	In axilla
Brachial . .	Inner edge biceps muscle, against humerus
Radial . .	Outer side wrist above thumb, as in taking pulse
Ulnar . . .	Inner side of front of wrist
Palmar Arch .	Pad in palm, fingers closed on to it, bandaged firmly in this position; or pressure opposite root of abducted thumb

Abdominal Aorta.	With fist closed, place back of fingers flat against anterior abdominal wall, to left of middle line, below umbilicus, patient lying with knees drawn up. Pressure is made against the lumbar vertebrae
Femoral . .	Patient lying, flex, abduct, externally rotate thigh, press against head of femur in groin
Popliteal . .	Flex knee, press against popliteal surface
Anterior Tibial .	On front of ankle joint
Posterior Tibial .	Behind medial malleolus

THE PRINCIPAL VEINS

Veins carry blood towards the heart. They begin as small vessels formed by the union of capillaries. These small veins unite and become larger veins, eventually forming the venous trunks which increase in size as they near the heart. Veins are more numerous and larger than arteries. Veins may be divided into *superficial* and *deep*.

The Deep Veins or Venae Comites accompany the main arteries and are named after them; some arteries have two accompanying veins. In *the upper limb* there are the *radial* and *ulnar* veins in the forearm; these unite at the elbow and become the *brachial* vein; this becomes the *axillary*, and finally the *subclavian* vein. The subclavian vein from each side then unites with the vein from the head forming the right and left *innominate* veins and these two innominate veins unite to form the *superior vena cava.*

In *the lower limb* the *anterior and posterior tibial* veins unite to become the *popliteal*, which then becomes the *femoral*, and finally becomes the *external iliac*. The internal and external iliac veins unite to form the *common iliac* vein. The right and left common iliac veins unite and the *inferior vena cava* is formed (*see also* page 171).

The Superficial Veins lie immediately beneath the skin, and communicate with the deep veins at certain points, before the great venous trunks reach the heart.

The Veins of the Head and Neck. The veins from the brain drain in the interior of the skull into channels called *venous sinuses*.

These are formed between two layers of the dura mater. The most important are: the *superior longitudinal* or *sagittal sinus* which corresponds in position to the upper border of the falx cerebri and receives blood from the brain and the *inferior sagittal* which drains the falx cerebri (*see* Fig. 113).

The *straight sinus* placed between the falx cerebri and the tentorium cerebelli.

Two *transverse sinuses* which lie close to the skull, receiving blood from other sinuses and, passing to an opening in the skull known as the jugular foramen, become, in the neck, the right and left internal jugular veins.

Other sinuses lie deep in the skull including the *cavernous sinuses* which lie one on each side of the sphenoid bone. These drain the regions of the orbit, nose and cheek. Infection of the face in these regions may cause thrombosis of the cavernous sinus which is a serious and often proves a fatal condition.

The *Internal Jugular Vein* lies *deep* in the neck, it contains the blood which has drained from the interior of the skull and it receives also the lingual, facial and thyroid veins. The internal jugular vein unites with the subclavian vein on each side to form the right and left innominate veins. These innominate veins unite to form the superior vena cava (*see* Fig. 118).

The *External Jugular Vein* is a *superficial vein* formed slightly behind and below the ear by the union of veins draining the regions of the side of the face and the ear. It enters the subclavian vein. Another superficial vein lying at the front of the neck—the *anterior jugular vein*—drains this area and joins the external jugular.

The Superficial Veins of the Upper Extremity begin as a network of small veins in the hands. Those from the palm drain into the median vein, those from the medial aspect of the dorsum into the basilic and those from the lateral aspect into the cephalic vein.

The *Median Vein* runs up the anterior aspect of the forearm and below the elbow divides into the *median basilic* and *median cephalic veins*. These two veins enter the basilic and cephalic veins.

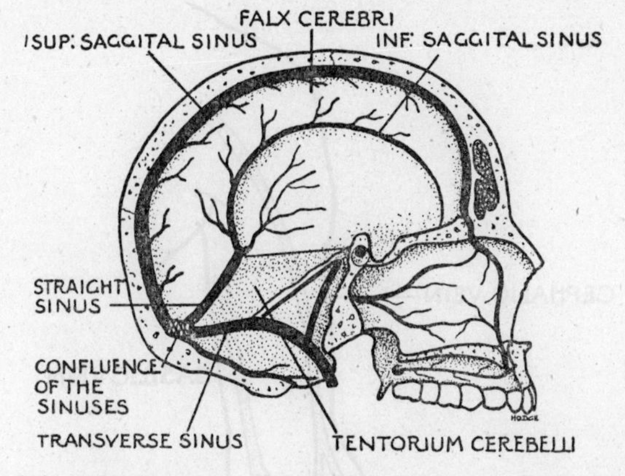

FIG. 113.—THE PRINCIPAL VENOUS SINUSES OF THE DURA MATER.

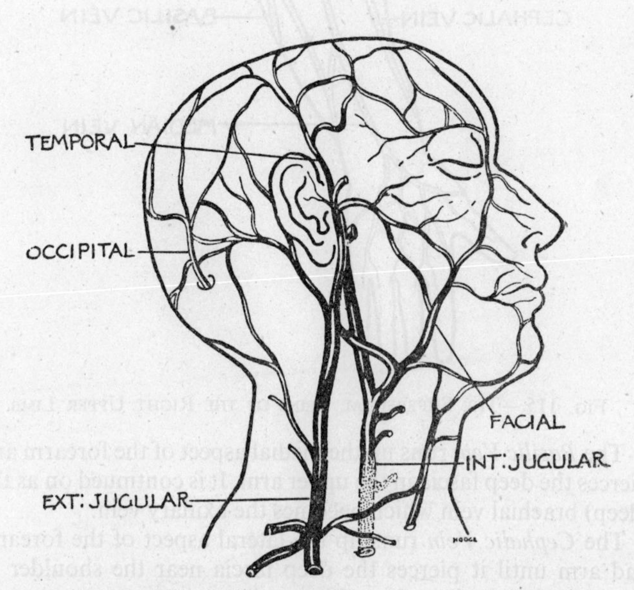

FIG. 114.—THE VEINS OF THE HEAD AND NECK (RIGHT).

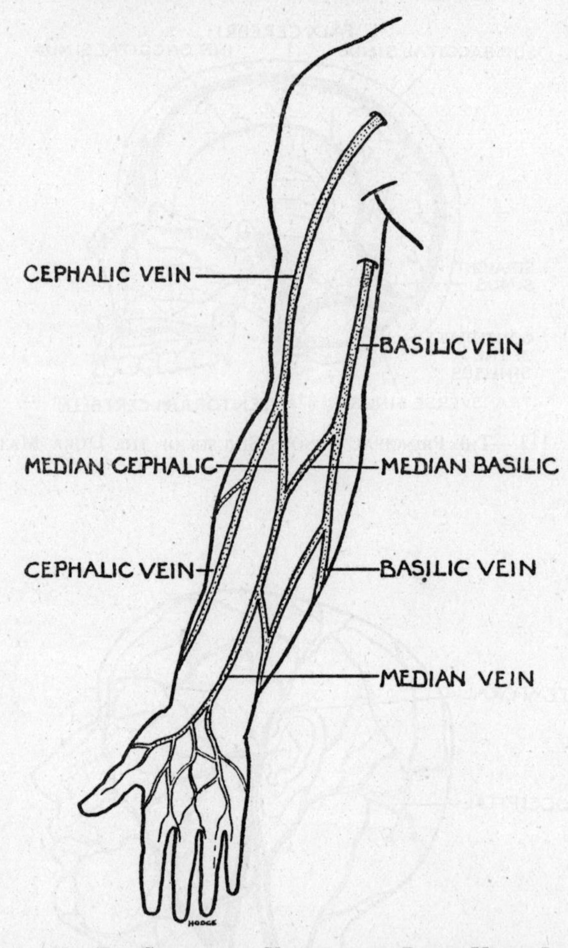

FIG. 115.—THE SUPERFICIAL VEINS OF THE RIGHT UPPER LIMB.

The *Basilic Vein* runs up the medial aspect of the forearm and pierces the deep fascia in the upper arm. It is continued on as the (deep) brachial vein which becomes the axillary vein.

The *Cephalic Vein* runs up the lateral aspect of the forearm and arm until it pierces the deep fascia near the shoulder to pour its contents into the axillary vein.

The Superficial Veins of the Lower Extremity. The long *saphenous* vein is the largest. It commences on the medial aspect of the dorsum of the foot, receiving tributary veins from this region; then passes up along the medial aspect of the leg,

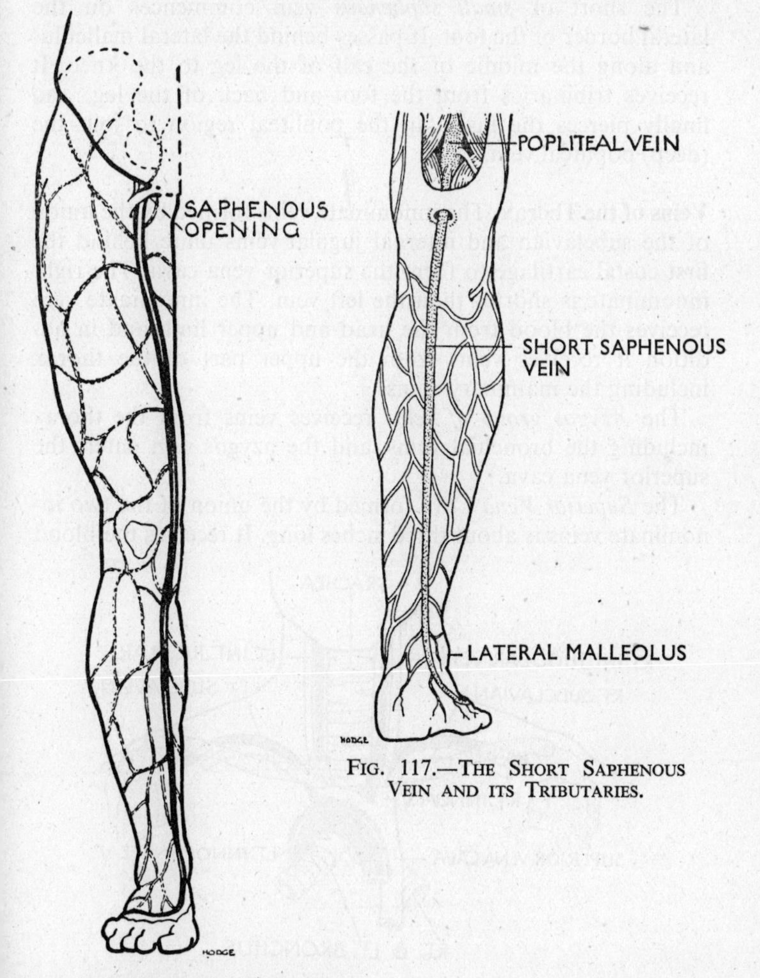

FIG. 116.—THE LONG SAPHENOUS VEIN AND ITS TRIBUTARIES.

FIG. 117.—THE SHORT SAPHENOUS VEIN AND ITS TRIBUTARIES.

behind the knee, to come forward again and finally pierce the femoral sheath, to empty its contents into the (deep) femoral vein. It receives tributary veins in its whole course, and is accompanied by numerous lymphatic vessels.

The short or *small saphenous* vein commences on the lateral border of the foot. It passes behind the lateral malleolus and along the middle of the calf of the leg to the knee. It receives tributaries from the foot and back of the leg, and finally pierces the fascia in the popliteal region to join the (deep) popliteal vein.

Veins of the Thorax. The innominate veins formed by the union of the subclavian and internal jugular veins unite behind the first costal cartilage to form the superior vena cava. The right innominate is shorter than the left vein. The innominate vein receives the blood from the head and upper limb and in addition it receives veins from the upper part of the thorax including the mammary veins.

The *Azygos group of veins* receives veins from the thorax including the bronchial veins, and the azygos vein enters the superior vena cava.

The *Superior Vena Cava* formed by the union of the two innominate veins is about three inches long. It receives the blood

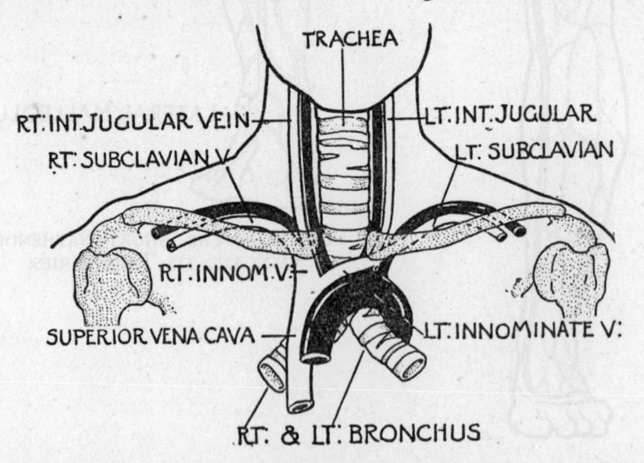

FIG. 118.—FORMATION OF THE SUPERIOR VENA CAVA BY THE UNION OF THE TWO INNOMINATE VEINS.

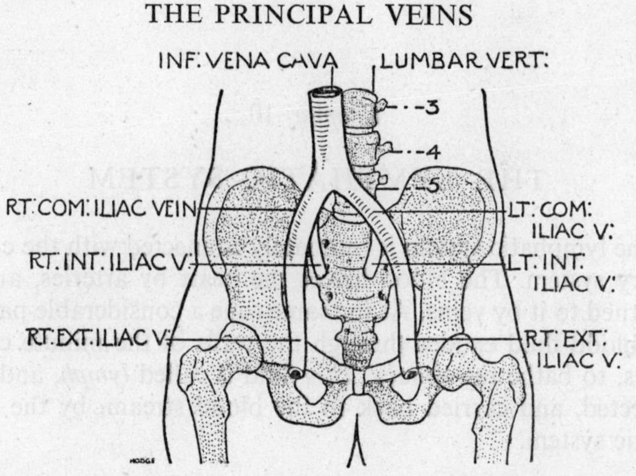

FIG. 119.—FORMATION OF THE INFERIOR VENA CAVA BY THE UNION OF THE COMMON ILIAC VEINS IN FRONT OF THE LUMBAR VERTEBRAE.

from the head, neck, both upper limbs and the walls of the thorax and empties its contents into the upper part of the right auricle of the heart.

Veins of the Pelvis and Abdomen. The *femoral veins* pass up one on each side beneath the inguinal ligament to enter the pelvis where it becomes the *external iliac vein.* Near the sacro-iliac joint it unites with the *internal iliac vein* which drains the blood from the organs in the pelvis. This union of external with internal iliac becomes the *common iliac vein*, right and left common iliac veins unite towards the right side of the fifth lumbar vertebra to become the inferior vena cava.

The *Inferior Vena Cava* receives many tributaries as it passes up through the abdomen and thorax to reach finally the right auricle of the heart. It receives the lumbar veins which drain the posterior abdominal wall, the renal veins from the kidneys, and the hepatic veins from the liver.

Chapter 10

THE LYMPHATIC SYSTEM

The lymphatic system is intimately connected with the circulatory system. The blood leaves the heart by arteries, and is returned to it by veins. At the same time a considerable part of the blood fluid exudes through the walls of the minute capillaries, to bathe the tissues. This fluid is called *lymph*, and it is collected, and carried back to the blood stream, by the lymphatic system.

Lymph forms the tissue fluid which bathes all cells. It is similar to blood plasma but contains a smaller quantity of protein material, about 4 per cent as compared with the 8 per cent contained in blood plasma. Lymph is alkaline in reaction, it contains lymphocytes, a few granular leucocytes but no red blood cells. It is by means of the lymph that nourishment and

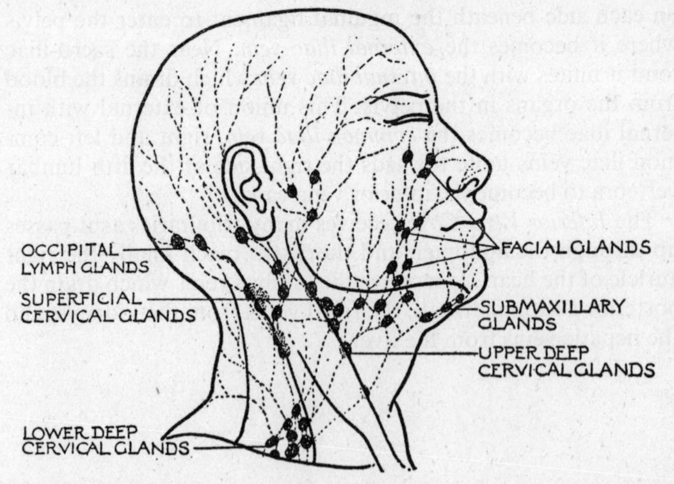

FIG. 120.—THE PRINCIPAL GROUPS OF LYMPHATIC GLANDS OF THE HEAD AND NECK.

oxygen reach the various tissue cells and that waste material, including carbon dioxide, is carried away.

Lymphatic Vessels. These are similar in structure to the small veins, but have more numerous valves which give the vessels a

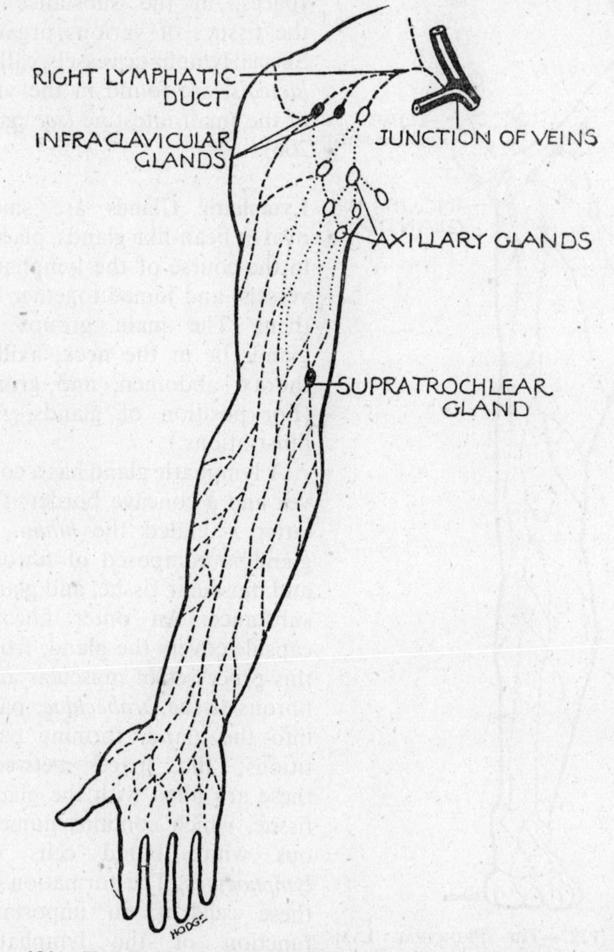

FIG. 121.—THE RIGHT LYMPHATIC DUCT AND THE LYMPHATIC GLANDS OF THE RIGHT UPPER LIMB.

beaded appearance. The smallest lymphatic vessels or *lymph capillaries* are larger than the blood capillaries, and consist of an endothelial coat only. The lymphatic vessels begin either as minute plexuses of very small capillaries, or in lymphatic spaces, in the substance of the tissues of various organs. Special lymphatic vessels, called *lacteals*, are found in the villi of the small intestine (*see* page 206).

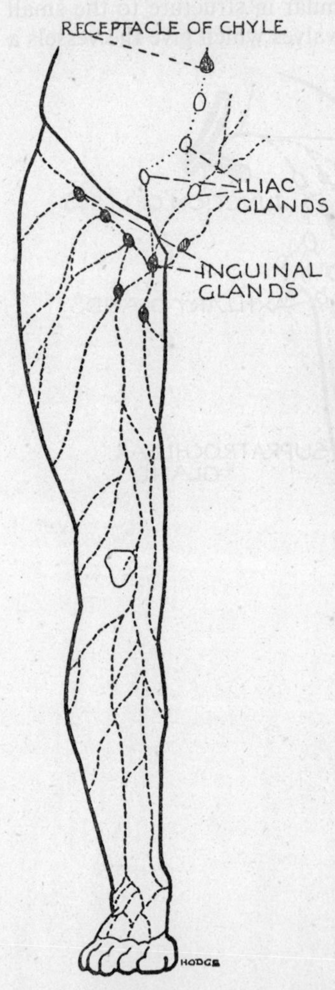

FIG. 122.—THE PRINCIPAL LYMPHATIC GLANDS OF THE RIGHT LOWER LIMB.

Lymphatic Glands are small oval or bean-like glands, placed in the course of the lymphatic vessels, and joined together by them. The main groups of glands lie in the neck, axilla, thorax, abdomen, and groin. (For position of glands, *see* illustrations.)

A lymphatic gland has a convex and a concave border; the latter is called the *hilum*. A gland is composed of fibrous and muscular tissue, and gland substance. An outer fibrous capsule covers the gland; from this processes of muscular and fibrous tissue, *trabeculae*, pass into the gland, forming partitions; the spaces between these are filled with the gland tissue, which contains numerous white blood cells or *lymphocytes*. The formation of these cells is an important function of the lymphatic glands.

An *afferent lymphatic vessel* passes through the capsule on the convex border of the gland, and empties its contents into the substance of the gland. This material comes into contact with the numerous lymph corpuscles, and together with many of these is collected by *efferent lymphatic vessels* which carry it away from the hilum. The arteries and veins also enter and leave the gland at the hilum.

Lymphatic Ducts. There are two lymphatic ducts, the thoracic duct and the right lymphatic duct.

The thoracic duct begins as the *receptaculum chyli* or *cisterna chyli* in front of the lumbar vertebrae. It then passes up through

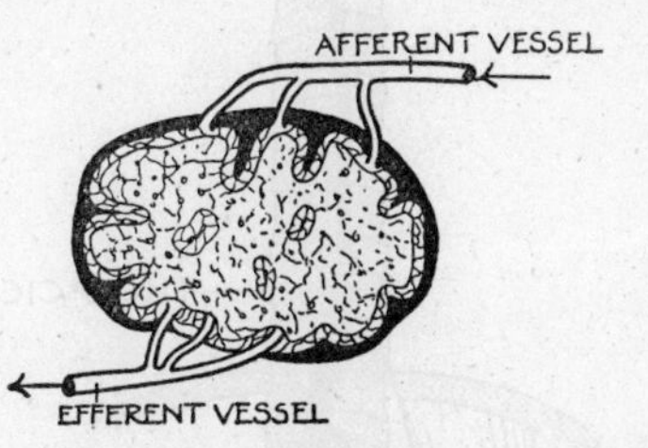

FIG. 123.—A LYMPHATIC GLAND, SHOWING AFFERENT VESSELS PASSING TO THE CONVEX BORDER, AND EFFERENT VESSELS PASSING FROM THE HILUM OF THE GLAND.

the abdomen and thorax, inclining to the left of the vertebral column, to unite with the great veins at the root of the left side of the neck, into which it pours its contents.

The thoracic duct collects the lymph from all parts of the body, except the parts drained by the right lymphatic duct.

The right lymphatic duct, which is a much smaller vessel, collects the lymph from the right side of the head and neck, the right upper limb and the right side of the chest, and empties it into the veins at the right side of the root of the neck.

It is through the lymphatic system that bacteria and toxins are eliminated. During this process the lymphatic vessels and glands may become inflamed, as will be seen in the swollen painful glands in the axilla or groin in the case of a septic finger or toe.

Other glands composed of lymph tissue are the *tonsils*. These lie one on each side of the fauces. They are freely supplied with lymphocytes, which also lie in the fluid on the surface, and in the crypts of the tonsils (*see* page 192).

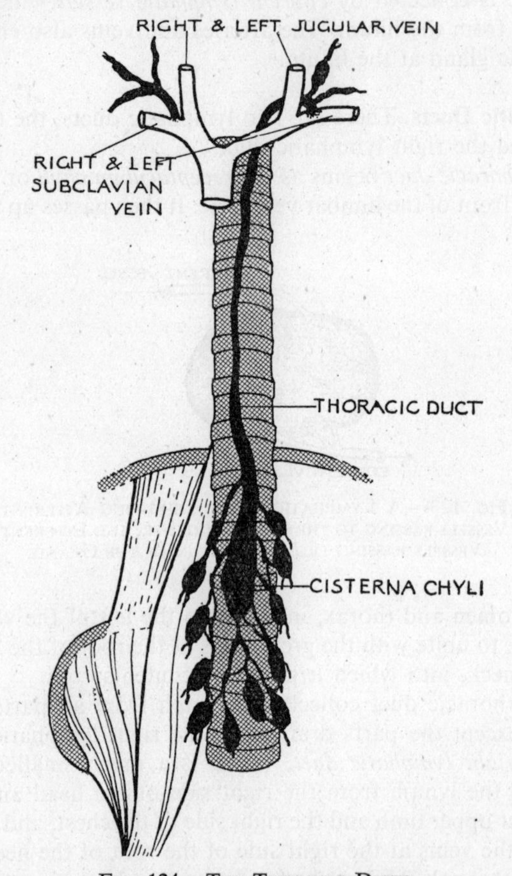

FIG. 124.—THE THORACIC DUCT.

The lymphatics from the right side of the head and chest and the right arm are seen draining into the junction of the right jugular and subclavian veins.

Considerable quantities of *lymphoid tissue* enter into the formation of the spleen, the serous membranes, and the lining of the small intestine. In the intestine it is contained in the mucous coat; in some parts nodules of lymph tissue are found; when single these are called the *solitary glands*, and when in groups they form *Peyer's patches* (*see* page 203).

The *villi* are largely lymph tissue; the central lacteal in the villus communicates with plexuses of lymphatic vessels in the submucous tissue, whence the lymph is passed on, finally reaching the receptaculum chyli.

Serous Membranes. The serous membranes, the most extensive of which is the peritoneum, will be described in the chapters dealing with the organs with which each is connected. The serous membranes are intimately associated with the lymphatic system. Their various folds carry lymphatics and blood vessels. These membranes are lined with pavement epithelium or *endothelium*, and many small openings are contained in this fine lining, these openings are called *stomata*, they lead into lymphatic vessels, and so prevent lymph collecting in the serous cavities.

Chapter 11

THE CLASSIFICATION OF FOOD

Food is needed to build up the body, to make good wear and tear, and to act as fuel for the production of heat and energy.

The rapid development of the body from foetal life onwards through infancy, childhood, and adolescence is an example of the continual demand for building material. The repair needed in the replacement of such tissue as skin and hair will be readily understood.

Cell analysis shows the protoplasm to contain carbon, oxygen, hydrogen, nitrogen, sulphur, and phosphorus; but the body cannot deal with these in their elemental state, therefore they are taken in complex forms as foodstuffs.

CLASSIFICATION OF FOODS

Food is divided into nitrogenous and non-nitrogenous foods. *Nitrogenous foods*, or proteins, contain nitrogen, oxygen, carbon, hydrogen, sulphur, and phosphorus. *Non-nitrogenous foods*, as carbohydrates and fats, contain hydrogen, oxygen, and carbon.

Besides these organic food substances, inorganic substances are also required. These are supplied as many varieties of salts and as water. In addition, many experiments in certain diets have proved the existence of still other vital principles which have been named *vitamins*.

Proteins contain nitrogen which is essential for the growth and repair of every living cell, therefore a certain amount of protein must be supplied daily. Protein is derived from both animal and vegetable foods. Examples of animal protein are *myosin* in lean meat and *albumin* in egg-white; amongst the vegetable proteins, *glutenin* in flour and *legumen* in peas and beans are good examples.

The protein substances contained in the various foods (described as *amino acids*) differ from one another. A large group of about eighteen are known, but only five of them are of such importance as to be essential to the body. A food containing all five of these is described as a *first-class* or *complete* protein; one containing perhaps only two or three of them is called an *incomplete* protein. Lean meat and milk are first-class foods. In the process of digestion each protein substance becomes chemically changed and split up by the enzymes of the various digestive organs into the several amino acids of which it is formed, as it is only when in this state that they can be utilized by the tissues of the body.

Nitrogen is not stored in the body. The waste products of protein are taken to the liver by the blood, where by the deamination of amino acids (*see* page 218) urea is formed.

Carbohydrates contain carbon which is combined in them with hydrogen and oxygen in the proportions in which these are present in water, H_2O. This class of food supplies the body with heat and energy; the carbon combines with oxygen forming carbon dioxide and producing energy.

The examples are divided into two groups, sugars and starches. With the exception of lactose or milk sugar, the sugar group is derived from the vegetable kingdom, e.g. the beet and cane sugars, and glucose and laevulose. Starch is mainly derived from green plant life in the first instance and then stored in the stems, roots, and seeds of these plants. Examples include wheat, maize, and barley, rice, sago, and cornflour, the root vegetables of which potato is a good example, and banana.

Some forms of carbohydrate are more digestible and more easily assimilated than others and for practical purposes these are divided into three groups as follows.

Monosaccharides are the most easily digestible ones and the group into which all classes must be reduced before they can be used by the tissues of the body. They are also called the *simple sugar group* and include *glucose*, *dextrose*, *fructose*, and *galactose*.

Disaccharides. These include *sucrose* or *cane sugar*, *lactose* or *milk sugar*, and *maltose* or *malt sugar*.

Polysaccharides include *starch, dextrin, cellulose,* and *glycogen.* The latter is also called animal starch.

During digestion, by a process of hydrolysis, all starch and sugar is reduced to the monosaccharide group before it can undergo combustion in the tissues. Sugar is soluble in water and cannot therefore be stored in the tissues of the body, and when this is necessary it is changed into a simple form of starch, *glycogen,* and stored in the liver and muscles, from whence it can be again turned into sugar when required.

Fats are derived from animal and vegetable sources. They are composed of carbon, hydrogen, and oxygen and stored as compounds of fatty acids and glycerin.

Examples are the animal fats of meat, and dairy produce such as milk, butter, cheese, and egg-yolk. Animal fats are an essential constituent of diet as they contain stores of Vitamin A and D. Of the vegetable fats olive oil and the nut fats are the best-known examples.

Fats are of the same use to the body as carbohydrates, they produce heat and energy, but fats are less easily oxidized. Fat is stored in the body as adipose tissue. It forms the chief reserve store of energy.

Water forms two-thirds of the weight of the body. It is essential to well-being, and deprivation of water is more immediately serious than of any other article of diet. It forms a large part of the tissues, especially of liquid tissues such as blood.

It is taken in the form of many varieties of liquid as drinks. A large proportion of all food is composed of water, particularly the fruits and vegetables, which contain from 75 per cent water, as in potato. Many of the fruits contain over 90 per cent water. In addition to the needs of the body, a large quantity has to be supplied to make good the 4 to 5 pints of water which is excreted daily by the kidneys, skin, and lungs.

Water has many functions in the body. In addition to forming a large part of the tissues, which it keeps moist, it dissolves many substances and so helps in the chemical changes in the digestive system, for example. It is an aid to peristalsis and it forms the medium in which the various secretions are conveyed.

It maintains the normal salt concentration of the tissues, thus regulating many of the processes of the body and rendering the process of osmosis possible.

Salts. There are various salts in the body. These form the mineral content of most foods. Every cell in the body requires mineral salts.

Calcium is supplied by milk, egg-yolk, and by many vegetables, particularly cabbage and carrots. It is required by all tissues, is carried by the blood serum and its use is regulated by the parathyroid secretion. It is particularly necessary for the ossification of bone, the formation of the teeth, and the clotting of blood.

Sulphur is supplied by all protein substances. It is essential for the well-being of all tissue.

Iron is present in egg-yolk, in spinach, cabbage, and lettuce and many cereal foods. It is needed for the composition of haemoglobin and in combination with it oxygen is distributed to the body.

Sodium Chloride is present in most food and also supplied as table salt. It is important and necessary for the formation of hydrochloric acid in the gastric secretion. It regulates the density of the body fluids upon which the function of many of the processes of the body depend.

Chlorine is mainly supplied in combination with sodium as sodium chloride.

Phosphorus is present in every cell in the body. It is essential for the production of muscular and nervous energy and for the correct composition of hard tissues such as bone and dentine. Phosphorus is supplied in milk, egg-yolk, fish-roe, and green vegetables.

Iodine is present in the products of the sea. The presence of it in the body balances the metabolic processes stimulated by the secretion of the thyroid gland.

In addition to these salts other necessary ones, *magnesium* and *potassium*, are contained in cereals and vegetables.

VITAMINS

Modern research has described the presence of several vitamins, which are essential to health, life, and growth but knowledge regarding vitamins is incomplete and as constant research is made new information arrives. The vitamins are distinguished by letters. Some are soluble in fats whilst others are soluble in water. They are termed respectively, fat-soluble and water-soluble vitamins.

Fat-soluble Vitamins. *Vitamin A* is present in animal fats, fish oils, dairy produce, and in some green vegetables. It is also present in carrots in the form of a substance called *carotene*, which may more correctly be termed a precursor of Vitamin A —this substance can be changed into Vitamin A in animal tissue, particularly in liver. Milk contains a considerable quantity of Vitamin A—2,000 international units per pint.

Vitamin A is described as the *growth vitamin*. Children need a good supply of it. Deficiency of Vitamin A gives rise to a disease of the eyes called *xerophthalmia*; deficiency also lowers the resistance to infection, particularly to catarrhal infection of the mucous membranes, a condition known as *xerosis*, and it gives rise to *night blindness*.

Vitamin D is associated with Vitamin A. It is the *anti-rachitic vitamin*, and is present in fish oil, milk, egg-yolk, cream and butter (especially of pasture-fed cows), in animal fats and in some vegetables. It is also synthetically prepared by the action of ultra-violet rays on ergosterol—irradiated ergosterol. It promotes the absorption of calcium and phosphates and is essential for bone and tooth formation. Absence of it gives rise to rickets. Children do not receive sufficient Vitamin D in their food and always require to have either one of the fish oils—cod liver or halibut oil, or synthetic Vitamin D —added to their diet.

Vitamin E. At present little is known of its value. It is present in green vegetables, cereals, and many other foods. Experiments on animals have shown that it is necessary for animal reproduction and that it prevents sterility. It is thought that it may prevent abortion in women and is therefore given, as a preventive, to pregnant women with a history of abortion or miscarriage.

Vitamin K is a fat-soluble vitamin, the *anti-haemorrhagic* or 'Koagulation vitamin' when deficient, the clotting time of blood is prolonged and there results a tendency to bleed particularly after the operation of tonsillectomy and after operations on the gall-bladder in cases of obstructive jaundice. It is present in green leaves, pigs' liver and in some cereals.

Water-soluble Vitamins. *The Vitamin B Complex* is a group of vitamins found in most foods, particularly in seeds and eggs —in the seeds of peas, beans, and lentils and in the germ layer and bran of cereals. It is present in bread in proportion to the wheat germ content of flour. It is found in yeasts and to a certain extent in meat.

Vitamin B_1 is also called Vitamin F. It is the anti-neuritic and anti-beri-beri factor. Beri-beri is a disease of nutrition common in countries where the natives are fed on polished rice. The aleurone layer and the germ of rice contains B_1 which is deficient in polished rice.

Vitamin B_2 contains several factors including the anti-pellagra and anti-dermatitis factor. Pellagra is a disease characterized by soreness of the mouth and dermatitis. Amongst the factors contained in the vitamin B_2 complex are substances and enzymes which are active at different stages of carbohydrate metabolism. These include *nicotinic acid*, *riboflavine* and *folic acid.* Deficiency of the vitamin B group causes debility, with loss of weight and anaemia; it has been used with success in the treatment of nutritional disorders affecting most of the systems of the body.

Vitamin C is anti-scorbutic. It is contained in fresh fruits, particularly in the citrous fruits and black-currants, and in vegetables. Deficiency gives rise to scurvy which is characterized by weakness and haemorrhages from the gums with loosening of the teeth. This vitamin is *ascorbic acid* and synthetic preparations of it are available in large quantities.

Vitamin P or *citrin* is a substance which is found in lemon juice which increases the action of ascorbic acid.

The chemical composition of most of these vitamins is well recognized and the amount of some of them has been standardized in 'international units' so that the essential amount of the type of vitamin taken can be regulated and controlled.

Protective Foods. Foods rich in vitamins, particularly A and D, sugars, fats, especially milk fat, first-class proteins, and minerals, especially calcium, iron, phosphorus, and sulphur, are described as 'protective foods' because they are essential to the well-being of the body.

To summarise. A normal diet to be complete should contain the six classes of essential substances described above, carbohydrates, fat, proteins, mineral salts, water and vitamins. In this way fuel, body building and protecting or health regulating foods are assured.

Examples of the Composition of Foods. Milk is a complete food. It contains all classes of foods in the following proportions:

Cow's Milk:		
	Water	87.00 per cent
	Protein	4.00 ,, ,,
	Fat	3.75 ,, ,,
	Carbohydrates	4.50 ,, ,,
	Salts	0.75 ,, ,,
	Total	100.00 ,, ,,

Eggs, a complete food for the developing chick, are very nourishing, and are easily digested by most people. The protein of egg hardens in cooking, therefore the longer an egg is cooked the less digestible it becomes. Egg contains protein 12.2 per cent, salts 0.6 per cent, and a little sugar. Egg-yolk contains nutritive substances necessary for the developing chick, including fats and cholesterol.

Meat contains 75 per cent water. Its main solid constituent is protein, and it is therefore rich in nitrogen and sulphur, and most meat protein contains phosphorus. It also contains fat, which is found even in lean meat, the fibres of pork and ham being particularly rich in fat.

Carbohydrates are in excess in most vegetable foods. Other classes of foods described as accessory articles of diet, are condiments, stimulants, etc.

A Well-balanced Diet provides for the requirements of the body, i.e. protein to replace wear and tear of tissue, and heat-producing foods sufficient to provide the necessary energy without loss of weight.

A *mixed diet* should contain a suitable proportion of all the different classes of food. The diet should suit the *age of the person,* the *climate* in which he lives, and the needs of the *occupation* he follows.

Heat is measured by means of the small calorie, and is the amount required to raise the temperature of a cubic centimetre of water one degree centigrade. In dietetics the large Calorie is used and it is spelt with a capital C. It is the amount of heat required to raise a litre of water one degree centigrade, and is known as the kilo Calorie.

The heat-producing foods are proteins, fats, and carbohydrates, and the amount of heat each type will produce has been estimated by careful investigation and been expressed in the following figures—as so many Calories per gramme, or ounce.

29 grammes = 1 ounce.

	Per gramme	*Per ounce*
Protein . . .	4.1 C.	116 C.
Fat . . .	9.3 C.	260 C.
Carbohydrate . .	4.1 C.	116 C.

Calorie requirements. The number of Calories required by a person may be expressed as so many per day, or per pound of body weight. It has been suggested by many authorities that an average number of Calories required by a workman weighing 140 pounds (10 stone) should not be less than 3,500—this figure allows for 25 Calories per pound body weight. A working woman requires less as a woman's body is more economical in the use of heat-producing food—the usual figure given is about 2,500. An adult at rest in bed only requires from 1,200 to 1,800 Calories.

Proportionate Requirements. Growing children require a relatively large proportion of Calories, to provide for their rapid growth and disproportionate expenditure of energy. An infant needs from 40-50 Calories per pound; a child under 5 requires about 1,500 per day, between 5 and 10 years, about

1,800, and from 10 to 12 about 2,000. A girl in her teens requires as much as a working woman, and a boy needs the same amount as a man.

Several tables giving the Calorie value of food per pound or per ounce can be obtained and the value of any given diet calculated from these. The proportion of each kind of food must also be considered, and for general purposes it is usually taken that a man of the weight mentioned above (10 stone) needs from 80-100 grammes of protein and fat, and the remainder can be supplied as carbohydrates. It is generally considered that carbohydrate forms over 50 per cent of the diet, fat about 35 per cent, and protein about 12 per cent. Of this at least half the amount must be first-class protein (*see* page 179). An adult requires a minimum of 40 grammes of first-class protein per day. The proportions mentioned will be found in a diet composed of 100 grammes of protein equal 410 Calories; 100 grammes of fat equal 930 Calories; and 400 grammes of carbohydrate equal 1,640 Calories, making a total of 2,980. But in many instances, particularly in that of the working classes, the percentage of carbohydrate will be found to be increased and the amount of fat and protein often lower. The example given below more nearly represents the proportions of the average dietary, and is quite adequate.

For example:

80 grammes or about 3 ounces of protein, of which 1 ounce must be first-class protein =	320 C.
The same amount of fat—80 grammes—provides	720 C.
The remainder can be carbohydrate, 615 grammes =	2,460 C.
	3,500 C.

In addition to the proper proportion of carbohydrate, fat, and protein, a well-balanced mixed diet must also include adequate amounts of all the necessary minerals—calcium, sulphur, iron, sodium chloride, phosphorus, iodine, magnesium, and potassium, the necessary vitamins and an adequate amount of water.

Chapter 12

THE ALIMENTARY CANAL AND THE DIGESTION OF FOOD

The digestive system deals with the reception of food and with the preparation of it for assimilation by the body. The *alimentary canal* consists of the following parts:

Mouth
Pharynx
Oesophagus
Stomach
Large and Small Intestine.

In addition the mouth contains the *teeth*, which masticate the food. Several glands or groups of glands pour important *digestive fluids* into the alimentary tract:

The *Salivary Glands*
The *Pancreas* } these two glands are described in
The *Liver* } Chapter 13.

The entire alimentary canal is lined by mucous membrane, from the lips to the end of the oesophagus this is a stratified epithelium. From the stomach to anal canal it is composed of columnar cells, and in the anal canal of stratified epithelium.

During the processes of digestion food is broken down into simple substances which can be absorbed and used by the cells of the body tissues. The various changes in the character of food are brought about by the activity of ferments or *enzymes* contained in the different digestive fluids. These substances have a specific action—they select and act on one type of food and have no effect on other types. *Ptyalin* for example acts only on cooked starch, and *pepsin* only on protein. One digestive fluid, the pancreatic fluid for example, may contain several enzymes, each enzyme acting only on one type of food.

An Enzyme is a chemical substance which produces changes in the chemistry of other substances, foods for example, without itself undergoing any change. The healthy action of the various enzymes depends to a great extent on the presence of mineral salts, especially calcium and iron. That is why mineral salts are so important a part of the diet and are included under the protective and essential food materials.

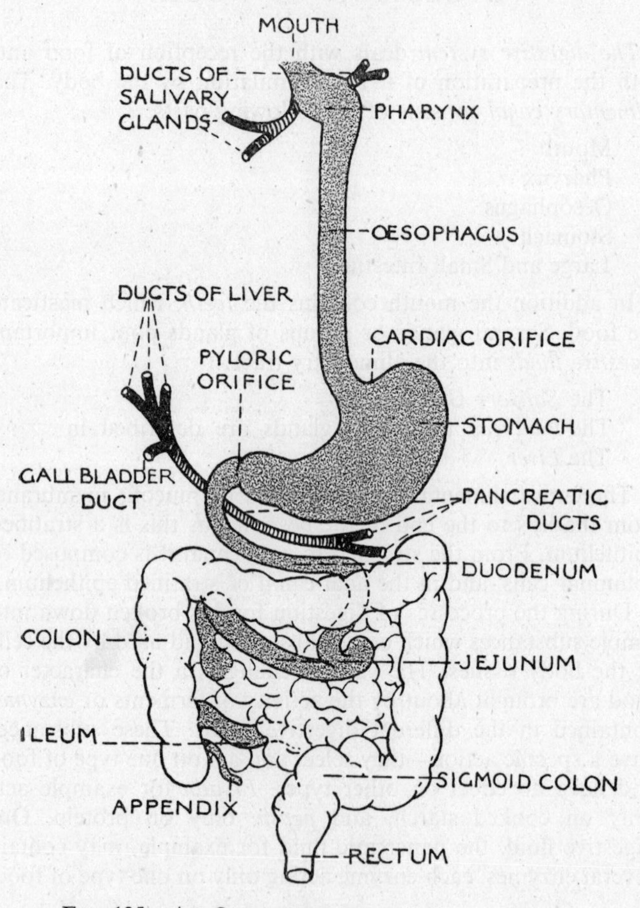

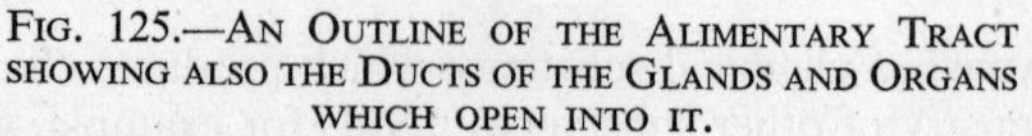

FIG. 125.—AN OUTLINE OF THE ALIMENTARY TRACT SHOWING ALSO THE DUCTS OF THE GLANDS AND ORGANS WHICH OPEN INTO IT.

THE MOUTH

The mouth is an oval cavity at the beginning of the alimentary canal. It consists of two parts, an outer small part, the *vestibule*, which is the space between the gums and teeth, and the lips and cheeks. The inner part, the *cavity of the mouth*, is bounded at the sides by the maxillary bones and the teeth, and communicates behind with the oral pharynx. The *roof of the mouth* is formed by the palate, and the tongue lies in the *floor* attached to the hyoid bone. In the middle line a fold of mucous membrane (*the frenulum linguae*) connects the tongue with the floor of the mouth. On each side of this lies the *sublingual papilla* which contains the opening of the submaxillary salivary gland; slightly external to this papilla lies the *sublingual fold*, where the tiny openings of the sublingual salivary gland lie.

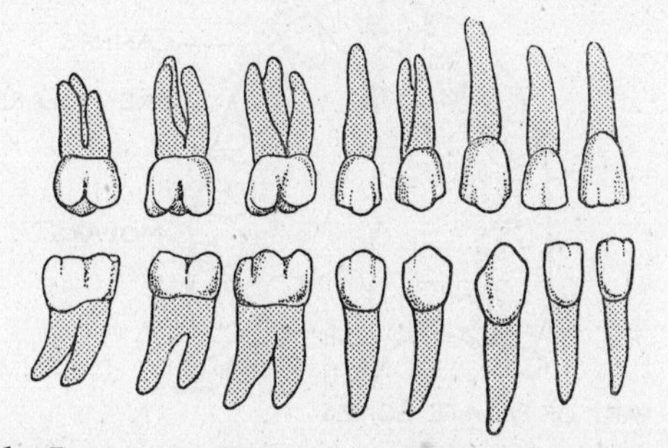

FIG. 126.—PERMANENT TEETH OF THE RIGHT SIDE OF THE JAW.
Note that the upper molars have three and the lower ones two roots. The lower molars are larger than the upper.

The mucous membrane of the mouth is covered by stratified epithelium. Beneath this lie tiny glands, which secrete mucus. This membrane is very vascular, it contains also numerous sensory nerve endings.

The lips are two fleshy folds which form the orifice of the mouth. They are covered externally with skin and internally with mucous membrane. The orbicularis oris muscle closes the lips, the levator anguli oris raises, and the depressor anguli oris depresses the corners of the mouth. The junction of the upper and lower lips form the angle of the mouth.

The palate consists of two parts, *the hard palate*, which is composed of the palatine processes of the upper maxillary bones and the palate bones and *the soft palate*, which is a movable hinged flap of muscle and mucous membrane at the back of the hard palate. From the middle of the soft palate a conical process, the *uvula*, hangs. Arching downwards and outwards from this are the *pillars of the fauces*, which are double folds of muscle and mucous membrane in which lie the tonsils.

The cheeks form the fleshy sides of the face and are joined to the lips at the naso-labial fold which runs from the side of the nose to the corner of the mouth. The cheeks are lined by mucous membrane which contains tiny papillae.

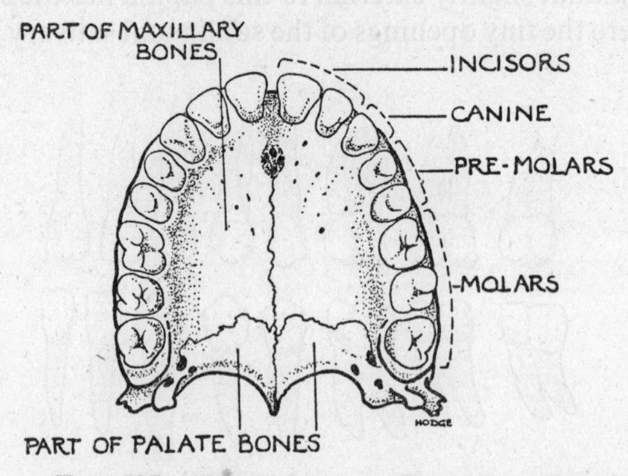

FIG. 127.—THE TEETH AND BONY PALATE.

The Teeth and Mastication. There are two sets of teeth, *the temporary set* and *the permanent set*. There are twenty temporary or milk teeth, ten in each jaw, named from the middle line on each side. Two incisors, one canine, two molars. The permanent teeth are increased to thirty-two, sixteen in each jaw, as follows: named from the centre, two incisors, one canine, two pre-molars, three molars.

As a rule an infant cuts his first teeth at the age of six months. The central incisors are cut first, then the lateral incisors; the first molars at about fifteen months, the canines at eighteen months, and lastly at about twenty months, the remaining molars. An infant of twelve months should have eight teeth, two central and two lateral incisors in upper and lower jaws. At the age of two the child has the complete temporary set of teeth. The teeth in the lower jaw are cut before the corresponding teeth in the upper jaw as a rule.

The permanent teeth begin to replace the temporary ones at about the age of six years. A molar is cut first behind the temporary teeth on each side, then the incisors at seven to eight years, pre-molars nine to ten years, canines at eleven years, second molars about twelve years, and the last molars which are called 'wisdom teeth' later.

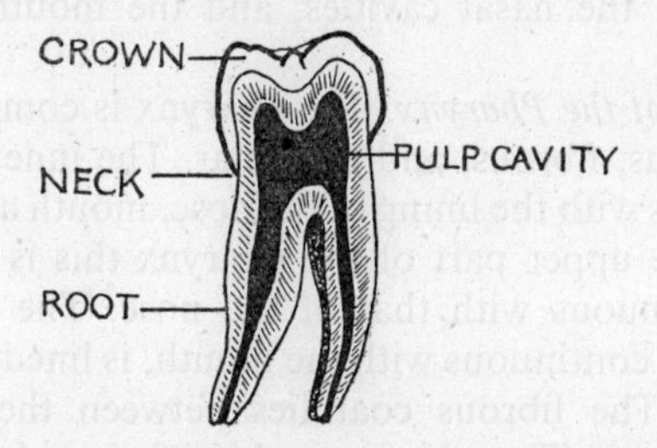

FIG. 128.—DIAGRAM OF SECTION OF TOOTH.

A *tooth* possesses a *crown*, a *neck* and a *root*. The crown projects above the gum, the neck is surrounded by the gum and the root lies beneath it. A tooth is made of a very hard material, *dentine*; in the centre of the structure is the *pulp cavity*. Tooth pulp contains connective tissue cells, blood vessels, and nerves. The part of the tooth projecting above the gum is covered with *enamel*, which is much harder than dentine.

Mastication is the biting and grinding of food between the upper and lower teeth. Movements of the tongue and cheeks assist, by manipulating the soft foods against the hard palate and the teeth.

The tongue is described on page 314.

THE PHARYNX AND OESOPHAGUS

The pharynx lies behind the nose, mouth, and larynx. It is a cone-shaped musculo-membranous passage with the widest part uppermost and extends from below the skull to the level of the sixth cervical vertebra. It is about five inches long and is divided into three portions:

The nasopharynx, behind the nose; into the walls of this part the Eustachian tubes open.

The oral pharynx, behind the mouth; the tonsils lie in the lateral walls of this part of the pharynx (*see* below).

The laryngeal pharynx which is the lowest part, lies behind the larynx.

There are seven openings into the pharynx—two Eustachian tubes in the walls of the nasopharynx, two posterior nares from behind the nasal cavities, and the mouth, larynx, and oesophagus.

Structure of the Pharynx. The pharynx is composed of three coats, mucous, fibrous, and muscular. The inner mucous coat is continuous with the lining of the nose, mouth and Eustachian tubes; in the upper part of the pharynx this is ciliated membrane, continuous with that of the nose. The lower part of the pharynx, continuous with the mouth, is lined with stratified epithelium. The fibrous coat lies between the mucous and muscular coats. The chief muscles of the pharynx are the *constrictor muscles*, which contract on the food received into the pharynx, and force it on to the oesophagus.

The tonsils are two glands placed one on each side of the pharynx between the pillars of the fauces. They are composed of lymphoid tissue permeated with blood and lymphatic vessels and containing masses of lymphocytes. The surface of the tonsil is covered with stratified epithelium continuous with that of the lower part of the pharynx. This surface is studded by crypts and into these crypts numerous mucus-secreting glands pour their secretion. This mucus contains many lymphocytes.

The mucous membrane of the pharynx near the opening of the posterior nares and the Eustachian tubes also contains lymphoid tissue rather like that of the tonsils. When this tissue is hypertrophied it obstructs the posterior nares and the condition described as *enlarged adenoids* is produced.

The Oesophagus is a muscular tube from nine to ten inches long, reaching from the pharynx above, to the cardiac orifice of the stomach below. It lies behind the trachea and in front of the vertebral column. Passing through the thorax it pierces the diaphragm, to enter the abdomen where it communicates with the stomach.

The oesophagus consists of four coats, an outer *fibrous* coat, a *muscular* coat, composed of two layers of muscle fibres, longitudinal and circular, a *sub-mucous* coat and an inner *mucous* membrane lined by stratified epithelium.

Swallowing. The act of swallowing follows mastication and may be described in three parts:

A voluntary act in which the food is formed into a *bolus*, by the action of the tongue and cheeks, and passed to the back of the mouth.

The food enters the pharynx, the soft palate rises to shut off the posterior nares, the glottis closes by contraction of its muscles and the constrictor muscles of the pharynx grasp the food and pass it on to the oesophagus.

The food passes through the oesophagus by *peristaltic action*, the circular muscle fibres are inhibited in front of the food and stimulated behind it, and in this way the bolus of food reaches the stomach.

The second and third parts of swallowing are involuntary and the first part, although a voluntary act, is for the most part performed automatically.

THE SALIVARY GLANDS AND SALIVA

The salivary glands are compound racemose glands which means they are composed of groups of sac-like alveoli, which form small lobules; ducts from each alveolus unite to form a larger duct which conveys the secretion towards a main duct through which the salivary secretion is poured into the mouth.

The principal salivary glands are the *parotid*, *submaxillary*, and *sublingual* glands.

The Parotid Glands are the largest. These lie one on each side, below and slightly in front of the ear. They weigh from half to one ounce each, and pour their secretion into the mouth through the parotid or *Stenson's duct*, which opens on the inside of the cheek, opposite the second upper molar tooth. The parotid gland is traversed by two important structures, the external carotid artery and the 7th cranial (facial) nerve.

The Submaxillary Glands are the next largest. These lie on each side beneath the jaw-bone, and are about the size of a walnut. Their secretion is poured into the mouth through the submaxillary or *Wharton's duct*, which opens into the floor of the mouth, near the *frenulum linguae*.

The Sublingual Glands are the smallest pair. These lie beneath the tongue on each side of the *frenulum linguae*, and pour their

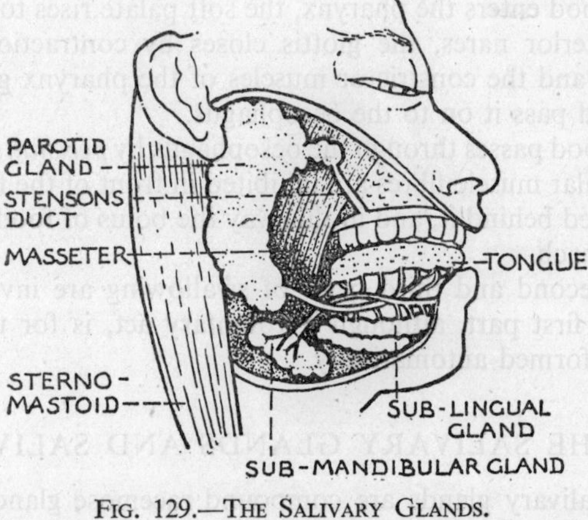

FIG. 129.—THE SALIVARY GLANDS.

secretion into the floor of the mouth, through several small openings.

The function of the salivary glands is the secretion of saliva, which is the first digestive fluid to act upon the food.

Saliva is a watery, alkaline fluid, having specific gravity of from 1002-1006. It contains a very small proportion of solids, mucin and a starch-splitting ferment *ptyalin*.

The action of saliva is both physical and chemical. By its physical action it moistens the mouth and assists talking, lubricates the food in the mouth and makes swallowing easier, and by moistening the food it dissolves particles, so that the chemical action upon these is facilitated.

The *chemical action* of saliva is due to a ferment *ptyalin* which in an alkaline medium acts on sugar and cooked starches. Ptyalin can only act on starch when the cellulose covering of the starch granules has been burst as by cooking, and then the cooked starches are converted into a soluble form of sugar, maltose. This action commences in the mouth, the saliva is swallowed with food and the action of ptyalin continues in the stomach for about twenty minutes or until the food is rendered acid by the action of the gastric fluid.

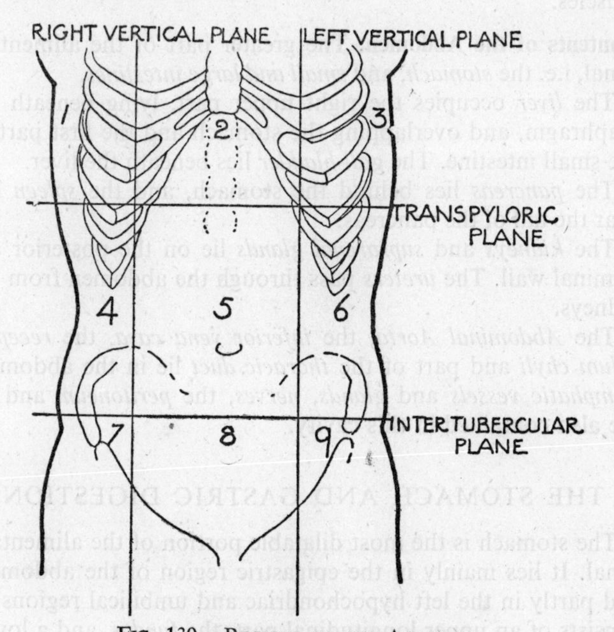

FIG. 130.—REGIONS OF THE ABDOMEN.

1. The Right Hypochondriac.
2. The Epigastric.
3. The Left Hypochondriac.
4. The Right Lumbar.
5. The Umbilical.
6. The Left Lumbar.
7. The Right Iliac.
8. The Hypogastric.
9. The Left Iliac.

THE ABDOMINAL CAVITY

The abdomen is the largest cavity in the body. It is oval in shape and extends from the diaphragm above to the pelvis below. The abdominal cavity is described in two parts—the abdomen proper, which is the upper and larger cavity, and the pelvis, the lower and smaller cavity.

Boundaries of the Abdomen. *Above* the diaphragm. *Below*, the brim of the true pelvis. *At the front and sides*, the abdominal muscles, the iliac bones, and the lower ribs. *At the back*, the vertebral column, and the psoas and quadratus lumborum muscles.

Contents of the Abdomen. The greater part of the alimentary canal, i.e. the *stomach*, and *small and large intestines.*

The *liver* occupies the right upper part, lying beneath the diaphragm, and overlapping the stomach and the first part of the small intestine. The *gall-bladder* lies beneath the liver.

The *pancreas* lies behind the stomach, and the *spleen* lies near the tail of the pancreas.

The *kidneys* and *suprarenal glands* lie on the posterior abdominal wall. The *ureters* pass through the abdomen from the kidneys.

The *Abdominal Aorta*, the *inferior vena cava*, the *receptaculum chyli* and part of the *thoracic duct* lie in the abdomen. *Lymphatic vessels* and *glands*, *nerves*, the *peritoneum* and *fat* are also contained in this cavity.

THE STOMACH AND GASTRIC DIGESTION

The stomach is the most dilatable portion of the alimentary canal. It lies mainly in the epigastric region of the abdomen, and partly in the left hypochondriac and umbilical regions. It consists of an upper longitudinal part, the *fundus*, and a lower horizontal part, the *pyloric antrum*. It communicates with the oesophagus by means of the cardiac orifice, and with the duodenum by the pyloric orifice.

The stomach lies below the diaphragm, in front of the pancreas, and the spleen lies against the left side of the fundus.

Structure. The stomach consists of four coats:

An outer peritoneal coat, which is a serous covering.

Muscular coat, which is in three layers, (*a*) *longitudinal fibres* which lie superficially and are continuous with the muscle of the oesophagus, (*b*) *circular fibres*, which are thickest at the pylorus where they form the sphincter muscle, lie beneath the first layer, and (*c*) *oblique fibres*, which are found chiefly at the fundus of the stomach and pass from the cardiac orifice and sweep downwards over the lesser curvature.

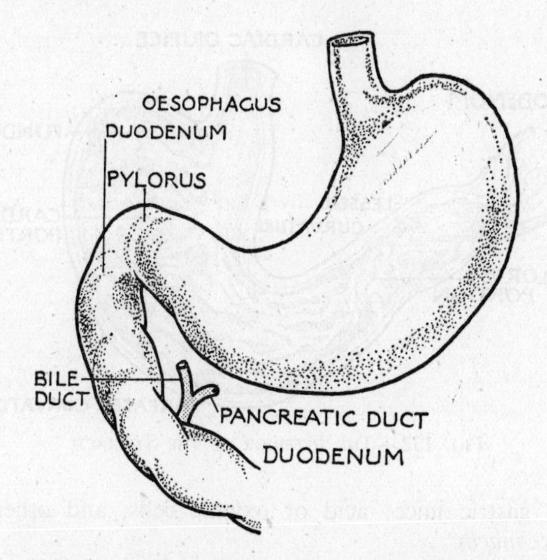

FIG. 131.—THE ANTERIOR ASPECT OF THE STOMACH.

A sub-mucous coat of areolar tissue contains the blood vessels and lymphatics.

A mucous coat, the inner membrane, is thick and soft, and is arranged in corrugated folds, *rugae*, which disappear when the organ is distended by food.

The mucous membrane is lined by columnar epithelium, all the cells secrete mucus, it contains numerous lymphatics. The surface is covered by the tiny ducts of the gastric glands. These lead from the branched tubular gastric glands, and the ducts opening on to the surface are lined by columnar epithelium continuous with that of the mucous surface of the stomach. The epithelium of the secreting part of the gland is modified and varies in different areas of the stomach.

Cardiac glands lie nearest to the oesophageal opening. These are tubular glands, either simple or branched.

Glands of the Fundus. These predominate, they are tubular glands and contain different types of cells, some produce *pepsin*—the peptic cells. Other cells produce the *acid* contained

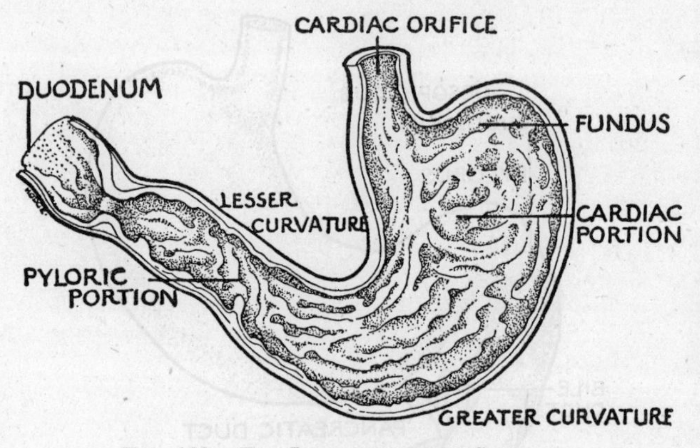

FIG. 132.—THE INTERIOR OF THE STOMACH.

in the gastric juice—acid or oxyntic cells, and other cells produce *mucin*.

Pyloric glands. The glands in the pyloric canal are also tubular in character. They produce mainly mucin and do not secrete any acid.

Blood and nerve supply. The stomach receives a very liberal blood supply from the gastric and splenic arteries; the nerve supply is derived from the vagus and from the solar plexus of the sympathetic system.

Function. The stomach receives the food from the oesophagus through the cardiac orifice and the fundus grasps the food and maintains steady pressure towards the pyloric end. Vigorous peristalsis in the pyloric antrum results in a thorough mixing of the contents of the stomach.

The passage of the food into the stomach during a meal is practically continuous; but the passage of food out of the stomach does not begin at once. Food must first be rendered liquid, then small quantities, about half an ounce at a time, are passed through the pyloric opening into the duodenum. The stomach contents are acid, the contents of the duodenum alkaline, and when a small quantity of the acid stomach contents has entered the duodenum the pyloric sphincter closes, until this has been rendered alkaline by the action of other digestive juices. When the sphincter muscle relaxes, the duodenum receives another instalment of stomach contents.

The glands in the mucous coat of the stomach secrete an important digestive fluid, *gastric juice*. This is a clear colourless acid fluid, of a low specific gravity, containing over 99 per cent water; the remainder is partly organic and partly inorganic matter in solution. It contains 0.4 per cent of free *hydrochloric acid* (HCI) which acidifies all foods, and acts as an antiseptic and disinfectant, rendering many organisms taken in with food harmless, and providing a medium for the digestion of protein foods.

Several digestive ferments are present in gastric juice, *pepsin*, which in the presence of hydrochloric acid is obtained from pepsinogen and acts on protein foods, converting these into more soluble substances called *peptones*; *rennin*, a milk-curdling ferment, which forms *casein* from the soluble caseinogen. Casein is milk protein, and thus separated it can be acted upon by the ferment pepsin. A fat-splitting ferment described as *gastric lipase*—in order to distinguish it from the lipase of the pancreatic juice—is present in small amounts in the stomach, and the digestion of fats commences here. The origin of this ferment is not yet clearly defined, some authorities consider it is pancreatic lipase which has regurgitated from the duodenum into the stomach through the pyloric valve; other authorities consider that it may be secreted by special cells in the gastric mucous membrane.

The stimulation of the secretion of gastric juice is partly psychical and partly mechanical. The *psychic stimulation* depends on impulses reaching the central nervous system through the senses as by the smell, thought, or sight of food. The *mechanical stimulation* is due to the presence of food in the stomach in contact with its walls which causes the glands to secrete gastric juice.

The secretion of gastric juice may be inhibited by the sympathetic nervous system, as may happen in strong emotion such as anger or fear. We speak of a person being sick with fear, and in this case the stomach may actually reject its contents.

Gastric juice contains a number of bacteria principally b. coli, staphylococci and some non-haemolytic streptococci. The bacterial properties of gastric juice is instrumental in preventing organisms entering the duodenum. Normal gastric fluid also contains a ferment known as the *blood forming factor of Castle*. This is an *anti-anaemic* or *haematinic* factor which is present in the stomach, passes from it to the liver and finally reaches the bone marrow where it is concerned with the making of red blood cells. In treating patients with pernicious anaemia this anti-anaemic haematinic or erythropoietic factor may be given by means of liver or liver extract or alternatively the patient may be treated by administration of gastric extract combined with the well balanced diet containing adequate quantities of meat. To summarise, the organs concerned in the manufacture, storage and use of the blood forming, factor of Castle are the stomach, liver and bone marrow.

Summary of the Functions of the Stomach

(1) The stomach receives the food and acts as a reservoir for a short time.
(2) All foods are liquefied and mixed with hydrochloric acid, and in this way prepared for intestinal digestion.
(3) Proteins are converted into peptones.
(4) Milk is curdled and casein set free.
(5) The digestion of fat commences in the stomach.
(6) An anti-anaemic factor is formed.
(7) Chyme, that is liquefied stomach contents, is passed on into the duodenum.

THE SMALL INTESTINE AND INTESTINAL DIGESTION

The small intestine is a tube about twenty feet long which extends from the stomach to the ilio-colic valve where it joins the large intestine.

The small intestine lies in the umbilical region of the abdomen and is surrounded by the large intestine. It is divided into several parts (*see* Figs. 125 and 134).

The Duodenum, the first ten inches of the small intestine, is shaped like a horse-shoe, the curve encircling the head of the

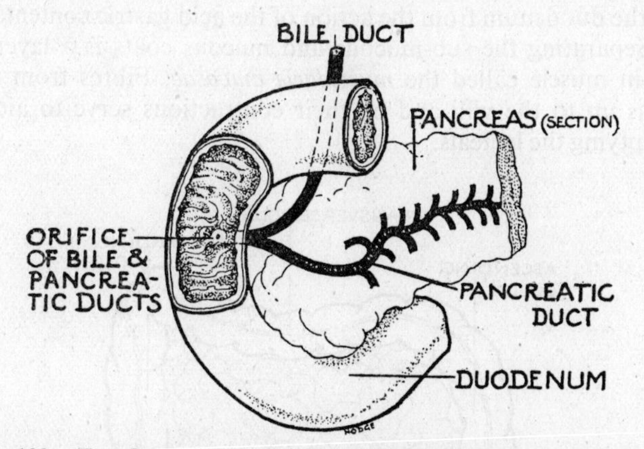

FIG. 133.—THE OPENINGS OF THE BILE AND PANCREATIC DUCTS AT THE AMPULLA OF VATER, IN THE DUODENUM.

pancreas. The bile and pancreatic ducts open into the duodenum at an eminence known as the papilla of the bile duct or the *ampulla of Vater*, four inches from the pylorus.

The Jejunum occupies the upper two-fifths of the remaining small intestine.

The Ileum occupies the last three-fifths.

Structure. The small intestine is composed of the same four coats as the stomach.

The *outer coat* is a serous membrane, the peritoneum, which closely invests the intestine.

The *muscular coat* consists of two layers of fibres only, an outer layer of *longitudinal fibres*, and beneath these an inner thick layer of *circular fibres*. Between these layers of muscular fibres lie blood vessels, lymphatics, and a plexus of nerves.

A *sub-mucous* coat lies between the circular muscle and the innermost coat or lining. This sub-mucous coat is composed of areolar tissue, it contains numerous blood vessels, lymphatics, glands and a nerve plexus called the plexus of Meissner. In the duodenum there are some characteristic glands known as *Brunner's glands*. These are tiny racemose glands which secrete a viscid alkaline fluid, which serves to protect the lining of the duodenum from the action of the acid gastric contents.

Separating the sub-mucous and mucous coats is a layer of plain muscle called the *muscularis mucosae*. Fibres from this pass up to the villi and by their contractions serve to aid in emptying the lacteals.

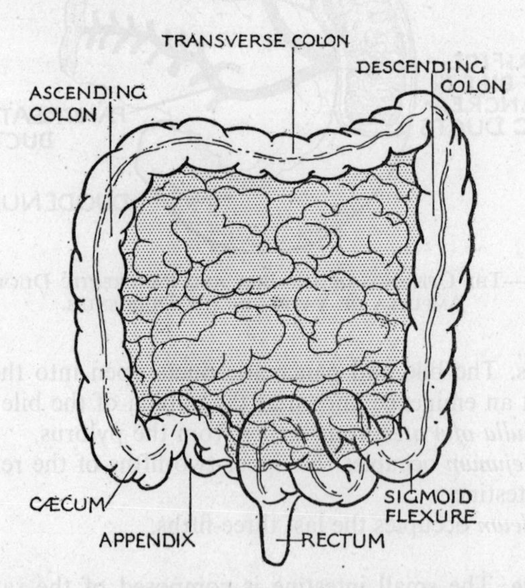

FIG. 134.—THE POSITION OF THE SMALL INTESTINE IN RELATION TO COLON.

The *inner mucous* lining is arranged in permanent tuck-like folds, called *valvulae conniventes*, which give it the appearance of fine pleating. These folds increase the extent of the secreting and absorbing surface. They also tend to prevent the too rapid passage of the contents along the intestine, thus giving the digestive juices longer time to act on the food. The mucous coat contains the *crypts of Lieberkühn* which open on to the surface between the villi. These are simple tubular glands (*see* page 25) lined by columnar epithelium. This epithelium is continuous with that covering the villi. Several varieties of cells including many leucocytes lie in the mucous coat; here and there nodules of lymphatic tissue are found, these are called the solitary glands. In the ileum masses of these nodules are present. They constitute the *Peyer's patches* and may contain 20 to 30 solitary glands and measure from half an inch to several inches long. These glands exercise a protective function and are the site of inflammation in enteric fever.

To the naked eye the surface of the *valvulae conniventes* has the appearance of soft velvet due to the presence of minute hair-like projections called *villi.* Each villus contains a central *lacteal* and a plexus of capillary blood vessels and is covered by a layer of columnar epithelium continuous with that of the mucous surface and containing also goblet cells.

Glands of the small intestine.

Name	*Character*	*Position*	*Function*
Crypts of Lieberkühn	Simple tubular glands	Throughout the mucous membrane of the small intestine	Secretion of intestinal juice, succus entericus
Brunner's glands	Small racemose glands	Sub-mucous coat of the intestine, particularly the duodenum	Secretion of alkaline substance protective to the duodenum
Solitary glands	Single follicles or nodules of lymphatic tissue	Throughout the mucous membrane of the small intestine	Protection of the intestine from bacterial invasion
Peyer's glands	Groups of solitary glands	Mucous surface of ileum	

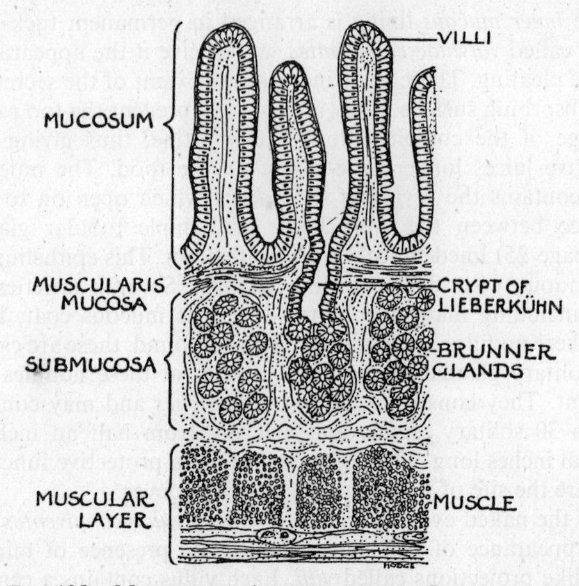

FIG. 135.—MICROSCOPIC APPEARANCE OF A SECTION OF THE COATS OF THE DUODENUM.

The Functions of the Small Intestine are digestion and absorption of the *chyme* from the stomach. The contents of the duodenum are alkaline.

The fluid contents are passed along the small intestine by *peristaltic movement*, similar to that occurring in the oesophagus, but slower. Two other movements are also described.

A *segmental movement*, in which segments of the intestine are cut off by constricting movements of the circular muscle fibres. This enables the liquid contents to be retained temporarily in contact with the intestinal wall, for digestion and absorption. The segments disappear to reappear farther along the organ.

A *pendulum or swaying movement* which causes a mixing together of the intestinal contents.

Two important digestive fluids are passed into the duodenum by ducts, the *bile* from the liver and the *pancreatic fluid* from the pancreas.

Bile assists in the digestion of all classes of food, proteins, carbohydrates, and fats, as the presence of bile in the duodenum facilitates the action of all three pancreatic ferments, trypsin, amylase, and lipase. It also, by its action on fats, aids the mixing together of the intestinal contents and to some extent emulsifies fats. Bile is an alkalinc fluid and helps in maintaining the reaction of the intestinal contents. For a fuller account of the functions of bile *see* page 220.

Pancreatic Juice contains three digestive ferments which act respectively on all three classes of food.

Amylase digests carbohydrates; it is more powerful than ptyalin, and acts on uncooked as well as on cooked starches.

Lipase is a fat-splitting ferment, breaking fats up into glycerin and fatty acids. It is most powerful when acting in conjunction with bile.

Trypsin digests proteins. It is produced by the ferment trypsinogen, present in the pancreatic juice, and converted into the digestive ferment trypsin, by one of the ferments of the succus entericus, *enterokinase*. Trypsin is more powerful in action than the ferment pepsin of the gastric juice. It reduces proteins and peptones to the polypeptide group.

A milk-curdling ferment is also thought by some physiologists to be present in the pancreatic juice.

Succus Entericus. Several ferments are present in the succus entericus or intestinal juice which complete the digestion of all foods.

Enterokinase activates the proteolytic ferment of pancreatic juice as described above.

Erepsin completes the digestion of already altered proteins, converting peptones into the various amino-acids.

Three ferments act on carbohydrates, completing the digestion of starches.

Invertase acts on cane sugar.

Lactase splits lactose into glucose.

Maltase converts maltose into dextrose.

By the action of the various digestive juices, saliva, gastric juice, pancreatic juice, and the succus entericus, the different

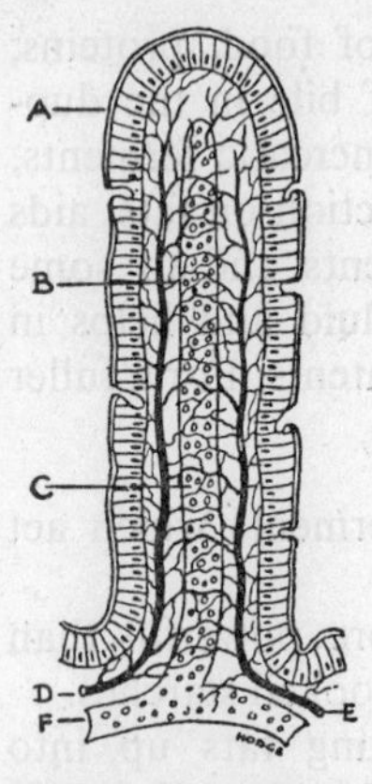

FIG. 136.—THE STRUCTURE OF A VILLUS.

A. Epithelial Covering.
B. Plexus of Capillaries round the Lacteal.
C. Central Lacteal.
D. Small Artery entering the Villus.
E. Small Vein leaving the Villus.
F. Lymphatic Vessel at the Base of the Villus.

food materials have by now been reduced to their final state ready for absorption. The proteins have been broken down into peptones by the gastric and pancreatic ferments, and into the *polypeptides* and *amino-acids* by the action of the succus entericus. Fats have been reduced to *fatty acids* and *glycerin*. Carbohydrates have been finally broken down into the *monosaccharides*, the main one, *glucose*, being very easily absorbed.

The digested food reaches the end of the small intestine in about four hours.

Absorption. The absorption of digested food takes place entirely in the small intestine through two channels, the capillary blood vessels and the lymphatics of the villi on the inner surface of the small intestine.

A *villus* contains a lacteal, blood vessels, epithelium, and muscular tissue, which are connected together by *lymphoid tissue* (*see* Fig. 136). The central lacteal ends in a blind extremity, plain muscle tissue lies along it, and it is surrounded by capillary blood vessels. The whole is then enclosed in a basement membrane and covered by epithelium. As the villi project from the intestinal wall, they are in contact with the liquid food or chyle. The fatty acids and glycerin pass into the columnar epithelial cells, and are re-combined into minute droplets of fat, which are passed on through the lymphoid tissue, into the central lacteal. The absorbed fats then pass by numerous lymphatic vessels to the *receptaculum chyli*, and thence by the *thoracic duct* to the blood stream.

All other digested foods pass directly into the capillary blood vessels of the villi, and are carried by the portal vein to the liver, where certain changes take place.

Summary of Digestive Processes

Organ	*Digestive Fluid*	*Reaction*	*Enzymes*	*Chemical Action of Enzymes*
Mouth . .	Saliva	Alkaline	Ptyalin	Converts cooked starches into a soluble sugar—Maltose
Stomach .	Gastric Juice	Acid	(1) Rennin	Converts caseinogen into Casein
			(2) Pepsin	Converts proteins into Peptones
			(3) Gastric Lipase	Begins the hydrolysis of fats
Duodenum .	Bile	Alkaline	—	Aids action of pancreatic enzymes. Emulsifies fats
,, .	Pancreatic fluid	Alkaline	(1) Trypsin	Reduces proteins and peptones into polypeptides and Amino-acids
			(2) Amylase	Converts all sugars and starches into Maltose
			(3) Lipase	Reduces fats to Glycerin and Fatty acids
Small Intestine	Succus entericus	Alkaline	(1) Enterokinase	Sets free the trypsin in pancreatic fluid
			(2) Erepsin	Reduces all protein substances to Amino-acids
			(3) {Sucrose, Maltase, Lactase}	Reduce all carbohydrate substances into the monosaccharides, Glucose, Galactose, and Laevulose

Summary of Absorption

Source of Food	*Final Digested Product*	*Organ of Absorption*
Proteins . .	Amino-acids	Epithelium of villi into blood vessels and blood stream
Fats . .	Glycerin and fatty acids	Epithelium of villi into lacteals and lymph stream
Carbohydrates .	Monosaccharides: Glucose Laevulose Galactose	Epithelium of villi and walls of blood vessels into blood stream

THE LARGE INTESTINE AND DEFAECATION

The large intestine or colon is attached to the small intestine at the *ileocolic* or *ileocaecal valve*. It is about five feet long and ends at the anus.

It begins as a dilated pouch, the *caecum*, to which the *vermiform appendix* is attached. The *appendix* is composed of the same four coats as the intestine but the sub-mucous coat contains a considerable amount of lymphoid tissue, which is thought to have a function similar to that of the tonsils. It may lie below or behind the caecum; in the latter case it is described as retrocaecal. The caecum lies in the right iliac region resting on the iliopsoas muscle, and from here the colon ascends through the right lumbar region as the *ascending colon*. It turns beneath the liver as the *hepatic flexure*, passes across the margins of the epigastric and umbilical regions as the *transverse colon*, turns beneath the spleen as the *splenic flexure*, and passes down through the left lumbar region as the *descending colon*. In the left iliac region a bend called the *sigmoid flexure* or *pelvic colon* is formed, and it then enters the true pelvis and becomes the *rectum*. The rectum is the lowest five inches of the large intestine, it begins at the pelvic colon and ends in the *anal canal* which is about one and a half inches long. This ends in the *anus*, which is guarded by internal and external sphincter muscles.

Structure. The *colon* consists of the same four coats as the small intestine, the longitudinal fibres of the muscular coat are arranged in three bands which give the colon a puckered and sacculated appearance. The inner mucous coat is smoother than that of the small intestine, it has no villi. It contains glands similar to the tubular intestinal glands and is lined by columnar peithelium which contains many secreting or goblet cells.

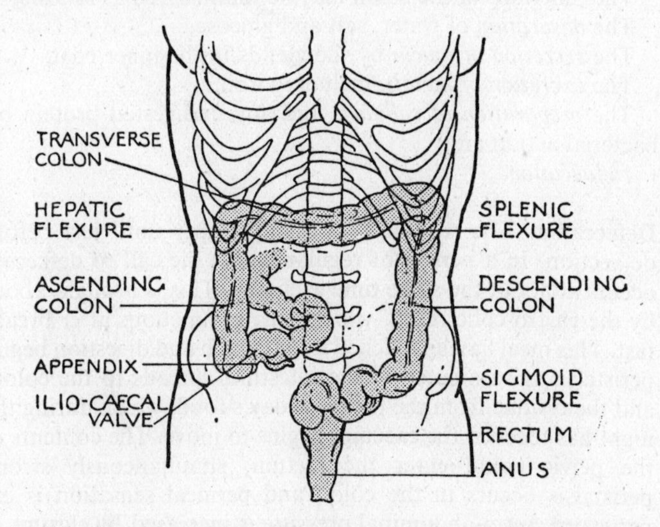

FIG. 137.—DIAGRAM OF THE POSITION OF THE LARGE INTESTINE IN RELATION TO THE SKELETON.

The structure of the *rectum* is similar to that of the colon, but the muscular coat is thicker and the mucous membrane is arranged in longitudinal folds called the *columns of Morgagni.* These are continued into the anal canal. At the area where the rectum joins the anal canal, the circular muscular fibres are thickened to form the *internal* anal *sphincter*. The cells lining the anal canal change in character, stratified epithelium replaces columnar cells and is continuous with the skin.

The Functions of the Large Intestine. The large intestine does not take part in the digestion or absorption of food. When the contents of the small intestine reach the caecum all the nourishment has been absorbed, and the contents are liquid. In passing along the colon the contents become more solid as water is absorbed, and when the rectum is reached the faeces are of a soft-solid consistence. Peristalsis is very slow in the colon. It takes about sixteen to twenty-four hours for the contents to reach the sigmoid flexure.

The functions of the colon may be summarized as follows:

The *absorption* of water, salt and glucose,

The *secretion of mucin* by the glands in the inner coat,

The *excretion of metals*, including iron,

The *preparation of cellulose* and any undigested protein by bacterial action and

Defaecation.

Defaecation. The rectum is normally empty until just before defaection. In a person of regular habits the call to defaecate occurs at about the same time each day. This is brought about by the gastro-colic reflex, which usually functions after breakfast. This meal having reached the stomach and digestion begun peristalsis is stimulated in the intestine, spreads to the colon, and the residue from the previous day's food, which during the night has reached the caecum, begins to move. The contents of the pelvic colon enter the rectum; simultaneously strong peristalsis occurs in the colon and perineal sensation is experienced. Intra-abdominal pressure is increased by closure of the glottis and contraction of the diaphragm and the abdominal muscles; the anal sphincters relax, and the act is complete.

Composition of faeces. Faeces contain about 70 per cent water, shed epithelium from the intestine, a considerable quantity of bacteria, most of them dead, a small quantity of nitrogenous matter, mainly mucin; also salts, principally calcium phosphate and a little iron, and cellulose when present in the diet.

THE PERITONEUM

The peritoneum is a double *serous membrane*. It is the largest serous membrane in the body and is described as consisting of two main parts, the *parietal peritoneum* which lines the walls of the abdominal cavity, and the *visceral peritoneum* which is reflected over the organs contained in that cavity. The potential space between these two layers is called the *peritoneal space* or sac.

Some of the organs are completely covered by peritoneum, these include the stomach, liver and intestines. Other organs such as the pancreas and spleen are only partly covered by it. The kidneys lie behind the peritoneum and are not contained in the peritoneal sac.

Special parts of the peritoneum are described as the *ligaments*, which are folds of peritoneum connecting the various organs to the abdominal wall, e.g. the ligaments of the liver and the uterus.

The omenta are three double folds of peritoneum which separate some of the organs from each other. The principal ones are the greater and lesser omentum. The *great omentum* is attached to the lower border of the stomach, and hangs down in front of the intestines like an apron. The *lesser* or *gastro-hepatic omentum* separates the liver from the lesser curvature of the stomach.

The *mesenteries* are folds of peritoneum which join the different parts of the intestine and sling them up to the posterior abdominal wall. The mesentery of the small intestine is a fan-shaped fold. The mesenteries also support the mesenteric vessels and contain numerous lymphatic glands.

The Pelvic Peritoneum. The peritoneum is continued into the pelvis; it covers the upper part of the rectum. In the male it is then reflected on to the base of the bladder. In the female, the peritoneum passes from the rectum to the upper part of the vagina, over the back and front of the uterus and then on to the bladder. The *Pouch of Douglas* is a sac of peritoneum which extends down for about three and a half inches in front of the rectum. In the female this area is called the recto-uterine fossa. In the male it is the recto-vesical fossa (*see* Fig. 170, p. 271).

The uterine peritoneum forms the broad ligaments, in the upper limits of which lie the *uterine tubes*. The peritoneum is continuous with the mucous membrane lining the uterine tubes, and as the uterine tubes open into the peritoneal cavity it is not a closed sac in the female.

The Functions of the Peritoneum. It covers most of the abdominal and pelvic organs, forming a smooth lining which

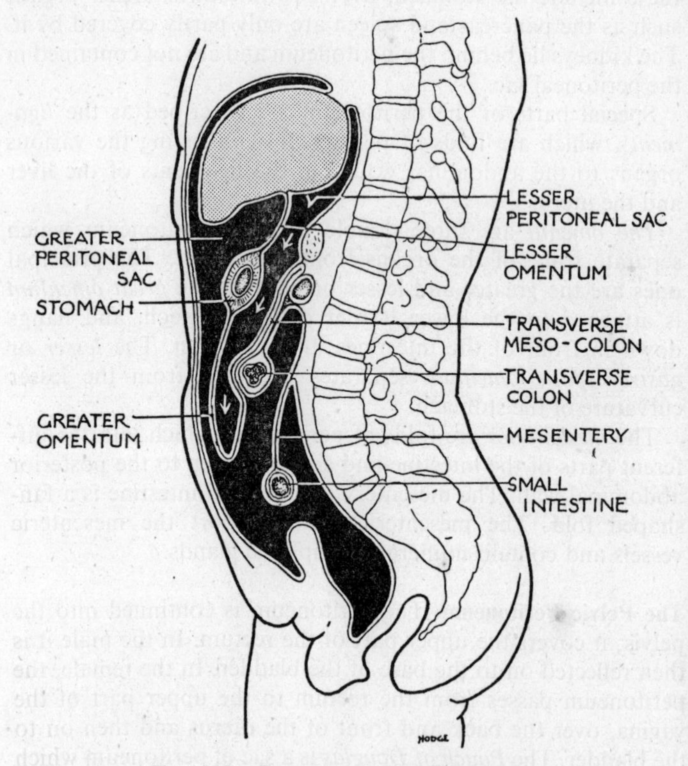

FIG. 138.—DIAGRAM OF THE PERITONEUM.

enables these organs to move upon each other without friction.

It attaches the organs together and keeps them in position and maintains the organs in relation to the posterior abdominal wall.

By means of the considerable amount of fat contained in the omenta, the peritoneum has great capacity to resist infection, the pelvic peritoneum is more resistant to sepsis than the peritoneum at the upper part of the abdominal cavity—that is why it is so important to keep patients with abdominal infection in Fowler's position.

Chapter 13

THE LIVER AND PANCREAS

THE LIVER

The liver is the largest gland in the body. It weighs from fifty to sixty ounces. It is situated on the right of the abdominal cavity beneath the diaphragm, and occupies part of the right hypochondriac, epigastric, right lumbar and left hypochondriac regions.

The liver is divided into two main lobes, right and left. The upper surface is convex and lies beneath the diaphragm, the under surface is irregular and presents the *transverse fissure*, the

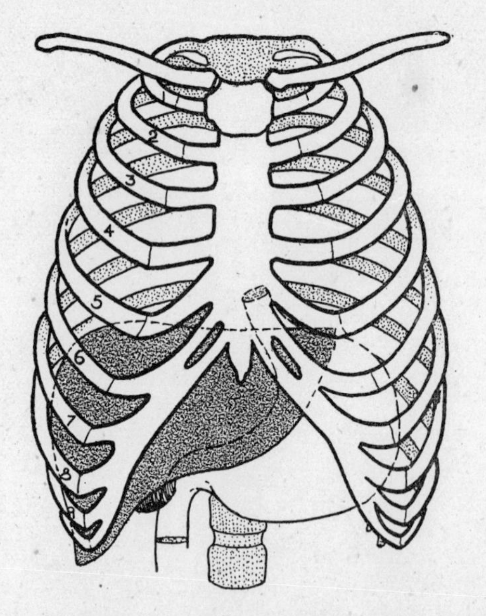

FIG. 139.—THE POSITION OF THE LIVER SHOWN RISING AS HIGH AS THE FIFTH RIB, AND EXTENDING AS LOW AS THE COSTAL MARGIN ON THE RIGHT SIDE.

surface being broken by the passage of the vessels which enter and leave the liver. The *longitudinal fissure* separates the right and left lobes on the under surface and the *suspensory ligament* occupies a similar position on the upper surface of the liver. The liver is further subdivided into five lobes, these are made up of lobules. The lobules, which are polyhedral in shape, are composed of cubical liver cells and the ramifications of the vessels of the liver, all connected together by liver tissue.

The Vessels of the Liver are :

The hepatic artery, which carries pure blood to the liver from the abdominal aorta,

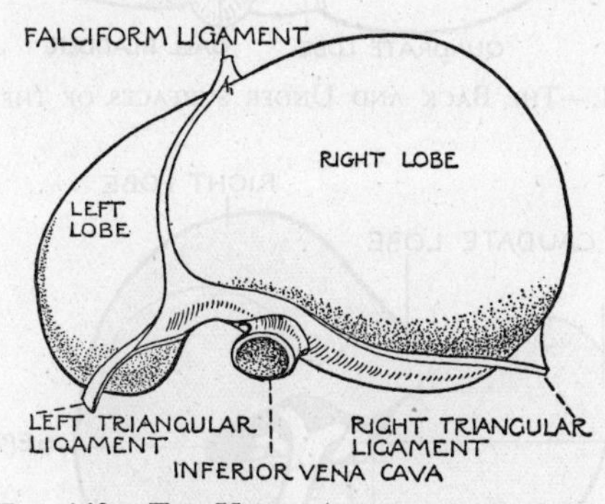

FIG. 140.—THE UPPER ASPECT OF THE LIVER.

The portal vein, which carries blood rich in nourishment collected from the stomach, pancreas, intestines, and spleen,

The hepatic vein, which is formed by the union of the capillaries from the hepatic artery and the portal vein; it carries the blood from the liver to the inferior vena cava, and

Bile ducts, which are formed by the union of the bile capillaries which collect the bile from the liver cells.

There are thus four main vessels traversing the substance of the liver, two entering, the hepatic artery and portal vein, and two leaving, the hepatic vein and the bile duct. Those vessels are supported by a connective tissue called *Glisson's capsule.*

Minute Structure. The liver cells are nucleated polyhedral cells. The protoplasm of the cells contains glycogen and fatty particles. Masses of these cells form the hepatic lobules which are roughly hexagonal in shape, about one millimetre in dia-

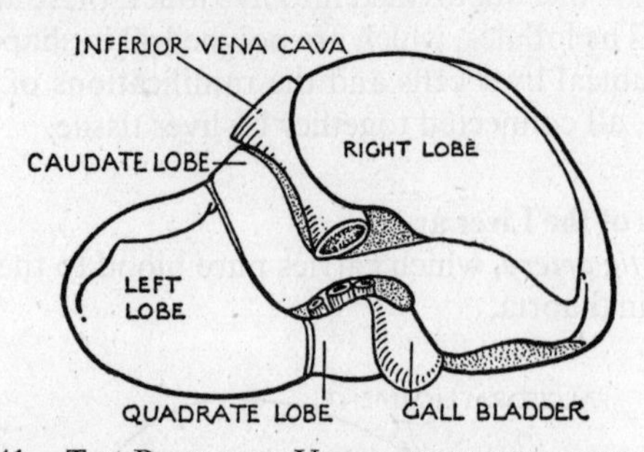

FIG. 141.—THE BACK AND UNDER SURFACES OF THE LIVER.

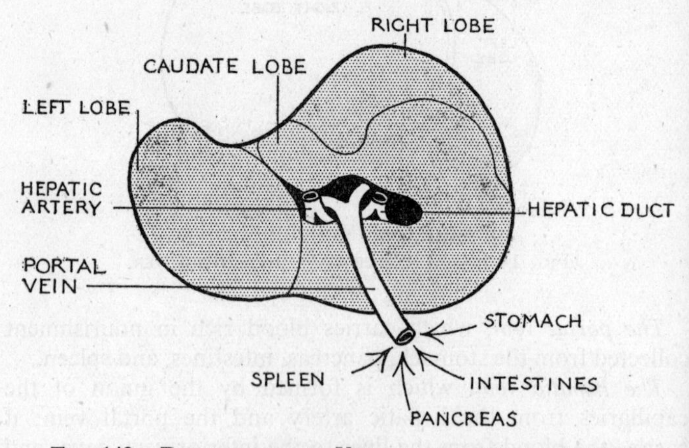

FIG. 142.—DIAGRAM OF THE VESSELS ENTERING AND LEAVING THE LIVER.

meter and separated from one another by a connective tissue in which run the ramifications of the vessels traversing the liver. Branches of the portal vein, the hepatic artery and the bile ducts are enclosed together in a connective tissue covering called Glisson's capsule, which forms portal canals. The blood from the portal vein comes into close proximity with the liver cells, each lobule is penetrated by a network of *blood sinusoids* or hepatic capillaries (*see* Fig. 144). Small vessels passing between the liver lobules are called *interlobular veins.* From these, capillaries branch into the substance of the lobules, and unite to form a small vein in the centres of the lobules, *intralobular veins.* These vessels pour their contents into other veins called *sublobular veins*, which unite and finally form several hepatic veins passing directly into the inferior vena cava.

Bile capillaries or *bile canaliculi* are minute channels which commence between the liver cells, lying between two cells, so that they are always separated from the blood capillaries. The bile capillaries then pass to the margins of the lobules, and pour their contents into the interlobular bile ducts which unite to form the *hepatic ducts.* The largest bile ducts are lined by columnar epithelium and have an outer coat of fibrous and muscular tissue, by means of these ducts bile is carried away from the liver.

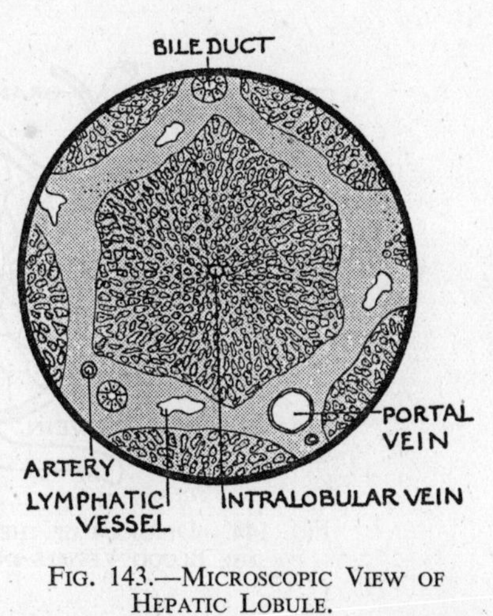

FIG. 143.—MICROSCOPIC VIEW OF HEPATIC LOBULE.

Note the hexagonal shape. In the Tissue surrounding the Lobule lie branches of the Portal Vein, Hepatic Artery, Bile Ducts and Lymphatics.

The Functions of the Liver are concerned with the metabolism of the body.

The glycogenic function. Stimulated by the action of an enzyme the liver cells produce glycogen (an animal starch) by concentration of the glucose derived from the carbohydrate food. This substance is stored temporarily by the liver cells, and converted back into glucose by enzyme action, when needed by the body tissue. By means of this function the liver aids in maintaining the percentage of sugar in the blood, but this is controlled by the internal secretion of the pancreas, insulin (*see* page 222).

The secretion of bile. Bile is secreted by the liver cells and is expelled by being forced into the bile ducts, and thence to the duodenum by the pressure of newly formed bile behind and by the contraction of the plain muscle in the walls of the bile ducts and gall-bladder.

Formation of urea. The liver receives the amino acids which have been absorbed by the blood. In the liver cells deamination

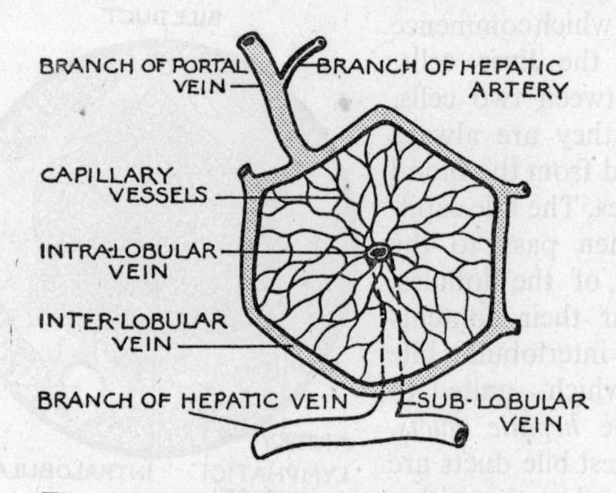

FIG. 144.—DIAGRAM OF THE ARRANGEMENT OF THE BLOOD VESSELS IN THE LIVER.

takes place, which means that the nitrogen is separated from the amino-acid part, and converted into urea. Urea is eventually removed from the blood by the kidneys and excreted in the urine.

Desaturation of fats. The liver prepares the fats for their final breaking down into the end products of carbonic acid and water.

Storage and distribution of the anti-anaemic principle. The blood-governing factor of Castle (*see* page 200) formed in the stomach is stored in the liver and from the liver it reaches the bone marrow to stimulate the formation of healthy red blood cells. It is from study of this function of the liver that the use of liver, or liver extract, in the treatment of anaemia has been introduced.

Maintenance of body temperature. The liver helps to maintain the temperature of the body, because the size of the liver and the number of its *metabolic activities* cause the blood passing through the organ to be raised in temperature.

THE GALL-BLADDER

The gall-bladder is a pear-shaped musculo-membranous bag, lying in a fossa on the under surface of the liver and reaching to the front margin of that organ. It measures three to four inches in length and holds from eight to ten drachms.

It is divided into a fundus, body, and neck, and consists of three coats:

An Outer serous peritoneal coat,

A Middle unstriped muscular tissue, and

An Inner mucous membrane, which is continuous with that lining the bile ducts. The mucous membrane is composed of columnar epithelial cells which secrete mucin and absorb water, thus concentrating the bile.

The cystic duct is about an inch and a half in length. It passes from the neck of the gall-bladder and joins the hepatic duct, thereby forming the common bile duct which conveys the bile to the duodenum.

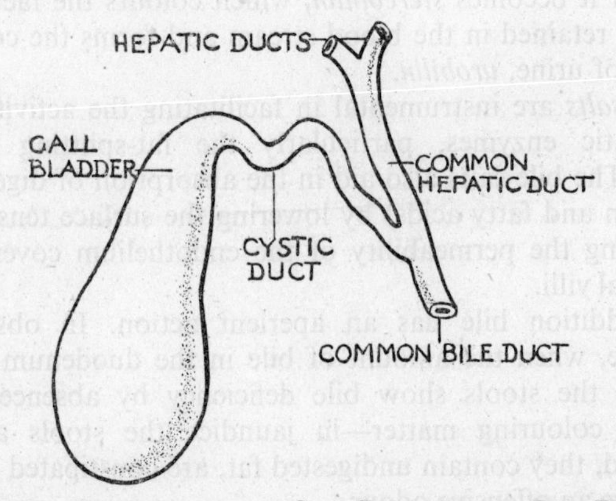

FIG. 145.—DIAGRAM OF THE GALL-BLADDER AND BILE DUCTS.

Function. The gall-bladder acts as a *reservoir* for the bile. It also performs the important function of *concentrating the bile* stored in it.

The gall-bladder is very liable to infection (cholecystitis), which may be conveyed to it either from the intestine or liver or through the blood stream. Gall stones may be formed in the gall-bladder and when these obstruct the hepatic or the common bile duct (*see* Fig. 145) the bile cannot escape from the liver and obstructive jaundice occurs.

Composition and Function of Bile. Bile is an alkaline fluid secreted by the liver cells. The amount secreted daily in man is from 17 to 35 ounces, the secretion is continuous, but the rate of production is accelerated during digestion, especially during the digestion of fats (*see* page 205). It contains about 86 per cent water, bile salts, bile pigments, cholesterol, mucin, and other substances.

Bile pigments. There are two bile pigments, *bilirubin*, which gives an orange-red colour to the bile, and *biliverdin*, which gives a greenish colour. Bilirubin is obtained from the haemoglobin as the result of the breakdown of the red blood cells after the iron has been separated in the spleen and liver. Some of the pigment is changed in the liver into biliverdin. These pigments are conveyed by the bile to the small intestine; some of it becomes *stercobilin*, which colours the faeces, and some is retained in the blood stream and forms the colouring matter of urine, *urobilin*.

Bile salts are instrumental in facilitating the activity of all pancreatic enzymes, particularly the fat-splitting ferment lipase. The bile salts also aid in the absorption of digested fat (glycerin and fatty acids) by lowering the surface tension and increasing the permeability of the endothelium covering the intestinal villi.

In addition bile has an aperient action. In obstructive jaundice, when the amount of bile in the duodenum is diminished, the stools show bile deficiency by absence of the normal colouring matter—in jaundice the stools are clay coloured, they contain undigested fat, are constipated and dry and have an offensive odour.

THE PANCREAS

The pancreas is a compound racemose gland, very similar in structure to the salivary glands. It is about seven inches long, extending from the duodenum to the spleen, and is described as consisting of the following three parts.

The head of the pancreas, the broadest part, lies to the right of the abdominal cavity and in the curve of the duodenum, which practically encircles it.

The body of the pancreas is the main part of the organ; it lies behind the stomach and in front of the first lumbar vertebra.

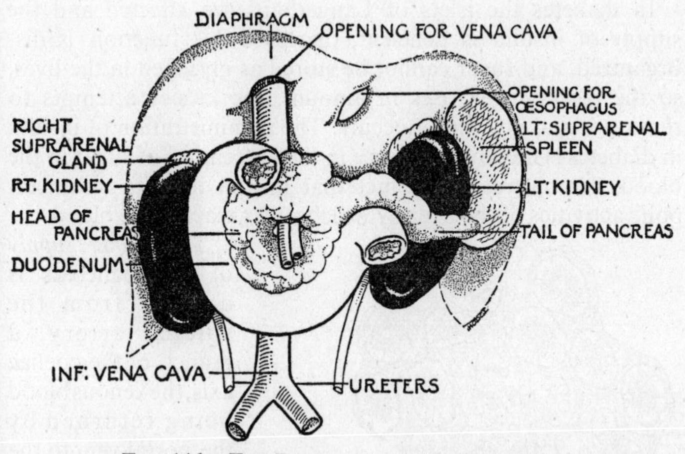

FIG. 146.—THE PANCREAS AND ITS RELATIONS.
The head of the pancreas is encircled by the duodenum, and the tail touches the spleen.

The tail of the pancreas is a narrow part to the left, which actually touches the spleen.

The substance of the pancreas is composed of lobules of secretory cells arranged round tiny ducts, which unite to form the main duct, the *duct of Wirsung*. This conveys the pancreatic digestive fluid to the duodenum.

Scattered amongst the lobules of the pancreas are to be found groups of smaller cells of entirely different structure and function; these scattered groups are known as the *islets of*

Langerhans which together form a ductless gland. The pancreas therefore has two functions, the secretion of a very important digestive fluid (*see* page 205), and the production of an internal secretion, which plays an important part in the metabolism of carbohydrate food. Commercial preparations of this internal secretion have been named *insulin*.

Insulin acts by controlling the storage of sugar as glycogen in the liver. It thus provides a ready store of glucose to the blood. As a rule the percentage of glucose in the blood is fairly constant at 80–120 milligrams per 100 cubic centimetres after starving twelve hours. It rises suddenly for half an hour after the intake of food.

In diabetes the islets of Langerhans are affected and the supply of insulin is deficient, therefore this function is disorganized, and sugar cannot be stored as glycogen in the liver, so the blood sugar rises in amount, the kidney attempts to remove it and glycosuria occurs. The administration of insulin in diabetes is met by a decrease in the percentage of sugar in the blood, demonstrating the fact that insulin inhibits the metabolic activities of the liver by which sugar reaches the blood.

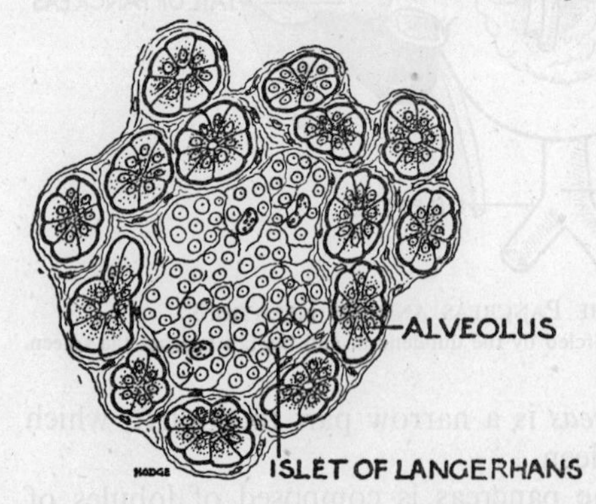

FIG. 147.—FROM A MICROSCOPIC SECTION OF PANCREAS SHOWING ISLET OF LANGERHANS SURROUNDED BY ALVEOLI.

The *blood supply* of the pancreas is derived from the splenic artery, a branch of the coeliac axis, the venous blood being returned by the portal vein to the liver. The islets of Langerhans, which form an endocrine organ producing an internal secretion, have a very liberal blood supply.

Chapter 14

THE RESPIRATORY SYSTEM AND RESPIRATION

It is by means of the respiratory system that every cell in the body receives its supply of oxygen and at the same time gets rid of the products of oxidation. Oxygen combining with the carbon and hydrogen of the tissues enables the metabolic processes of each individual cell to proceed, with the result that work is effected and waste products in the form of carbon dioxide (CO_2) and water (H_2O) are eliminated.

Respiration is a two-fold process whereby the *interchange of gases* takes place in the tissues, 'internal respiration'—and in the lungs, 'external respiration' (for description of the physiology of respiration, *see* page 232).

The thorax is a closed cavity, and by means of a negative pressure kept up by the elasticity of the lung tissue, air is drawn into the lungs during inspiration and expelled from the lungs during expiration. The air enters through the respiratory passages which are enumerated and briefly described below.

The bony framework of the nose is described on page 49, and the olfactory region on page 317. The respiratory portion forms the upper part of the respiratory passages.

THE RESPIRATORY PASSAGES

The *anterior nares* are the openings into the nostrils. They open into the portion known as the *vestibule of the nose* which is lined with stratified epithelium continuous with that of the skin. The lining of the anterior nares contains a number of sebaceous glands and is covered by hairs. It opens into the nasal cavities.

The *nasal cavities* are lined with mucous membrane which is highly vascular, and which is composed of columnar ciliated epithelium and goblet cells.

As air passes through the nose it is *filtered* by the hairs contained therein, *warmed* by contact with the fairly extensive mucous surface, and *moistened* by evaporation of moisture from this surface.

The *posterior nares* are the openings from the nasal cavities to the nasopharynx.

The *nasopharynx* lies behind the nose, and is lined with columnar ciliated epithelium.

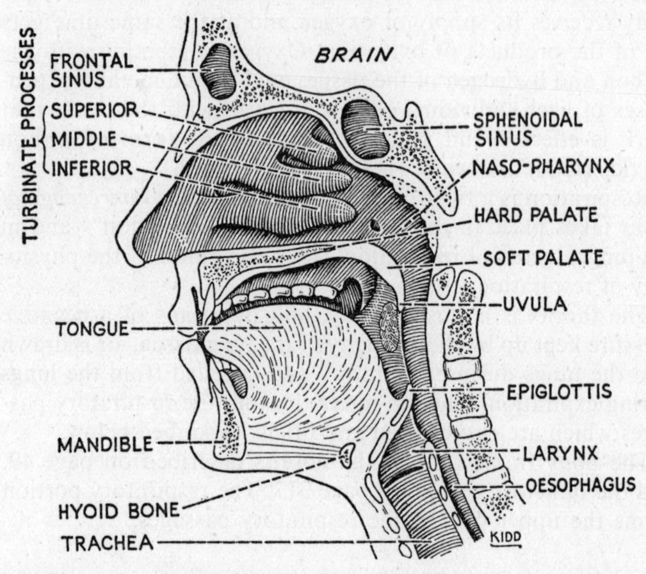

FIG. 148.—SECTION OF THE FACE AND NECK, SHOWING THE UPPER RESPIRATORY PASSAGES.

The *pharynx* lies below the nasopharynx and communicates with two other organs, the larynx in front and the oesophagus behind. The structure of the pharynx is described on page 191.

The *larynx* or voice box forms the upper prominent part of the windpipe and is continuous with the pharynx above and opens into the trachea below. The larynx lies in the front of the neck, extending from the lower part of the oral pharynx to the 6th cervical vertebra and lying in front of the 3rd and the 6th cervical vertebrae (*see* Fig. 31) from which it is separated by the oesophagus.

The *larynx* is composed of pieces of cartilage connected together by ligaments and membrane. The largest of these is the *thyroid cartilage*, the front of which forms the subcutaneous prominence known as Adam's apple in the front of the neck.

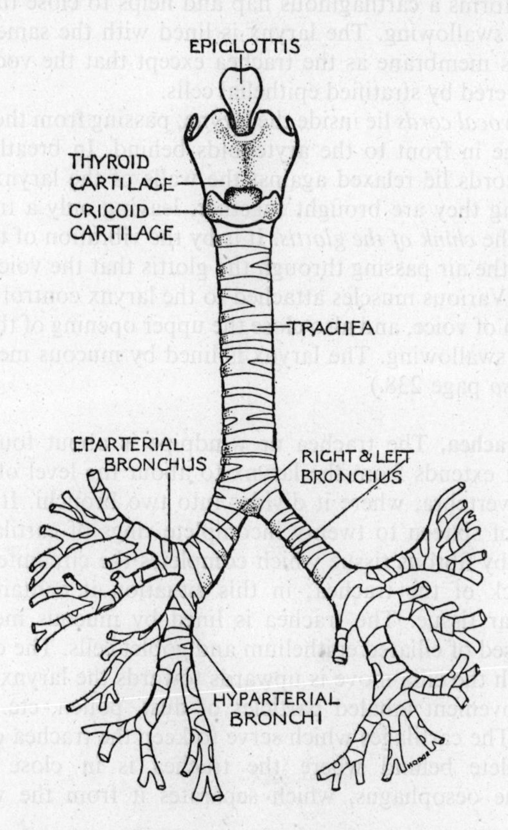

FIG. 149.—THE LARYNX, TRACHEA, AND BRONCHI, WITH THEIR RAMIFICATIONS.

It consists of two plates or laminae joined in the middle line. The superior border is marked by a V-shaped notch. The *cricoid cartilage* lies below the thyroid and is shaped like a signet ring with the signet part of the circle at the back. (This is the only cartilage which is a complete ring.) Other cartilages are the two *arytenoid cartilages* perched on the back of the cricoid and the *cartilages of Santorini and Wrisberg* which are very small. Attached to the top of the thyroid cartilage is the *epiglottis*, which forms a cartilaginous flap and helps to close the larynx during swallowing. The larynx is lined with the same type of mucous membrane as the trachea except that the vocal cords are covered by stratified epithelial cells.

The *vocal cords* lie inside the larynx, passing from the thyroid cartilage in front to the arytenoids behind. In breathing, the vocal cords lie relaxed against the walls of the larynx, but in speaking they are brought together, leaving only a tiny aperture—the *chink of the glottis*. It is by the vibration of the cords due to the air passing through the glottis that the voice is produced. Various muscles attached to the larynx control the production of voice, and also close the upper opening of the larynx during swallowing. The larynx is lined by mucous membrane. (*See also* page 238.)

The Trachea. The trachea or windpipe is about four inches long. It extends from the larynx to about the level of the 5th dorsal vertebra, where it divides into two bronchi. It is composed of sixteen to twenty incomplete rings of cartilage connected by fibrous tissue which completes the circumference at the back of the trachea; in this situation it contains some muscular tissue. The trachea is lined by mucous membrane composed of ciliated epithelium and goblet cells. The direction in which the cilia move is upwards towards the larynx, and by this movement inhaled particles of dust, pollen, etc. are got rid of. The cartilages which serve to keep the trachea open are incomplete behind where the trachea is in close contact with the oesophagus, which separates it from the vertebral column.

The *cervical trachea*, which passes through the neck, is crossed by the isthmus of the thyroid gland, the lobes of the gland embracing the sides of the trachea. The *thoracic trachea* passes through the superior mediastinum (*see* Fig. 150) lying behind the sternum, in contact with the innominate artery and the arch of the aorta. The oesophagus lies behind the trachea.

The Bronchi, which are formed by the bifurcation of the trachea at about the level of the 5th dorsal vertebra, are similar in structure to the trachea, and are lined by the same types of cells. The bronchi pass downwards and outwards towards the roots of the lungs. The *right bronchus* is shorter and wider than the left; it gives off one branch at a level higher than that of the pulmonary artery called the *eparterial bronchus*; the other branch arising after the main branch has passed below the artery is the *hyparterial bronchus*. The *left bronchus* is longer and slimmer than the right and as it passes below the pul-

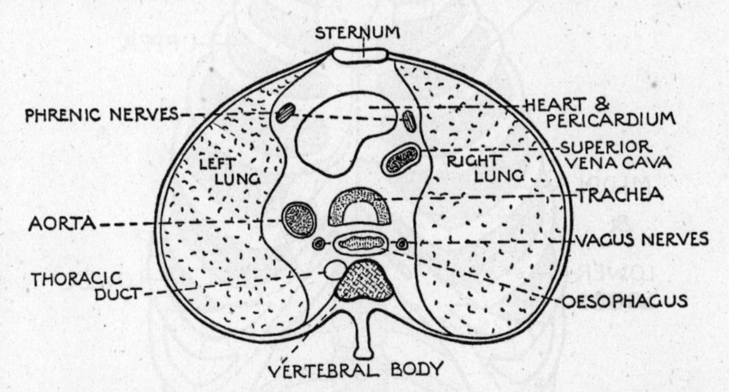

FIG. 150.—A DIAGRAM SHOWING THE RELATIVE POSITIONS OF STRUCTURES IN THE MEDIASTINUM.

monary artery before dividing into branches all its branches are hyparterial (*see* Fig. 149).

THE THORACIC CAVITY

The thoracic cavity is situated at the upper part of the trunk. *The boundaries of the thorax* are:

The sternum and costal cartilages in front,
The twelve thoracic vertebrae with their invertebral discs of cartilage behind,
The ribs and intercostal muscles at the sides,
The diaphragm below, and
The root of the neck above.

Contents. The sides of the thoracic cavity are completely filled by the lungs with their pleural covering; these lie each side of, and form the lateral boundaries of, the mediastinum.

The mediastinum is the space in the thoracic cavity between the two lungs. It contains the heart and great blood vessels, the oesophagus, thoracic duct, descending aorta, and superior vena cava, the vagi and phrenic nerves and numerous lymphatic glands.

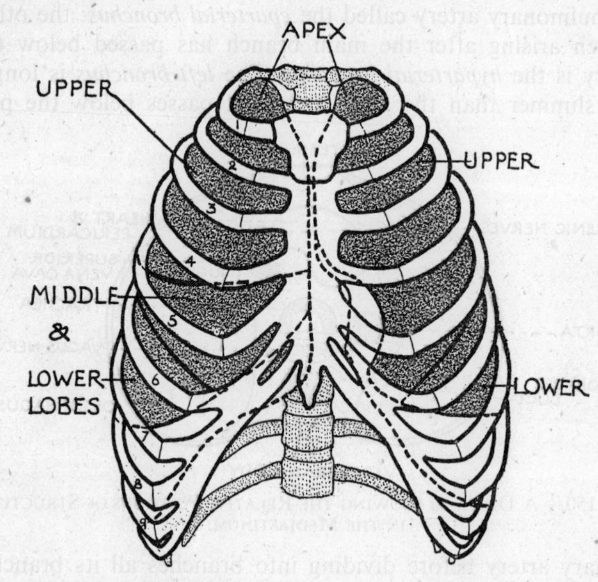

FIG. 151.—THE POSITION OF THE LUNGS IN THE THORAX.
The *black lines* indicate the division of the lungs into lobes. The *dotted lines* indicate the position of the pleura.

THE LUNGS

The lungs, two in number, are the principal organs of respiration. They fill the chest cavity, lying one on each side separated in the middle by the heart and its great blood vessels, and by the other structures lying in the mediastinum (*see* above). The lungs are cone-shaped organs, with the *apex* above, rising a little higher than the clavicle into the root of the neck. The *base of the lungs* lies at the lowest point; it rests on the diaphragm and is accommodated by its concave lower surface to the upper dome-shaped surface of the diaphragm. The lungs present an *outer surface* in contact with the ribs, an *inner surface* where the root of the lung lies, a *posterior border* in contact with the vertebral column, and an *anterior border* which overlaps the anterior aspect of the heart.

The Lobes of the Lungs. The lungs are divided into lobes by fissures. The right lung has three and the left lung two lobes. Each of these lobes is composed of a number of lobules. A small bronchial tube enters each lobule and as it divides and subdivides its walls become thinner and thinner and finally

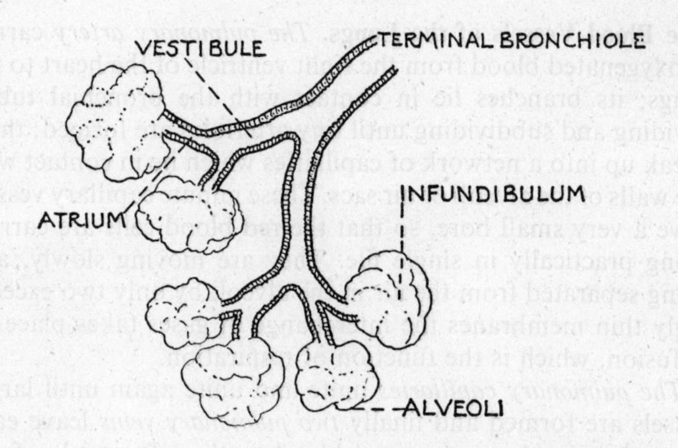

FIG. 152.—DIAGRAM OF THE TERMINATION OF A BRONCHIOLE INTO GROUPS OF ALVEOLI.

end in small dilated sacs, the air sacs of the lungs. Lung tissue is elastic, porous and spongy and it floats in water because of the air contained in it.

The Pulmonary Bronchi. The trachea divides into two main bronchi, these divide again before they enter the lungs (*see* page 227). As the *pulmonary bronchi* pass through the lungs they divide and subdivide a great number of times. The larger vessels retain a structure similar to that of the trachea, having a fibrous muscular wall containing cartilage and lined by ciliated epithelium. The cartilage gradually disappears from the smaller vessels leaving the fibrous-muscular coat and the ciliated lining. The *terminal bronchi* open into a slightly altered passage called the *vestibule*, and here the lining membrane begins to change its character; the ciliated epithelial lining gives place to one of flattened endothelial cells. From the vestibule (*see* Fig. 152), several *infundibula* open, and in the walls of these the air sacs lie. The *air sacs* or *alveoli* consist of one layer of flattened epithelial cells, and it is here that the blood comes into almost direct contact with the air—a plexus of blood vessels surrounds the alveoli and the interchange of gases takes place.

The Blood Vessels of the Lungs. *The pulmonary artery* carries deoxygenated blood from the right ventricle of the heart to the lungs; its branches lie in contact with the bronchial tubes, dividing and subdividing until tiny arterioles are formed; these break up into a network of capillaries which lie in contact with the walls of the alveoli or air sacs. These minute capillary vessels have a very small bore, so that the red blood cells are carried along practically in single file. They are moving slowly, and being separated from the air in the alveoli by only two exceedingly thin membranes the interchange of gases takes place by diffusion, which is the function of respiration.

The pulmonary capillaries unite and unite again until larger vessels are formed and finally *two pulmonary veins* leave each lung carrying the oxygenated blood to the left auricle of the heart for distribution all over the body by means of the aorta.

Vessels described as *bronchial arteries* carry oxygenated blood direct from the thoracic aorta to the lungs in order to nourish and bring oxygen into the substance of the lungs. The terminal branches of these arteries form a capillary plexus, which is distinct and separate from that formed by the terminal branches of the pulmonary arteries, but some of these capillaries finally unite with the pulmonary capillaries and this blood is then carried into the pulmonary veins. The remainder of the blood is conveyed from each lung by the *bronchial veins*, and it eventually reaches the superior vena cava through the azygos veins (*see* page 170).

The Root of the Lung is formed by the following structures:

Pulmonary arteries, which carry deoxygenated blood into the lungs for purification,

Pulmonary veins, which return the oxygenated blood from the lungs to the heart,

Bronchi, which branch into the bronchial tree, form the principal air passages,

Bronchial arteries, which arise from the thoracic aorta, convey arterial blood to the lung substance,

Bronchial veins, which return some of the blood from the lungs to the superior vena cava, and

Lymphatic vessels, which pass in and out of the lungs, are very numerous.

Nerves. The lungs are supplied by the vagus and sympathetic nerves.

Lymphatic glands. All the lymphatic vessels which pass through the lung structure are drained eventually into glands lying at the root of the lung.

The Pleura. Each lung is surrounded by a double serous membrane, the pleura. The *visceral* or *pulmonary pleura* closely invests the lung, passing into the fissures and so dividing the lobes from each other. This membrane is then reflected back at the root of the lung and forms the *parietal pleura*, which covers the interior of the chest wall. The pleura lining the ribs is the *costal pleura*, the portion covering the diaphragm, the *diaphragmatic pleura*, and the portion which lies in the neck, the *cervical pleura*. This is strengthened by a strong membrane called *Sibson's fascia*, on which the subclavian artery lies.

Between the pleural layers there is a slight exudate which lubricates the surfaces, and prevents friction between the lungs and the chest wall during the respiratory movements. In health the two layers of pleura are in contact one with the other, the pleural space or cavity is only a potential space; but when, in abnormal states, air or fluid lies between the two layers of pleura separating them, the space then becomes distinct.

THE PHYSIOLOGY OF RESPIRATION

The function of the lungs is the interchange of gases. In the minute structure of the lungs the pulmonary capillaries break up and surround the numerous alveoli; here the red blood cells pass through the tiny capillary vessels slowly and almost in single file, in order that the *reduced haemoglobin* may liberate its load of carbonic acid gas to the air and receive oxygen in exchange, so that the newly constituted *oxy-haemoglobin* may be conveyed to the tissue cells. This is what happens in the lungs, but the interchange of gases is a two-fold process, as described below.

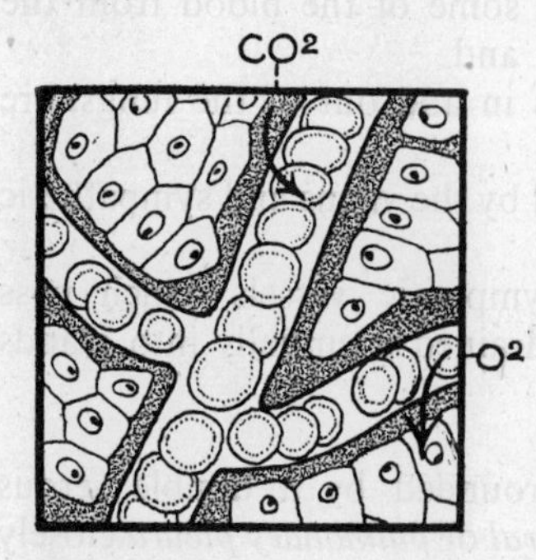

FIG. 153.—DIAGRAM ILLUSTRATING TISSUE RESPIRATION.

An arrow at the top indicates the passage of $C.O._2$ from the tissue fluid to the red cells within a capillary. An arrow below indicates the passing of Oxygen from the red blood corpuscles to the cells floating in tissue fluid.

Tissue or Internal Respiration. The blood, having its haemoglobin saturated with oxygen (oxy-haemoglobin), circulates throughout the body and finally reaches the capillary bed where the blood is moving extremely slowly. The tissue cells take oxygen from the rich haemoglobin to enable oxidation to go on, and the blood receives in exchange the waste product of oxidation (carbonic acid gas).

Pulmonary Respiration or External Respiration. The blood which has circulated in the tissues is now a dusky red colour, owing to the reduced amount of haemoglobin contained in its red cells and it also contains a fairly large amount of carbonic acid gas. When the blood circulating in the capillary blood vessels in the lungs comes into contact with the air in the alveoli, carbon dioxide is given off and oxygen received in exchange. Not all the CO_2 is lost, however, a small percentage is retained in the blood, as it is required in order to stimulate the respiratory centre for the control and regulation of the

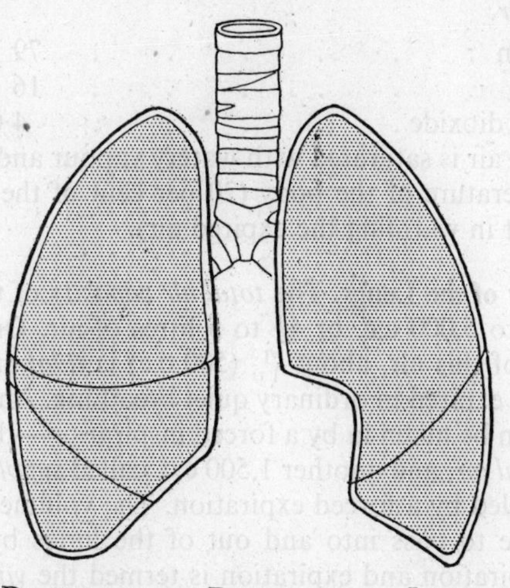

FIG. 154.—DIAGRAM OF THE DIVISION OF THE LUNGS INTO LOBES.
The right lung has three and the left lung two lobes.

respiratory movements (*see* page 235). As the result of these two respiratory processes the following changes take place in the tissues and in the lungs.

In the tissues.—Arterial blood provides oxygen to the cells and receives carbonic acid in exchange, thus leaving the tissues as *de-oxygenated blood.*

In the lungs.—The *venous blood* brought to the lungs gives up its load of carbonic acid and receives oxygen in exchange, thus becoming *oxygenated blood.*

During pulmonary respiration the following changes take place in the composition of air in the alveoli:

Inspired (atmospheric) *air:*

Nitrogen	79	per cent
Oxygen	20	,, ,,
Carbon dioxide	0·04	,, ,,

Air entering the alveoli is of the temperature and humidity of the atmosphere.

Expired air:

Nitrogen	79	per cent
Oxygen	16	„ „
Carbon dioxide	4·04	„ „

Expired air is saturated with watery vapour and it is of the temperature of the body (20 per cent of the body heat is lost in warming the expired air).

Air Capacity of the Lungs. The *total air capacity* of the lungs is from 4,500 to 5,000 c.c. or 4½ to 5 litres of air. Only a small proportion of this air, about $\frac{1}{10}$ (500 c.c) is *tidal air*, which is inspired and expired in ordinary quiet breathing. An additional 1,500 c.c. can be taken in by a forced inspiration—this is called *complemental air*, and another 1,500 c.c. called *supplemental air* can be expelled by a forced expiration. The volume of air that can be made to pass into and out of the lungs by the most forcible inspiration and expiration is termed the *vital capacity of the lungs*, and this is made up of the sum total of tidal, complemental, and supplemental air.

Vital Capacity:

Tidal air	500 c.c.
Complemental air	1,500 c.c.
Supplemental air	1,500 c.c.
	3,500 c.c.

Even then from 1,000 to 1,500 c.c. of *residual air* remains in the lungs, so that the lungs are never empty.

The vital capacity of the lungs is measured by means of a spirometer. It varies with the degree of physical fitness of the subject and the vital capacity is taken as an indication of physical fitness and is higher in strong healthy subjects than in those who are weak and feeble.

RATE AND CONTROL OF RESPIRATION

The mechanism of respiration is regulated and controlled by two principal factors, (*a*) the chemical, and (*b*) the nervous control. Certain factors stimulate the respiratory centre, which lies in the medulla oblongata, and when stimulated the centre generates impulses which are transmitted by spinal nerves to the muscles of respiration—the diaphragm and intercostals.

Nervous Control. The respiratory centre is an automatic centre in the medulla oblongata from which *efferent impulses* pass to the muscles of respiration. By means of some of the cervical nerve roots impulses are conveyed to the diaphragm by the phrenic nerves; and at a lower level of the spinal cord, impulses pass from the thoracic region via the intercostal nerves to stimulate the intercostal muscles. These impulses cause rhythmical contraction of the diaphragm and intercostal muscles at the rate of about sixteen to eighteen times per minute.

Afferent impulses stimulated by distension of the air sacs are carried by the vagus nerves to the respiratory centre in the medulla. When artificial respiration is performed it is with the object of stimulating the vagus nerves to action; as air is mechanically pressed out of the lungs, it is anticipated that the elastic lung tissue will respond and the air sacs become distended, so that the vagus nerve being stimulated, afferent impulses will be carried to the respiratory centre and these impulses may—in health they do—cause the efferent impulses to be discharged via the phrenic and intercostal nerves to the muscles of respiration.

Chemical Control. It is this which is the ultimate factor in controlling and regulating the frequency, rate, and depth of the respiratory movements. The respiratory centre in the medulla is extremely sensitive to the reaction of the blood; the alkaline reserve of blood must be maintained (*see* page 149). Carbon dioxide is an acid product of metabolism, and this acid chemical substance stimulates the respiratory centre to send out the impulses which act on the muscles of respiration.

Both controls, nervous and chemical, are essential; without either one of them man cannot continue to breathe. In cases of paralysis of the muscles of respiration (intercostals, and diaphragm), the iron lung or some other means of continual artificial respiration is employed, because the chest must move in order that air may be carried in and out of the lungs. On the other hand, where the movements of respiration have failed, but the mechanism, nerves, and muscles remain intact, as in poisoning by carbon monoxide, or when a patient stops breathing during an anaesthetic, inhalations of carbon dioxide 7 per cent in oxygen are given in order to increase the amount of carbon dioxide in the blood, which is the acid substance needed to stimulate the respiratory centre to begin again to send out its impulses which will regulate and control the nerves and muscles.

Certain other factors will cause increase in the rate and depth of respiration. *Vigorous exercise*, by using up the oxygen in the

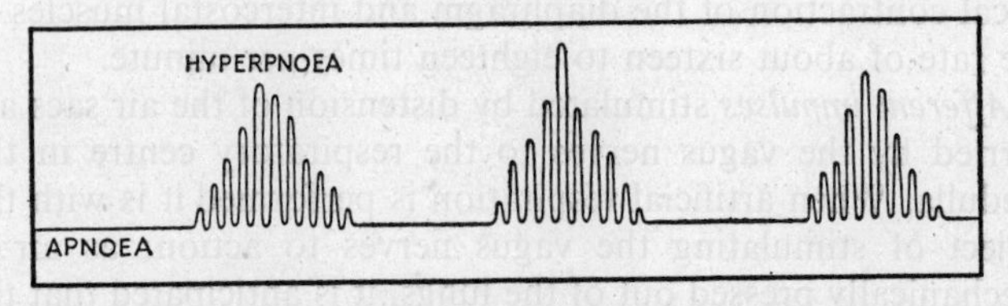

FIG. 155.—CHEYNE-STOKES'S BREATHING (*see* note below).

muscles in order to provide the energy (work) needed, will give rise to a slight increase in the amount of carbon dioxide in the blood and result in fuller ventilation of the lungs.

Emotion, *pain*, and *fear*, for example, cause impulses to be registered which stimulate the respiratory centre and give rise to the sharp intake of breath with which we are all familiar. *Afferent impulses from the skin* will produce a similar effect—when the body is plunged into cold water, or feels the first shock of a cold shower-bath, a sharp deep inspiration follows.

Voluntary control of the movements of respiration is possible but slight, as the movements are automatic. Any attempt to hold the breath for a longish time fails because of the discomfort caused by any increase above the normal amount of carbon dioxide in the blood.

Cheyne-Stoke's breathing is an irregularity of respiration in which periods of excessive deep breathing alternate with periods of apnoea. During *hyperpnoea* carbon dioxide is excessively exhaled and thus the normal chemical stimulant of respiration is removed. A period of *apnoea* (cessation of breathing), follows, and then, when sufficient carbon dioxide has collected in the blood to stimulate again the respiratory act breathing recommences.

This phenomenon is met in many diseases particularly in the late stages of heart disease and in toxaemias such as uraemia. It can also be produced artificially for a time by taking a rapid succession of deep breaths.

The Rate of Respiration is slightly quicker in women than in men. In normal breathing expiration succeeds inspiration, and is followed by a slight pause. Inspiration—expiration—pause. In sick babies this order is sometimes reversed and the sequence becomes: inspiration—pause—expiration. This is described as *inverse breathing*.

Normal rate per minute:

In the newly born	40
At twelve months	30
From two to five years . . .	24
In adults	16–18

The Mechanism of Respiration. Two movements occur during respiration (*a*) inspiration and (*b*) expiration. In quiet breathing the diaphragm does the work. The external intercostals are brought into play as accessory muscles only when inspiration becomes a conscious effort.

Inspiration is brought about by muscular action. Contraction of the diaphragm enlarges the chest cavity from above downwards, that is vertically. Elevation of the ribs and sternum, brought about by contraction of the intercostals, enlarges the chest cavity from side to side and from back to front. The elastic lungs expand to fill this increased space, and air is drawn into the air passages.

In *expiration* the air is forced out by relaxation of the muscles and the elastic recoil of the lungs.

In *forced respiration* the movements of the chest are greatly increased. The muscles of the neck and shoulders help to raise the ribs and sternum. The muscles of the back and abdomen are also brought into action and the *alae nasi* of the nose.

A *cough* is a forcible expiration when the air is expelled noisily. *Sighing* and *yawning* are prolonged inspirations, and in illness denote a failing heart. They are seen as signs of haemorrhage. *Hiccough* is caused by a spasm of the diaphragm, the movement is sudden, and the sound is caused by the air being forced through the glottis.

VOICE AND SPEECH

Voice is produced by the larynx, which is situated at the upper end of the trachea (for anatomy of larynx, *see* page 225). Folds of membrane, the *vocal cords*, are placed across the cavity of the larynx from front to back. These consist of two sets of folds, the *ventricular folds* or false cords, which consist of two thick folds of mucous membrane. Placed medially to these are the *vocal folds* or true vocal cords, which contain some yellow elastic tissue and which are concerned in the production of the voice. When these are brought together the air is forced to pass through a mere slit, 'the chink of the glottis'. The sound thus produced is then modified as it passes through the air passages above the larynx, and contraction of the muscles forming the soft palate, movements of the tongue, the position of the teeth, and lips, and air passing through the sinuses of the bones of the skull all serve to give tone to the voice.

Chapter 15

METABOLISM

Metabolism is the word used to indicate the chemical changes which take place in the body necessary for the fulfilment of its vital functions. Each cell is made up of protoplasm, which has the power to take in oxygen and other necessary substances, and to discard certain other properties as waste matter, including carbon dioxide, but between these changes taking place in the cells lies a large 'no man's land' of chemical activity upon which all the functions of the body intimately depend. Metabolism is divided into two classes of activity.

Constructive Metabolism or Anabolism, by which the body is built up and heat and energy are stored. This is most active in infancy and the growing years of childhood and adolescence, when increase in size and weight has to be provided for. Later, in adult life, when development is completed, the processes constituting anabolism prevent loss of weight, maintain the normal temperature of the body, and also repair and replace the tissues of the body as they become broken down or worn out.

Destructive Metabolism or Katabolism is concerned with the breakdown of tissues and the using up of energy. This is a constant unceasing process most highly active during muscular exercise and least active during restful sleep.

The rate of metabolism varies with age, sex, climate, with the type of clothing worn and work performed, and also with the state of mind of the subject, being more highly active during nervous tension than during relaxation.

Rate of Metabolism. *Basal Metabolism* is the term used to describe the rate of metabolic activities with the body in a condition of physical and mental rest. In this state the minimum of oxygen will be required as the tissues are working at a minimum and therefore the least possible amount of carbon dioxide will be excreted. The *basal metabolic rate* is therefore that obtained by measuring either the intake of oxygen or the output of carbon dioxide under the condition of rest stated.

The various vital activities of the body have been described in the different sections of this book. It is sufficient to summarize here that the activities which constitute *metabolism* include the functions of the heart and circulatory system, respiration, and digestion; the activities of all glands and the production of all secretions and excretions, and the maintenance of the body temperature.

It is obvious that the rate of metabolism will depend on the activity of the animal or man. The metabolic rate will be higher in a manual worker than in an indoor office worker leading a sedentary life. To compensate for heat lost and to maintain the necessary production of energy to be used as heat or work, man requires food. The energy value of food has been standardized and is expressed in large Calories—the amount of heat needed to raise the temperature of one litre of water from freezing point to 1 degree Centigrade is 1 Calorie.

	Calories
1 gramme of carbohydrate when oxidized gives	4·1
1 gramme of fat " " "	9·3
1 gramme of protein " " "	4·1

The proportionate Calorie requirements of man have been given on page 185. It is sufficient to give examples here, in order to show how the rate of metabolism determines the food intake necessary, in order:

To prevent loss of weight,
To maintain the body temperature, and
To provide for the functional activity of all cells, tissues, glands, and organs.

	Calories
A man doing heavy manual work requires	3,500
A sedentary worker requires	2,500
A man at rest needs	1,800
A man asleep needs even less, probably .	1,500

The foods which provide heat and energy are, as enumerated above, carbohydrates, fats, and proteins, and a résumé of the process of the metabolism of these three types of food is given below.

METABOLISM OF CARBOHYDRATE

Digestion.

Atyalin converts cooked starch into maltose.

Pmylase converts all starches into maltose.

Intestinal ferments:

Invertase *Maltase* *Lactase*	produce the final breaking down of maltose into the *monosaccharides:*	*laevulose,* *glucose,* and *galactose.*

Absorption.

The *monosaccharides* are absorbed into the blood—the percentage of blood sugar is maintained by the insulin control and liver activity.

In the tissues—carbohydrates are oxidized to provide heat and energy.

During the process of combustion CO_2 is eliminated as a waste product.

The waste products which result from the burning up of carbohydrates in the tissues are excreted—

By the lungs . Water (H_2O) and Carbon Dioxide (CO_2)
From the skin " " " "
In the urine . "

METABOLISM OF FAT

Digestion.

Gastric lipase produces slight hydrolysis of fat.

Pancreatic lipase, *Intestinal lipase* } break down fats into glycerin and fatty acids.

Absorption of glycerin and fatty acids by the lacteals—passed to thoracic duct, and enter the blood stream.

In the blood—fat is carried to every cell of the body.

The liver assists in the oxidation of fats and prepares fats for deposition in the tissues. The term *desaturation of fats* is sometimes used to describe this preparatory action of the liver on fats.

In the tissues—some of the fat is oxidized (in the presence of carbohydrates) to give heat and energy. Some of the fat is stored in the fat depots. (This stored fat contains vitamins A and D.)

The waste products which result from the combustion of fat in the tissues are excreted:

By the lungs, water and carbon dioxide,
By the skin, water and carbon dioxide, and
By the kidneys, water.

METABOLISM OF PROTEIN

Digestion.

In the stomach:

Pepsin (with HC1) converts proteins to peptones,
Rennin produces casein from caseinogen, and
Pepsin (with HC1) turns casein into peptones.

In the intestine:

Trypsin reduces protein and peptone to polypeptides, and
Erepsin further reduces polypeptides to amino-acids.

Absorption. Into the blood, the amino-acids bring nitrogen and sulphur to every cell in the body.

The body cells select the special amino-acids each cell needs for repair and growth.

The liver deaminates amino-acids and from this process urea is formed, and carbon compounds liberated for oxidation.

The waste products which result from the metabolism of protein in the tissues are—urea, uric acid, and creatinine. These substances are excreted in urine.

Control of Metabolism. Consideration of the co-ordination of the activities of the different organs of the body will make it clear that some marvellous controlling mechanism is functioning in order to ensure that each cell does not function merely as a unit but as part of an organization—the body. The two most important controlling factors are:

The nervous system, central, and involuntary. An example of what happens when a muscle is deprived of its nerve supply is seen in infantile paralysis, when the muscle wastes, the part ceases to function, and growth is retarded.

The endocrine organs. It is known that certain organs, described as endocrine (*see* page 245), produce substances of a chemical nature which control the well-being of the body, and so doing effect changes in other organs. For example, when the secretion of the thyroid gland is diminished, metabolic activities are decreased; and conversely, when the secretion is increased or abnormal in character, metabolism is carried on at a greater rate as instanced by the rise in temperature and increased pulse rate characteristic of hyperthyroidism.

Another point which must be considered in regard to the control and regulation of metabolism is the fact that increased activity of one organ may and often does lead to increase in the activity of other organs. For example, muscular activity results in better elimination of carbon dioxide; the presence of this gas in the blood stimulates respiratory activity, as a result there is greater intake of oxygen and the heart beats more forcibly in order to distribute the oxygen to the tissues, in this case to the muscles, where it is needed for the utilization of energy and the elimination of waste products.

THE MAINTENANCE OF BODY TEMPERATURE

The normal body temperature is 98·4 with a range of from 97 to 99 degrees Fahrenheit. The diurnal variation is about one degree, the lowest level being reached in the early hours of the morning and the highest point between 5 and 7 p.m.

This normal temperature is maintained by an exact adjustment between heat produced and heat lost, and this is controlled by the heat-regulating centre in the brain, which is extremely sensitive to the temperature of the blood passing through it.

Heat is produced by the metabolic activities in the skeletal muscles and liver. The glycogen stored in liver and muscles is converted into usable glucose and oxidized, with the result that heat is produced. In order to maintain the normal production of heat the requisite amount of fuel food is necessary (*see* page 186). The metabolic activities (the rate of oxidation) must be adjusted to meet the varying demands made, for example, by active work or conditions of rest, the intake of food at meal-times and the periods between meals, the emotional reactions of the body, the external temperature, the clothing worn, and so on.

Heat loss is mainly effected by the functional activities of the skin (the importance of the skin in regulating the temperature of the body is described on page 258). A certain amount of heat is lost by the evaporation of moisture from the lungs and by the excreta. To summarize, the organs concerned in producing heat and in losing heat:

Heat Production	*Heat Loss*	Per cent
Fuel food, oxidized in muscles and liver	Skin—evaporation of sweat, radiation and conduction	70
	Lungs—Evaporation of moisture . . .	25
	Excreta	5
		100

Pyrexia. An increase in body temperature above 99 and up to 105 degrees or more is called pyrexia. The temperature may be temporarily elevated by exposing the surface of the body to great heat as in the pyrexial treatment of disease. The reaction of the body to infection is another matter; in this case the rise of temperature is due to definite disorder of the heat-regulating mechanism. Heat is produced in excess of heat loss, and the body adapts itself to maintaining the temperature at a higher level. It is claimed that this rise in temperature is one of the protective mechanisms of the body, as by it the defence against invading organisms is increased.

Chapter 16

THE ENDOCRINE ORGANS AND SPLEEN

The endocrine organs or ductless glands are grouped together under this name because the secretion they make does not leave the glands by means of a duct, instead it is passed into the blood, circulating through the substance of the gland. The word *endocrine* comes from the Greek, and means 'internal secretion'; the active principle of an internal secretion is called *hormone*, from a Greek word meaning 'to excite'. Some of the endocrine organs produce a single hormone, others two hormones or more: the pituitary gland, for example, produces a number of hormones which control the activity of many of the other endocrine organs; for this reason the pituitary has often been described as 'the master gland of the body'.

The endocrine organs are:

The *Pituitary*, anterior and posterior lobes,

The *Thyroid* and *Parathyroid* glands,

The *Suprarenal glands*, cortex and medulla, and

The *Thymus* gland and possibly also the *Pineal* body.

The formation of an internal secretion is an important function also of many other organs and glands, such as the pancreas, stomach, ovaries, and testes.

The functions of these internal secretions can only be studied by removing the glands of animals, or in man when the glands are diseased.

The underlying causes of abnormal activity or under-activity of the glands (hypersecretion or hyposecretion) are not always understood, but it is derangement of their secretion that produces the symptoms of disease, e.g. Graves's disease and myxoedema.

Definite disease of the glands is another matter which also upsets their function, e.g. Addison's disease.

PITUITARY GLAND

The Pituitary Gland lies at the base of the skull, resting on the sella turcica of the sphenoid bone. It consists of two lobes, anterior and posterior, and an intermediate part, the pars intermedia.

The Anterior Lobe of the pituitary produces a number of hormones which are instrumental in controlling the production of the secretion of all the other endocrine organs and glands which produce an internal secretion. These various hormones are enumerated below.

The *growth hormone* (*somatotropic hormone*) controls the growth of the body. *Underproduction* results in *dwarfism* and *overproduction* in *gigantism* when the abnormal state arises before the growth is complete, and to a condition described as *acromegaly* in adult life. In acromegaly the feet and hands become large and spade-like, the skin thickens, and the lower jaw becomes enlarged giving the face a heavy appearance.

The *Thyrotropic hormone* controls the activity of the thyroid gland in the production of *thyroxin.*

The *Adrenotropic hormone* controls the activity of the suprarenal glands in the production of two secretions, *cortin* from the cortex of the gland, and *adrenalin* from the medulla.

The *Pancreaticotropic* (*diabetic*) *hormone* controls the activity of the pancreas in producing *insulin*; overproduction giving rise to hypoglycaemia and underproduction to diabetes mellitus.

The *Parathyrotropic hormone* controls the production of *parathormone* by the parathyroid glands.

The *Gonadotropic hormone* controls the activity of male and female sex glands. By two distinct hormones *Prolan A* and *Prolan B,* it controls the two internal secretions of the ovary—*oestrin* and *progesterone* (*see* page 278). In the male it controls the activity of the testis in the production of male sex hormone.

The *Mammotropic hormone* (*prolactin*) controls the secretion of milk in the breast during the latter half of pregnancy.

Posterior Lobe secretions. The posterior lobe of the pituitary gland makes an internal secretion called *pituitrin* which contains two hormones, *vasopressin* and *oxytocin.*

Vasopressin exercises an important influence on plain muscle fibre, such as that of the heart, intestine, and the blood vessels. *Overproduction* of vasopressin causes *hypertension* of the blood vessels; *underproduction* is thought to give rise to *diabetes insipidus.*

Oxytocin stimulates the contraction of the uterus.

THYROID GLAND

The thyroid gland consists of two lobes, placed one on each side of the trachea, and connected together by a strip of thyroid

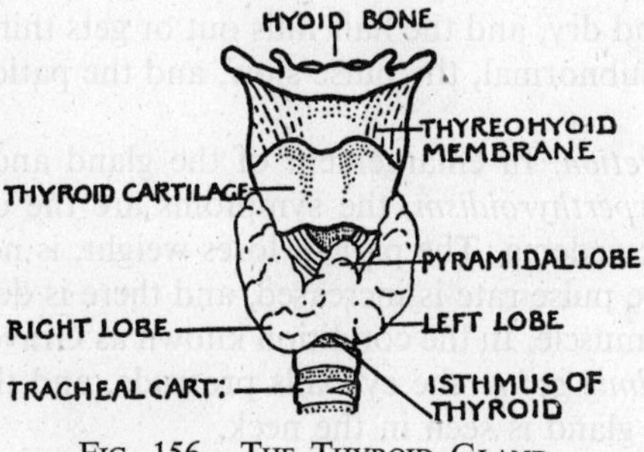

FIG. 156.—THE THYROID GLAND.

substance, called the *isthmus of the thyroid*, which lies across in front of, the trachea.

Structure. The thyroid gland is composed of numbers of vesicles lined with cubical epithelium (*see* Fig 8, page 24), abundantly supplied with blood, and held together by connective tissue. These cells secrete a sticky fluid *the colloid of the thyroid* which contains an iodine compound; the active principle of this compound is named *thyroxin.* This secretion fills the vesicles and from here passes to the blood stream either directly or through the lymphatics.

Function. The secretion of the thyroid is regulated by a hormone of the anterior lobe of the pituitary gland, the *thyrotropic hormone*, and by the sympathetic nervous system.

The thyroid gland is intimately concerned with the metabolic activities regulating the chemistry of the tissues and is instrumental in stimulating oxidation processes and in regulating the consumption of oxygen and consequently the output of carbon dioxide. Derangement or disease of the gland produces severe and serious changes and it is by the knowledge gained from the study of these changes (*see* below) that the function of the gland is understood.

Hyposecretion (*hypothyroidism*). Deficiency of the secretion of the gland at birth produces a condition known as *cretinism*, in which mental and physical growth are retarded. In adults deficiency of the secretion produces *myxoedema*, the symptoms of which are slowness of mind and speech, the skin becomes thickened and dry, and the hair falls out or gets thin. The temperature is subnormal, the pulse slow, and the patient puts on weight.

Hypersecretion. In enlargement of the gland and increased secretion, *hyperthyroidism*, the symptoms are the opposite of those of myxoedema. The patient loses weight, is nervous and excitable, the pulse rate is increased, and there is degeneration of the heart muscle. In the condition known as Graves's disease or *exophthalmic goitre* the eyeballs protrude, and the enlargement of the gland is seen in the neck.

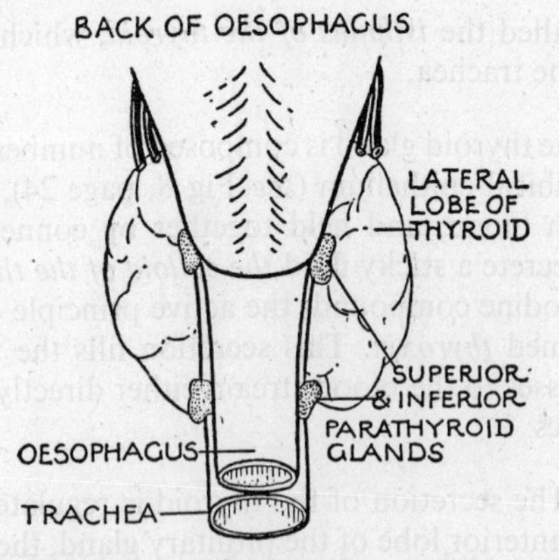

FIG. 157.—THE BACK OF THE OESOPHAGUS, SHOWING THE POSITION OF THE FOUR PARATHYROID GLANDS WHICH LIE *BEHIND* THE LOBES OF THE THYROID GLAND.

THE FOUR PARATHYROID GLANDS

The parathyroid glands are four small glands placed two on each side of the thyroid gland in the neck. The parathyroid secretion regulates the amount of calcium in blood and bone.

Hypoparathyroidism, in which there is deficiency of the blood calcium content, causes a condition described as *tetany* to develop. This condition is characterized by muscular twitchings and convulsions and there is increase in pulse and respiration rate; these symptoms are quickly relieved by the administration of calcium.

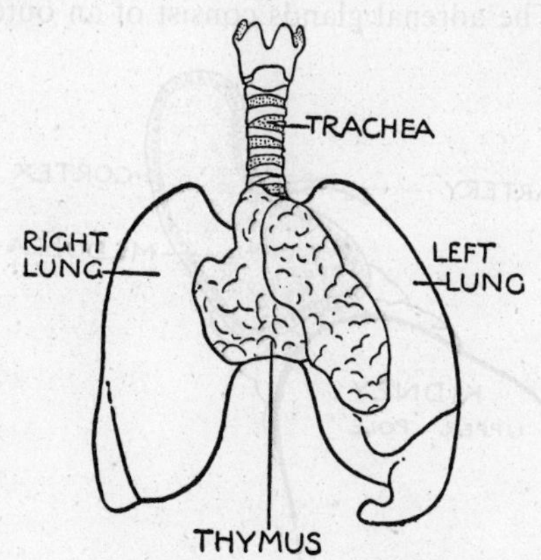

FIG. 158.—THE POSITION OF THE THYMUS GLAND.

Hyperparathyroidism, overactivity of the glands, is usually associated with enlargement (tumour) of the glands. The balance of calcium distribution is disturbed, calcium is attracted out of the bones into the blood serum, with the result that deformities of bones occur and a type of osteitis characterized by the formation of cysts develops.

THE THYMUS GLAND

The thymus gland lies in the thorax about the level of the bifurcation of the trachea. It is associated with the years of infancy and childhood; it increases in size during the first year or two, then decreases until, at the age of puberty, it is very small, and has entirely disappeared by the time adult years are reached.

It is thought to delay the development of the reproductive organs. When the gland persists in adult life, the patient is liable to sudden death under conditions such as those of general anaesthesia.

THE SUPRARENAL GLANDS

The *Adrenal* or *Suprarenal glands* lie on the upper pole of each kidney. The adrenal glands consist of an outer yellowish

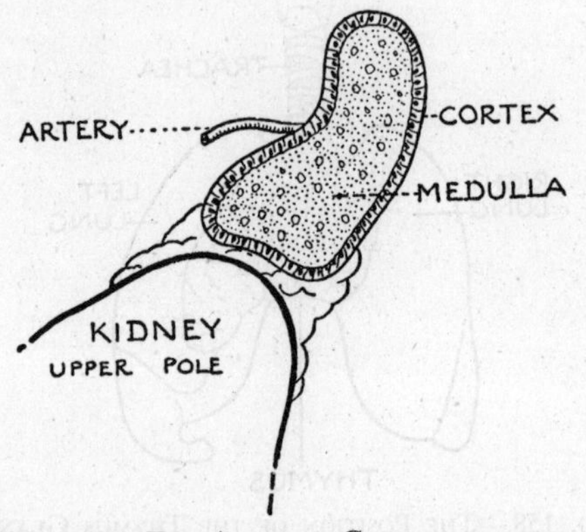

FIG. 159.—THE ADRENAL GLAND, SHOWING CORTEX AND MEDULLA.

part, the cortex, which produces *cortin*, and an inner medullary portion producing a substance known as *adrenalin.*

Adrenalin is constantly passing into the blood circulating through the suprarenal glands, which are very richly supplied with blood. The secretion is thought to be increased in conditions of emotion such as anger and fear, and in states of asphyxia and starvation, and it is believed that an increased output of adrenalin raises the blood pressure in order to combat shock produced by these emergencies.

Adrenalin raises the blood pressure by stimulating the muscular fibres in the walls of the blood vessels, causing them to contract. It also aids in carbohydrate metabolism by increasing the output of glucose from the liver.

Adrenalin is used in conditions of shock, and, when applied locally, will arrest haemorrhage by its action on the blood vessels.

Cortin is essential to life. In disease of the adrenal glands (Addison's disease) the patient becomes wasted and prostrated, getting gradually weaker. This disease can now be arrested by the use of cortical extract.

The Pineal Gland is a small red body, similar in shape to a pine cone, situated near the corpus callosum. Its function is obscure, it has been suggested that this gland produces an internal secretion but up to the present time there is no definite evidence in support of this theory.

Other glands which produce important internal secretion are the pancreas (*see* page 222), and the sex glands, which are described in Chapter 19.

THE SPLEEN

The spleen is a dark purplish gland lying on the left side of the abdomen in the left hypochondriac region beneath the ninth, tenth, and eleventh ribs. It lies against the fundus of the stomach and its outer surface is in contact with the diaphragm. It touches the left kidney, the splenic flexure of the colon, and the tail of the pancreas.

The spleen consists of a network of connective and lymphoid tissues, and contains numerous blood cells. It is surrounded by a capsule from which processes called *trabeculae* pass into the substance of the gland. The contents of the gland are collectively known as *spleen pulp*.

The splenic blood vessels enter and leave the gland at the hilum, which is on the inner surface. The blood vessels empty their contents directly into the spleen pulp, so that the blood comes into contact with the spleen substance, and is not as in other organs separated from it by blood vessels. There is no capillary system—the vessels do not anastomose, they are end arteries. The flow of blood through the spleen is helped by the contraction of muscle fibres in the capsule and in the trabeculae. It is collected in a system of venous sinuses which empty their blood into the branches which unite to form the splenic vein by which blood is carried from the spleen.

The Functions of the Spleen. The spleen does not make an internal secretion like the other ductless glands and very little is known of its functions but it is considered to be concerned with the elaboration of the blood. It makes lymphocytes, and in some obscure way it separates old worn-out red blood cells from the circulation; the stroma of these cells is broken down in the spleen, setting free the iron, which passes in the portal blood to the liver. It is also thought that the spleen has something to do with the formation of blood platelets. The spleen is not essential to life. When no other cause can be found for haemolytic anaemia splenectomy is performed, and as the result of this the fragility of the red cells may improve and relief be obtained.

The spleen is enlarged in some diseases, when it may be felt below the costal margin.

Chapter 17

THE SKIN

The skin covers and protects the surface of the body and is continuous with the mucous membrane lining the cavities and orifices which open on to the surface. The skin has many functions; it contains the tactile nerve endings, helps to regulate the temperature and to control the loss of water from the body, and possesses some excretory, secretory, and absorptive properties. The skin is divided into two layers:

The Epidermis or Cuticle, and
The Dermis or Corium.

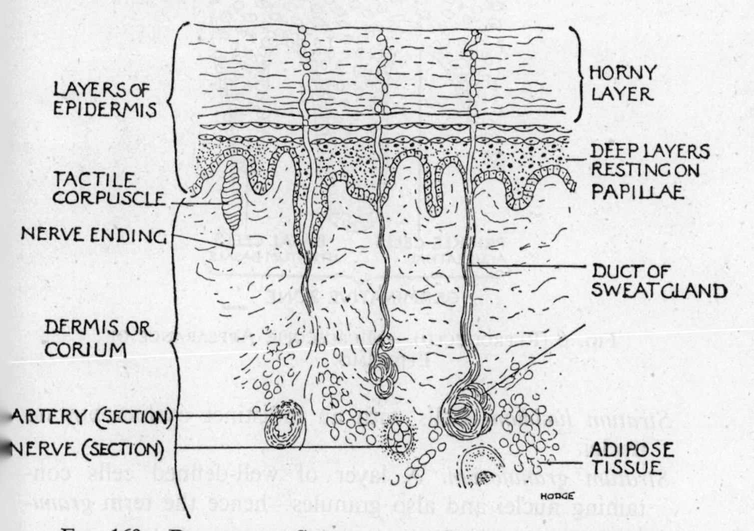

FIG. 160.—DIAGRAM OF SKIN SHOWING STRUCTURES IN DERMIS.

The Epidermis is composed of stratified epithelium and consists of a number of layers of cells arranged in two fairly well-defined zones: a horny zone and a germinal zone. The component parts of the epidermis can be distinguished microscopically and Fig. 6 is here reproduced for the convenience of the student.

Epidermal Layers. The *Horny Zone* lies superficial. It is made up of the *three upper layers* of the cells of which the epidermis is composed.

Stratum corneum. Thin, flat, scale-like cells which are constantly being cast off.

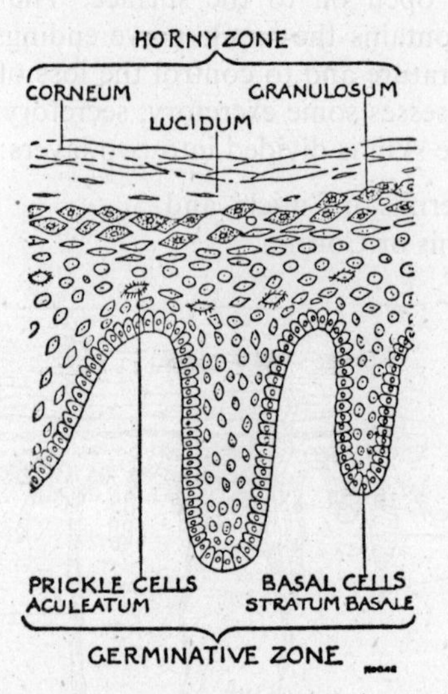

FIG. 6 (REPRODUCED).—MICROSCOPIC APPEARANCE OF EPIDERMIS.

Stratum lucidum. Cells with an indistinct outline but no nuclei.

Stratum granulosum. A layer of well-defined cells containing nuclei and also granules—hence the term *granulosum.*

The *Germinal Zone* lies beneath the horny zone and consists of two layers of well-formed epithelial cells.

Prickle cells which are so-named because minute fibrils which connect one cell with another in this layer give individual cells the appearance of having prickles.

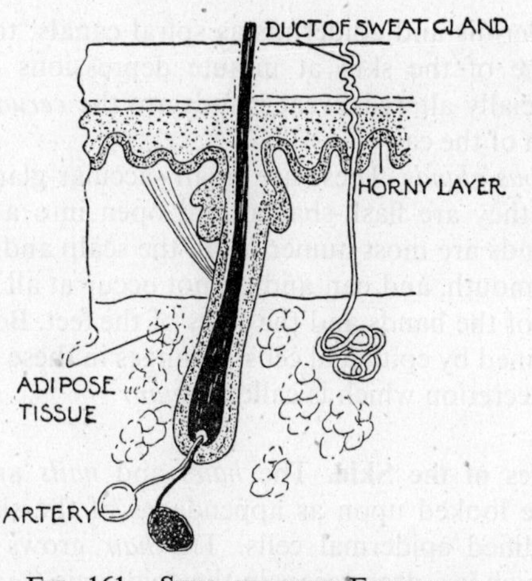

FIG. 161.—SKIN, SHOWING FORMATION OF A HAIR FOLLICLE.

Sebaceous glands are shown opening into the follicle.

Basal Cells. These are the cells from which new epidermal cells are constantly being produced. These cells are arranged in an orderly fashion, they are packed closely together and form the first layer or two of cells which rest on the papillae of the dermis.

The epidermis does not contain any blood vessels. The ducts of the sweat glands pass through it, and it accommodates the hairs. Epidermal cells line the hair follicles. The surface of the epidermis is marked by lines and ridges, these correspond to the papillae of the dermis which lie beneath. These lines vary; at the tips of the fingers and thumbs they form distinct patterns which differ in each individual. It is on this fact that the study of the fingerprints in criminology is based.

The Corium or Dermis is made up of fibrous and elastic connective tissue. The surface of the dermis is arranged in small papillae which contain loops of capillary blood vessels.

The nerve endings of the sensory nerves, the *tactile bodies*, lie in the dermis. The coiled tubes of numerous *sweat glands* lie in the deep parts of the dermis, and the ducts from these pass through dermis and epidermis as spiral canals, to open on to the surface of the skin at minute depressions called pores. Some specially altered sweat glands are the *ceruminous glands* in the skin of the ear.

Sebaceous glands. These are small saccular glands found in the skin, they are flask-shaped and open into a hair follicle. These glands are most numerous in the scalp and face, around the nose, mouth, and ear, and do not occur at all in the skin of the palm of the hands and the soles of the feet. Both gland and duct are lined by epithelial cells. Changes in these cells result in the fatty secretion which is called *sebum*.

Appendages of the Skin. The *hairs* and *nails* and sebaceous glands are looked upon as appendages of the skin. They are both modified epidermal cells. The *hair* grows from a hair follicle which is a deep recess in the epidermis (*see* Fig. 161).

The *hair follicle* is lined with epidermal cells and at the bottom of it is a papilla from which the hair grows. In health, when a hair drops out it is replaced by another hair grown from the same papilla. The root of the hair lies in the follicle. At its deepest extremity the hair is slightly thickened to form the hair bulb. This part fits over a vascular papilla and it is

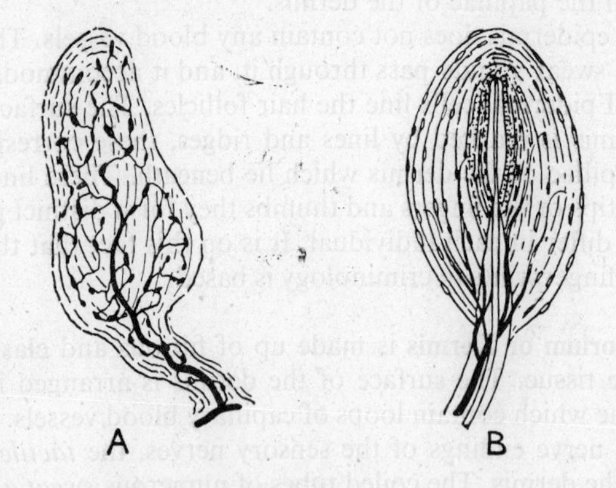

FIG. 162.—EXAMPLES OF SENSORY NERVE ENDINGS PRESENT IN THE SKIN.

from soft cells in this region that the hair grows. The part which projects from the surface is the *hair-shaft*. The colour of the hair is due to the amount of pigment in the epidermis. Associated with the hair follicles are minute involuntary muscles, the *arrectores pilorum* or 'the raisers of the hairs', also *sebaceous glands* which secrete a fatty substance called *sebum*, which keeps the skin soft and smooth, and the hair glossy.

Nails. The nail is composed of modified skin. It lies on a *nail bed* in which the dermis is arranged in ridges instead of in papillae as in the skin. The nail bed is well supplied with nerves and is very vascular. The proximal part of the nail lies in a groove of the skin—the *nail groove*, it is thinnest in this region and the white part, called the *lunula*, because of its shape, is the portion from which the nail grows forward. The *body of the nail* is the uncovered part, it is firmly attached to the nail bed. The distal extremity of the nail is free—the *free border*, and at each side the nail is bounded by a fold of skin termed the *nail wall*.

Summary of the Functions of the Skin

(1) It forms a protective covering for the body.
(2) Is the seat of the special sense of touch, the tactile sense.
(3) Is an excretory organ by means of sweat.
(4) Is important in the regulation of body temperature.
(5) Has power of absorption of oily substances.
(6) Secretes a fatty substance, sebum.
(7) When exposed to ultra-violet light it manufactures vitamin D.

The Skin as an Excretory Organ. Sweat glands are numerous all over the body, but most numerous in the skin of the palms of the hands and the soles of the feet.

The secretion of sweat is continuous. When small in amount it is said to be *insensible*, as we are not conscious of it. When so profuse that we are conscious of it, it is said to be *sensible perspiration*. The amount of sweat secreted by a man in twenty-four hours is about 30 ounces.

The secretion of sweat is controlled by the sympathetic nervous system, partly by means of the heat-regulating centre in the brain, acting through the vaso-motor nerves, and partly by stimulation of the function of the sweat glands by special secretory nerves. This control takes place automatically according to the needs of the body.

Sweat is composed mainly of water with about 1·2 per cent of solids in solution. It is acid in reaction, of a specific gravity of 1005, and saltish in taste.

Organic waste matter gives the perspiration its peculiar odours.

The Skin as a Heat-regulating Organ. The temperature of the body in man is constant. It is maintained by an adjustment between heat loss and heat production, which is controlled by the heat-regulation centre. This becomes aware of any change in the body temperature, by the temperature of the blood passing through the medulla.

The vaso-motor nerves control the state of the cutaneous arterioles by two actions, *vaso-dilatation* and *vaso-constriction.* In vaso-dilatation the arterioles are dilated, the skin reddens, and excess of heat is rapidly got rid of by radiation, by the increased activity of the sweat glands, and the subsequent evaporation of moisture from the surface of the body. In vaso-constriction the skin vessels are constricted, the skin becomes pale and cold, sweating is almost stopped, and the loss of heat is checked. By this control heat loss is increased or decreased according to the needs of the body.

The skin is the principal organ concerned in the loss of heat from the body. A considerable amount of heat is also lost by the lungs, and a little by the faeces and urine.

It is by means of the evaporation of sweat on the skin surface that this organ acts as a controller of the body temperature. Heat is lost by the skin in various ways:

By *evaporation*, the amount of sweat formed depends on the amount of blood passing through the skin vessels,

By *radiation*, heat is given off to the surrounding air,

By *conduction*, heat is transmitted to objects in contact, such as clothing, and

By *convection*, by movement of heated air in currents, the air in contact with the surface of the body is replaced by cooler air.

The Skin as an Organ of Special Sense. The sensation of touch resulting from the stimulation of the nerve endings in the skin, varies with the type of nerve ending stimulated. The sensations of heat, cold, and pain are all separate sensations. Certain spots exist in the skin called *sensory spots*, some of these are sensitive to cold, some to heat, and others to pain.

The sensations produced by deep pressure, and the sensation enabling a person to determine and judge the weight of an article, arise in the deeper structures such as the muscles and joints.

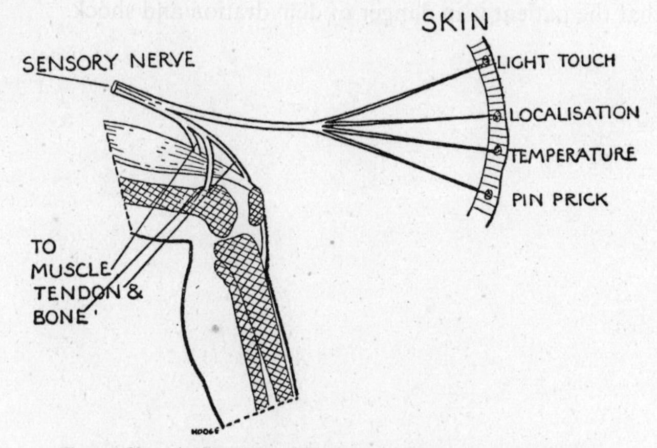

FIG. 163.—A SENSORY NERVE. A DIAGRAM SHOWING THE VARIETIES OF SENSATIONS COLLECTED FROM SUPERFICIAL AND DEEP STRUCTURES.

When the skin of a patient suffering from some nerve injury is examined two kinds of sensation are tested.

Protopathic deals with the sensations of pain and deep pressure and extremes of cold and heat.

Epicritic deals with the finer sensations of light touch such as touch by cotton wool, and differences in these sensations themselves, and in their localization, so that discrimination of the part touched is made and two points of a compass placed near each other on the skin can be distinguished as two points. The finer differences in temperature such as cool and warm shades can be differentiated.

Some of the Protective properties of the Skin. The skin is waterproof to the extent that it prevents loss of fluid from the tissues and it also prevents the passage of water into these tissues when, for example, the body is immersed in water. The epidermis prevents injury to the underlying structures and, covering as it does the sensory nerve endings in the dermis, it mitigates pain. When the epidermis is destroyed as in burns of the third degree this protection being removed every contact becomes painful, and evaporation of fluid from the now exposed dermis causes serious loss of body fluid with the result that the patient is in danger of dehydration and shock.

Chapter 18

THE URINARY SYSTEM

The urinary system consists of:
The Kidneys, which secrete urine,
The Ureters, to convey the urine from kidney to bladder,
The Bladder, which acts as a reservoir, and
The Urethra, for discharge of urine from the bladder.

The Kidneys lie on the posterior abdominal wall, mainly in the lumbar region, one on each side of the vertebral column, deeply embedded in fat, behind the peritoneum, and therefore outside the peritoneal cavity.

The position of the kidneys may be indicated, from behind, as extending from the level of the last dorsal vertebra to the third lumbar vertebra. The right kidney is slightly lower than the left, as the liver occupies considerable space on the right side.

Each kidney measures 4 to 5 inches in length, 2½ in breadth, and 1 to 1½ inches in thickness. An adult kidney weighs from 4 to 6 ounces.

The kidneys are bean-shaped organs with the inner border or *hilum* directed towards the vertebral column. The outer border is convex. The kidney vessels enter and leave at the hilum. Each kidney is surmounted by a *suprarenal gland.* The right kidney is shorter and thicker than the left.

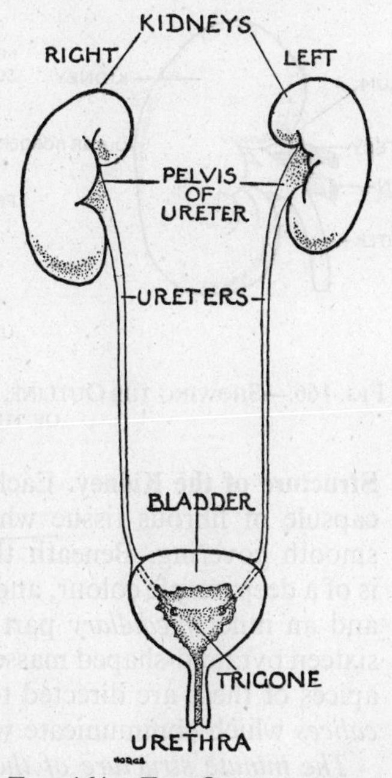

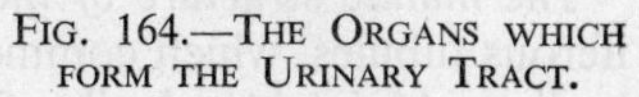

FIG. 164.—THE ORGANS WHICH FORM THE URINARY TRACT.

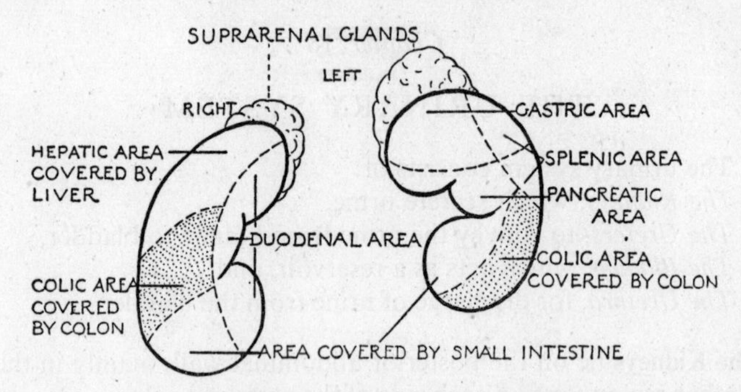

FIG. 165.—ANTERIOR SURFACE OF THE KIDNEYS, SHOWING THE POSITION OF THE ADRENAL GLANDS AND THE RELATIONS OF THE KIDNEY.

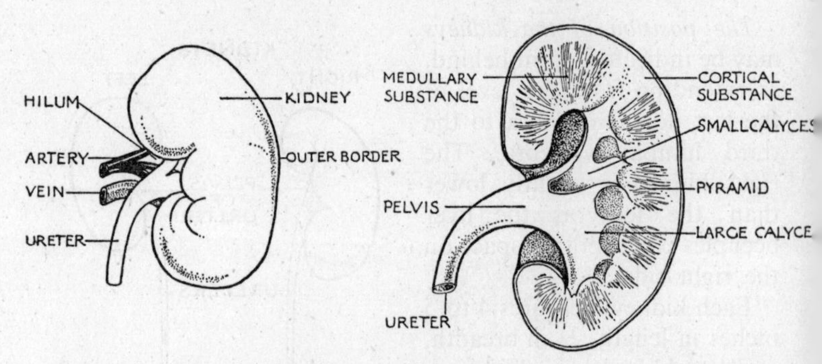

FIG. 166.—SHOWING THE OUTLINE, VESSELS, PELVIS AND GROSS STRUCTURE OF THE KIDNEY.

Structure of the Kidney. Each kidney is surrounded by a thin capsule of fibrous tissue which invests it closely, forming a smooth covering. Beneath this the kidney substance lies. It is of a deep purple colour, and consists of an outer *cortical* part, and an inner *medullary* part, which is made up of fifteen to sixteen pyramid-shaped masses, the *pyramids of the kidney*. The apices of these are directed towards the hilum, and open into *calices* which communicate with the *pelvis of the kidney*.

The minute structure of the kidney shows numbers of uriniferous tubules, which commence in the cortex as small round bodies—*Malpighian bodies*. These consist of a tuft of blood capillaries forming a *glomerulus*, tightly packed into the expanded upper end of a tubule known as *Bowman's capsule*. From the Malpighian bodies run the *uriniferous tubules*, partly convoluted and partly straight. The first part of the

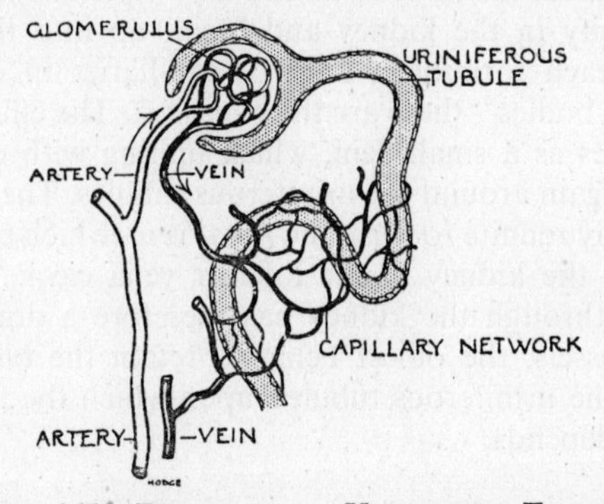

FIG. 167.—DIAGRAM OF A URINIFEROUS TUBULE.

The Artery or Afferent Vessel is shown passing into the Malpighian Capsule, where it breaks up into Capillaries. An Efferent Vessel, a vein, leaves the Capsule and is shown breaking up into a second set of Capillaries around the Tubule.

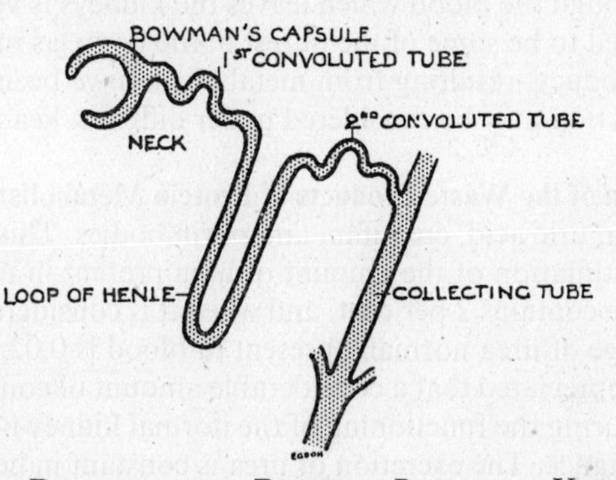

FIG. 168.—DIAGRAM OF THE DIFFERENT PARTS OF A URINIFEROUS TUBULE.

tubule is convoluted and is known as the *first convoluted tubule*; this is followed by a loop, the *loop of Henle*; then the tubule again becomes convoluted, the *second convoluted tubule*, which communicates with a *collecting tubule* that passes through the cortex and medulla to terminate at the apex of one of the pyramids.

Blood vessels. In addition to the uriniferous tubules the kidney structure contains blood vessels. The *renal artery* brings pure blood from the abdominal aorta to the kidneys. Branches of this ramify in the kidney and break up into the afferent arterioles, each forming a knot of capillaries in one of the Malpighian bodies—these are the *glomeruli.* The efferent vessel then emerges as a small vein, which uniting with other veins breaks up again around the uriniferous tubules. These capillaries eventually reunite to form the *renal vein,* which conveys the blood from the kidney to the inferior vena cava. The blood circulating through the kidney has therefore a double set of capillary vessels, the object being to retain the blood in the vicinity of the uriniferous tubules, upon which the function of the kidney depends.

RENAL FUNCTION

The Function of the Kidneys is the purification of the blood, and although the blood which leaves the kidneys is venous, it is considered to be some of the purest in the body, as many of the waste products resulting from metabolism have been removed. This function may be considered under different headings.

Excretion of the Waste Products of Protein Metabolism, particularly urea, uric acid, creatinin, and purin bodies. This is studied by the estimation of the amount of urea present in urine. Normal urine contains 2 per cent, and when it is considered that the percentage of urea normally present in blood is 0.02 per cent it will be appreciated that a considerable amount of concentration occurs during the functioning of the normal kidney in regard to this substance. The excretion of urea is constant in health.

The Removal of Excess Salt. The tissues of the body require the blood to convey to them 0.6 per cent sodium chloride. When salt is present in the tissues over this amount it is eliminated by the kidneys. Conversely, when the normal percentage of salt in the tissues is decreased the kidneys excrete more water, and thus, by eliminating water, make the blood more concentrated and so increase the percentage of salt in the tissues.

In some diseases the kidneys fail to remove excess salt from the tissues, water is then retained in the body and oedema occurs.

The Maintenance of the Reaction of the Blood. The kidneys remove acids from the blood. The blood is always alkaline, but if the kidneys fail in this function, what is called the *alkaline reserve* of the blood is diminished, which means it is slightly less alkaline as it contains slightly less sodium bicarbonate. Under these conditions acidosis occurs, which leads to the manifestation of symptoms and signs of toxaemia.

The Function of the Kidneys in Regard to Water. The normal amount of water excreted by the kidneys in health is from 30 to 60 ounces a day, but this is not invariable. Considering the size of the renal arteries and the vast amount of blood passing through the kidneys per minute the function of the kidney in concentrating its excretion and so conserving water is a very important one. Water is excreted in large quantities only when it is present in excess, and the amount is also adapted to the function of the skin in this respect. In cold weather, when the loss of fluid from the skin is slight, more water is eliminated by the kidneys, and conversely less is eliminated when the skin is acting profusely in hot weather and during vigorous exercise.

In addition the kidneys *help to maintain the constant composition of the blood* by removing any harmful products or abnormal substances which may be present, such as bacteria, toxins, chemical poisons, and drugs. In addition they remove some of the useful constituents of blood when these are present in excess. Excess of salt has been mentioned; similarly, when the blood contains an abnormally high percentage of sugar as occurs in diabetes mellitus, sugar appears in the urine and the condition known as glycosuria is present.

This power of the kidneys to remove substances which would be harmful to the body either because they are definitely waste products or because they are in excess in the blood is due to a selective action of the kidney cells.

The Secretion and Excretion of Urine. The structure of the kidneys may be physiologically considered to be of two parts: the *parenchyma*, that is the essential part of the organ, the kidney tubules, and the *interstitial tissue*, consisting of the blood vessels and the connective tissue binding all parts together.

The production of urine is a twofold process of filtration and secretion.

Filtration takes place in the Malpighian bodies, which, filled with capillary blood vessels, act as a simple filter. The diluted salts in solution pass from the blood in the capillaries into the tubules.

Secretion takes place mainly in the convoluted portion of the tubules. These are lined with columnar cells which have a special selective power and select the other constituents of urine from the blood in solution, particularly the end products of protein metabolism.

The concentration of urine, is a further process, which also occurs in the uriniferous tubules, principally in the loop of Henle. The water removed during this process of concentration passes back into the blood stream and in this way the loss of water is limited. Urine passes along the uriniferous tubules into collecting tubules, which pass it to the apices of the pyramids; from here it drips into the pelvis of the ureter and on into the ureters, where by peristaltic action it is conveyed to the bladder.

The *pelvis of the ureter* is the upper dilated end of the ureter, its extensions form the *calyces.*

The Ureters are two ducts or tubes, one attached to each kidney, passing from it to the bladder. Each ureter is about the thickness of a goose-quill and from 14 to 16 inches long. It consists of an outer fibrous covering, a middle muscular layer, and an inner mucous lining. The ureter commences as a dilatation at the hilum of the kidney, and passes down through the abdominal cavity into the pelvis to open obliquely into the posterior aspect of the urinary bladder.

THE URINARY BLADDER

The *bladder* acts as a reservoir for urine; it is a pear-shaped organ. It lies in the true pelvis in front of the other contents, and behind the symphysis pubis. In the infant it lies higher. The lowest part is fixed and is called the *base*, the upper part or *fundus* rises as the bladder becomes distended with urine. The apex lies forward beneath and behind the symphysis pubis.

The bladder consists of:

An outer serous coat,
A muscular coat,
A sub-mucous coat, and
A mucous lining, of transitional epithelium.

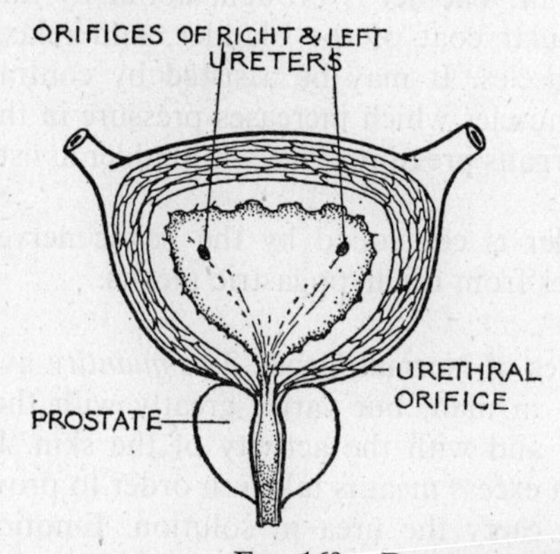

FIG. 169.—DIAGRAM SHOWING TRIGONE OF BLADDER.

Three vessels communicate with the bladder. The two ureters open obliquely into it at the base; their oblique direction prevents the regurgitation of urine into the ureters. The urethra opens out of the bladder in front. The triangular area between the openings of the ureters and the urethra is the *trigone of the bladder* (*see* Fig. 164). In the female, the bladder lies between the symphysis pubis and the uterus and vagina. It is separated from the uterus by a fold of peritoneum—the utero-vesicular pouch (*see* Fig. 170).

The urethra is a canal passing from the neck of the bladder to the external opening; it is lined by mucous membrane continuous with that lining the bladder. *The urinary meatus* is composed of circular muscle fibres, which form the *sphincter urethrae*. The female urethra is 1 to 1½ inches long, the male 7 to 9 inches (*see* page 285).

Micturition is the act of passing urine. As the urine is formed in the kidneys it passes along the ureters into the bladder. The desire to micturate is due to an increase of pressure in the bladder caused by the presence of urine there. This occurs when from 6 to 8 ounces have accumulated. Micturition is a reflex act which can be controlled and inhibited by the higher centres in man. The act is brought about by the contraction of the muscular coat of the bladder, and relaxation of the sphincter muscles. It may be assisted by contraction of the abdominal muscles which increases pressure in the abdominal cavity, the organs pressing upon the bladder assist in emptying it.

The bladder is controlled by the pelvic nerves, and sympathetic fibres from the hypogastric plexus.

Characteristics of Normal Urine. The *quantity* averages 30-60 ounces daily in man, but varies greatly with the amount of fluids taken, and with the activity of the skin. It is also increased when excess meat is taken in order to provide the fluid necessary to carry the urea in solution. Emotional disturbances will increase the urinary output.

The *colour* is a clear, pale amber with no deposits, but a light flocculent cloud of mucus may be seen floating in the specimen.

The *odour* is aromatic.

The *reaction* is slightly acid to litmus with an average pH of 6.

The *specific gravity* varies from 1015 to 1025.

Composition of Normal Urine. Urine consists mainly of water, urea, and sodium chloride. In a man taking an average diet with 100 grammes of protein in the twenty-four hours, the percentage of water and solids will be as follows:

96% Water
4% Solids, made up as follows: 2% Urea

2% { Uric Acid, Urates, Chlorides, Phosphates, Sulphates, Oxalates, &c.

Urea is one of the end products of protein metabolism. It is prepared from amino-acids, which are denitrified in the liver and reach the kidneys in the circulation. The quantity of urea depends on the amount of protein in the diet. A little ammonia is always present in urine, having reached the kidneys in the blood before it has been converted into urea.

Uric acid and other nitrogen compounds are derived from two sources, *endogenous* due to the breakdown of tissue protein and *exogenous*, which is that obtained from food taken.

Of the mineral constituents of urine, the chlorides form the greater part, the chief being sodium chloride. Some of the salt is decomposed to form hydrochloric acid in the stomach. The oxalates, phosphates, and sulphates are derived mainly from the vegetable foods.

Chapter 19

THE ORGANS OF THE REPRODUCTIVE SYSTEM

The mode of development of the generative organs is interesting. The germ cells of the testes in the male, and of the ovary in the female develop very early in embryonic life. Sex therefore is determined from the very earliest days but sex characters cannot be recognized. It is a great and wonderful mystery how these reproductive cells are carried to the exact areas for which they are designated, the ovary and testes. They are developed in front of the kidney and are then carried in as columns of cells which eventually form the glands of reproduction consisting of germ cells and surrounding structures. The *ovum* is the germ cell in the ovary and the *spermatozoon* the cell in the male. Many tens of thousands more are formed than will ever develop and in this way the most important function of the human being, that of reproduction, is assured. At adolescence these germ cells develop and bring about the changes which determine the sex qualities and characters of the male and female.

The organs of reproduction form what is known as the genital tract which is in relation to the urinary tract. In the male the two tracts are closely associated see fig. 179. In the female though in close relationship with the urinary tract the genital tract is distinct from it. The female genital tract communicates with the peritoneal cavity. The male tract does not do so, it is a closed tract. The female generative organs lie in the bony pelvis, the male organs lie mainly outside the pelvis.

THE PELVIC CAVITY

The *pelvic cavity* lies below and communicates with the abdominal cavity (*see* page 196). The *true pelvis* is the bony basin formed by the ischium and pubis which make up the sides and front, and the sacrum and coccyx which form the posterior boundary. The *brim of the pelvis* is formed by the promontory of the sacrum at the back, the ilio-pectineal lines at the sides, and the crest of the pubis in front. These form the rim or basin-like upper margin of the cavity.

The *outlet of the pelvis* is bounded by the coccyx in the median plane *behind*, by the symphysis pubis *in front*, and the pubic arch, the ischium, and ligaments passing from the ischium to the sacrum on *each side*. This outlet is filled in by the structures forming the floor of the pelvis.

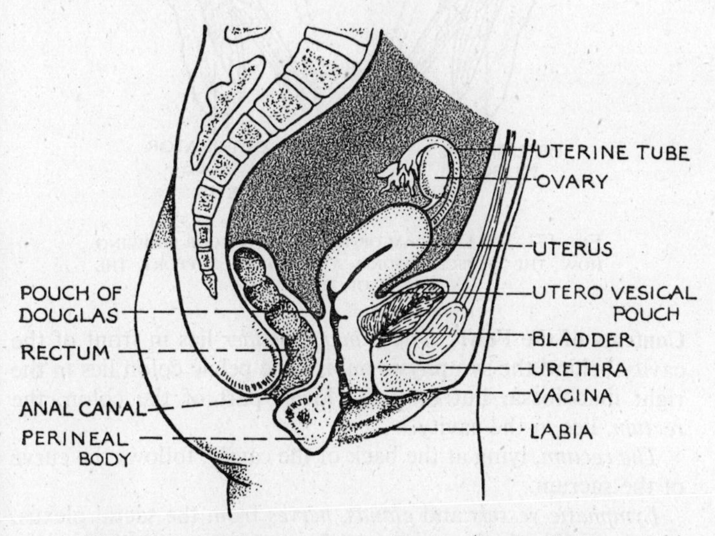

FIG. 170.—A SECTION OF THE FEMALE PELVIC CAVITY.

The Pelvic Floor. The structures which lie within the boundaries of the pelvic outlet form the floor of the pelvis. Two muscles, the levator ani and coccygeus, act as a *pelvic diaphragm* (*see* Figs. 171 and 172). The *perineum* is the lowest part of the trunk. It is divided into an anterior urogenital area and a posterior anal area. One central point is called the *perineal body*; it is a strong fibrous and muscular body lying, in the female, between the vaginal opening in front and the rectum behind. This structure may be torn during childbirth.

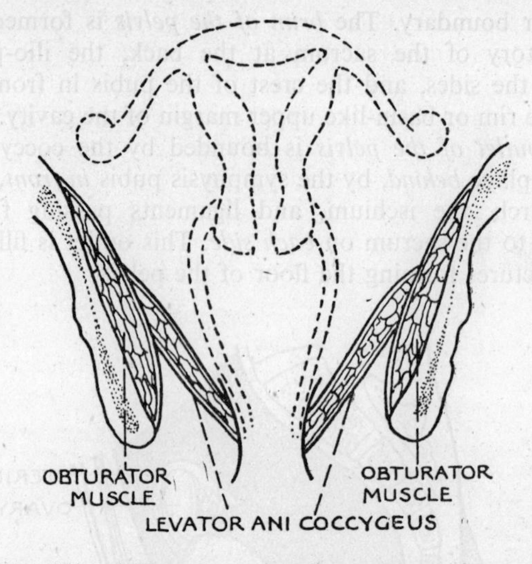

FIG. 171.—A DIAGRAM OF THE PELVIC FLOOR SHOWING HOW THE MUSCLES FORM A SLING TO SUPPORT THE CONTENTS OF THE PELVIS.

Contents of the Pelvis. The *urinary bladder* lies in front of the cavity behind the symphysis pubis. The pelvic colon lies in the right iliac fossa, but only the lower part of the colon, the *rectum*, lies in the cavity.

The rectum, lying at the back of the cavity, follows the curve of the sacrum.

Lymphatic vessels and *glands*, *nerves* from the sacral plexus, *blood vessels*, which are derived from the internal iliac artery, and numerous *veins*, and the *pelvic peritoneum* complete the contents of the pelvic cavity in the male.

The female pelvis contains the uterus and its ligaments, the uterine tubes and the ovaries. In illustration Fig. 170, the female pelvis is shown.

THE FEMALE ORGANS OF GENERATION

The organs of generation or the reproductive organs may be divided into the external organs and the internal organs.

The External Organs are collectively known as the *vulva*, and comprise the following parts:

The mons veneris, a pad of fat lying in front of the symphysis pubis. This area becomes covered with hair at puberty.

The labia majora are two thick folds which form the sides of the vulva. They are composed of skin and fat, and unstriped muscular tissue, blood vessels, and nerves. The labia majora are about three inches long.

The nymphae or *labia minora* are two small folds of skin situated between the upper parts of the labia majora.

The clitoris is a small erectile body which corresponds with the penis of the male. It is situated at the apex of the vestibule.

The vestibule is a smooth triangular surface, limited on either side by the labial folds. The urethral orifice opens into the vestibule.

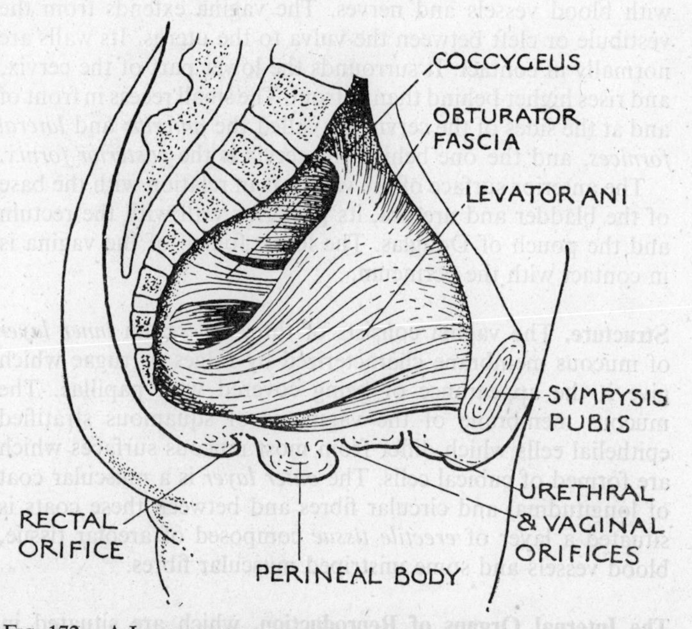

FIG. 172.—A LATERAL VIEW SHOWING THE ARRANGEMENT OF THE MUSCLES WHICH FORM THE FLOOR OF THE PELVIS (SEE also Fig. 171).

The perineum is the base of a triangular-shaped muscular wedge between the vagina and the rectum (*see* Fig. 172).

Bartholin's glands are glands which lie on each side towards the back of the labia majora.

The fossa navicularis is a depression lying between the hymen and the fourchette.

The hymen is a thin fold of membrane at the orifice of the vagina. It forms an incomplete curtain, varies in shape, and normally is perforated. The hymen separates the external from the internal genitals. It is placed at the orifice of the vagina, which is the canal leading to the internal organs of reproduction.

VAGINA

The vagina is a muscular tube lined with membrane comprised of a special type of stratified epithelium, well supplied with blood vessels and nerves. The vagina extends from the vestibule or cleft between the vulva to the uterus. Its walls are normally in contact. It surrounds the lower part of the cervix, and rises higher behind than in front. The small recess in front of and at the sides of the cervix are called the *anterior* and *lateral fornices*, and the one behind the cervix is the *posterior fornix.*

The anterior surface of the vagina is in relation with the base of the bladder and urethra, its posterior wall with the rectum and the pouch of Douglas. The lower fourth of the vagina is in contact with the perineum.

Structure. The vagina consists of three layers, an *inner layer* of mucous membrane characterized by ridges or rugae which give it the appearance of being covered with papillae. The mucous membrane of the vagina is of squamous stratified epithelial cells which differ from most mucous surfaces which are formed of cubical cells. The *outer layer* is a muscular coat of longitudinal and circular fibres and between these coats is situated a layer of *erectile tissue* composed of areolar tissue, blood vessels and some unstriped muscular fibres.

The Internal Organs of Reproduction, which are situated in the pelvis, are the uterus, ovaries and uterine tubes.

THE UTERUS

Structure. The uterus is a thick, muscular, pear-shaped organ covered by peritoneum. It is situated in the pelvis, between the rectum behind and the bladder in front (*see* Fig. 170, page 271). It lies slightly anteflexed and anteverted with the fundus lying forward on the bladder. It communicates below with the vagina, and above the uterine tubes open into it. The broad ligaments, ovaries and uterine tubes lie at the sides of the uterus. The blood supply is from the uterine and ovarian

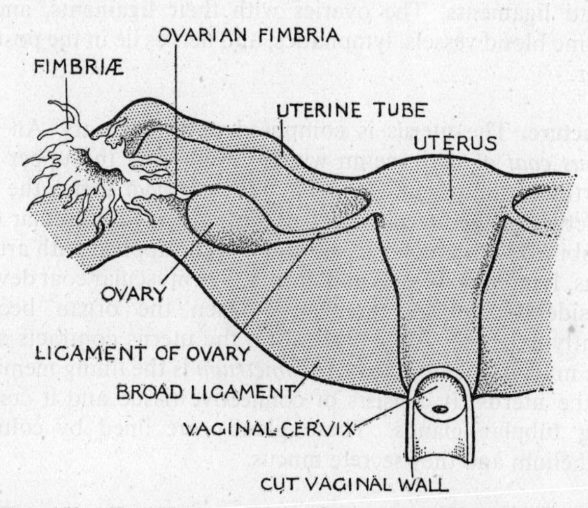

FIG. 173.—THE UTERUS, RIGHT OVARY, AND UTERINE TUBE.

arteries. The uterus is from 2 to 3 inches long, and weighs from 1 to 2 ounces. It is divided into the following three parts.

The fundus, a convex part above the openings of the uterine tubes.

The body of the uterus extends from the fundus to the cervix, from which it is separated by the isthmus.

The cervix is the lowest and most constricted part. It is continuous with the body of the uterus above by the *internal os*, and with the vagina below by the *external os*. The *os* is a constricted circular aperture closing the cervical canal.

Ligaments of the Uterus. The *round ligaments* are two bundles of connective and muscular tissue, containing blood vessels and covered by peritoneum, which pass from the upper angle of the uterus, forwards and outwards through the internal ring to the inguinal canal. Each round ligament is from four to five inches long. In addition several folds of peritoneum help to hold the uterus in position. These folds pass from the front, back and sides of the uterus. The lateral ones form the *broad ligaments* and pass from the sides of the uterus to the sides of the pelvis. The uterine tubes lie in the upper margin of the broad ligaments. The ovaries with their ligaments, and the uterine blood vessels, lymphatics, and nerves lie in the posterior layer.

Structure. The uterus is composed of three coats. An *outer serous coat* of peritoneum which covers only the upper three fourths of the organ. A *middle muscular coat* forms the main structure of the uterus. It consists of unstriped muscular tissue combined with areolar tissue and is well supplied with arteries, veins, lymphatic vessels and nerves. The muscular coat develops considerably during pregnancy when the organ becomes greatly enlarged. After parturition the uterus contracts again. The mucous membrane or *endometrium* is the lining membrane of the uterus. It consists of connective tissue and it contains long tubular glands. These glands are lined by columnar epithelium and they secrete mucus.

Function of the Uterus. To retain the fertilized ovum during development. The ova which are discharged from the ovaries are conducted along the uterine tubes to the uterus. (Fertilization of the ovum usually takes place in the uterine tube.) The endometrium has been prepared for the reception of the ovum (*see* page 279), which now becomes embedded in it. During the pre-natal period the ovum grows and develops and the uterus increases in size, its walls become thick and strong and it rises out of the pelvis into the abdominal cavity.

The *muscle* of the uterus is composed of several layers of fibres woven closely together. During pregnancy the uterine muscle develops and strengthens. When full term has been reached and labour commences, the uterus contracts and expels the baby and the placenta, and then contracts to approximately its normal size. This contraction is called involution of the uterus.

THE OVARIES

Structure. The ovaries are two almond-shaped glands placed one on each side of the uterus, below the uterine tubes. They are of greyish colour and are composed of Graafian follicles embedded in a stroma, which is a highly vascular soft tissue.

The *ovary* is covered by a layer of germinal epithelium. Down-growths of groups of these cells develop and become the Graafian follicles. One cell of the group becomes an *ovum*, the others remain clustered around it and form the *membrana granulosa*; as development of the Graafian follicle proceeds changes take place in these cells and fluid—the *liquor folliculi*—separates the cells of the membrana granulosa into layers. At this stage *oestrin* is formed. As the follicle approaches full development, or ripening as it is called, it lies near the surface of the ovary, gradually becoming more and more distended with fluid, until it projects as a cyst-like swelling from the surface of the ovary. Tension within the follicle causes it to rupture and the fluid and ovum escape into the peritoneal cavity. It is thought that each month one follicle develops and one ovum is set free and extruded. The ovum is then attracted into the uterine tube by the movements of its fimbriated end.

Ovulation. *Maturation of the Graafian follicle* and liberation of the ovum is termed *ovulation*. When the Graafian follicle ruptures bleeding occurs, a clot is formed in the empty follicle, and cells, which have a yellow appearance, grow into this clot and form the *corpus luteum* or yellow body. Should the escaped ovum be fertilized the corpus luteum continues to grow and persists throughout pregnancy; if the ovum is not fertilized the corpus luteum only persists for twenty-eight days. The corpus luteum produces the hormone, progesterone (*see* below).

The ovary has three functions:

(1) The production of ova.

(2) The production of the hormone, *oestrin.* ⎫ Control of menstruation.
(3) The production of the hormone, *progesterone.* ⎭

In addition and probably by virtue of its hormones the ovary controls the female sex changes at puberty, including development of the uterus and vagina. It controls the changes which take place in the uterus during menstruation, during pregnancy, and the development and activity of the breasts.

The Ovarian Hormones. The production of the ovarian hormones is controlled by two pituitary hormones, Prolan A and B.

Prolan A controls (1) the changes which the Graafian follicles undergo up to the moment of ovulation, when the ovum escapes from the follicle, and (2) the production of oestrin.

Oestrin stimulates increased blood supply to the endometrium, which results in slight thickening of this lining membrane of the uterus.

Prolan B controls the changes that take place in the Graafian follicles after ovulation—the formation of the corpus luteum, the length of time this persists, and the production of progesterone.

Progesterone continues the work begun by oestrin on the endometrium and causes it to become thick, soft, and velvety ready for the reception of the ovum. *Progesterone inhibits menstruation.* As long as the corpus luteum persists, progesterone is formed and menstruation cannot occur, therefore the lining of the uterus is kept intact and ready to receive the fertilized ovum. If pregnancy occurs the placenta, which serves to feed and nourish the foetus, is formed, but *if the ovum is not fertilized* the corpus luteum disappears, the production of progesterone ceases, and the endometrium is broken up and discharged during menstruation.

The menstrual cycle consists of changes in ovary and uterus.

The *menstrual period* lists about *five days;* during this period the surface epithelium is stripped off the lining of the *uterus* and bleeding occurs.

The *post-menstrual period* is a *stage of repair* lasting about *nine days*, when the lining membrane is renewed.

A *resting stage* follows. This is a period of inactivity which lasts about *four days.*

The *pre-menstrual stage* comes next and lasts about *ten days.* In the early days the endometrium becomes thick and soft ready for the implanting of a fertilized ovum, but if no ovum

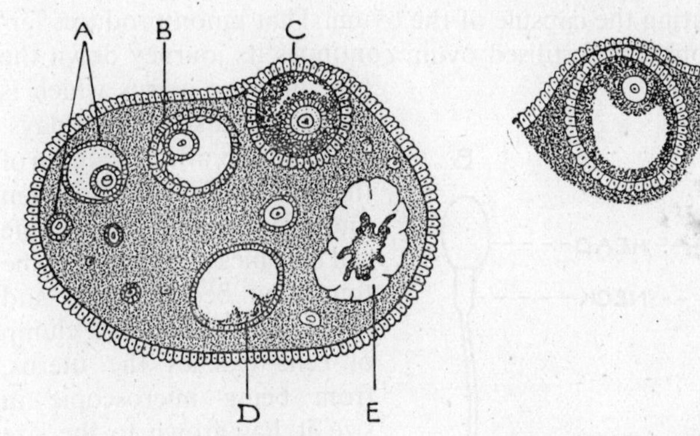

FIG. 174.—DIAGRAM OF THE OVARY SHOWING SOME OF THE STRUCTURE.

FIG. 175.—A MATURE GRAAFIAN FOLLICLE READY TO RUPTURE.

A, B and C indicate stages in the development of a Graafian follicle. D, a follicle recently ruptured and E the formation of corpus luteum.

is fertilized congestion occurs in the capillaries ready for the menstrual period to follow. The cycle is repeated. The periodicity of this cycle averages 28 days but it may be a little longer or a little shorter.

The changes in the *ovary* (*see* page 277) are the processes of development and ripening of a Graafian follicle which results in the discharge of an ovum. This occurs about fourteen days before each menstrual period. Afterwards the ruptured follicle collapses and the changes which give rise to the corpus luteum occur. This persists for about fourteen days and then, if fertilization has not occurred atrophies and dies leaving a small scar on the uterus.

Fertilisation is the result of the fusion of the male reproductive cell, the *spermatozoon*, with the *ovum* or egg cell which normally takes place in the uterine tube. A number of spermatozoa are deposited in the vaginal vault. They pass through the uterus and find their way into the uterine tube. Here resistance is met as the activity of the ciliated lining of the tube is directed to carrying the ovum along, from the other end of the tube, towards the uterus, but the spermatozoa are propelled by the activity of their tails. (One only is needed to effect fertilisation.) Union of both cells is brought about by the spermatozoon penetrating the capsule of the ovum. That union produces fertilisation. The fertilised ovum continues its journey down the tube into the uterus which is thought to take about 7 days. All this time, after the union of the two cells the fertilised ovum undergoes rapid division, one cell becomes two, two become four, four become eight and so on. By the time this clump of cells reaches the uterus, from being microscopic in size it has grown to the size of a pin-point. It then becomes embedded in the wall of the uterus and development, which is giving rise to the formation of an entirely new complete individual, continues. Pregnancy has occurred. During pregnancy ovulation and menstruation do not occur and this is thought to be due to the persistence of the corpus luteum which produces progesterone, the hormone inhibiting menstruation.

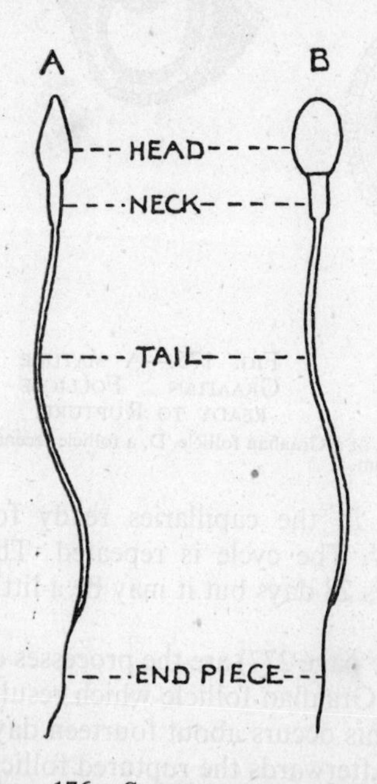

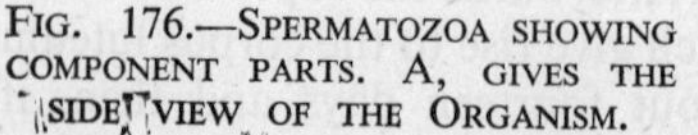
FIG. 176.—SPERMATOZOA SHOWING COMPONENT PARTS. A, GIVES THE SIDE VIEW OF THE ORGANISM.

UTERINE TUBES

The *uterine tubes* pass one on each side from the upper angles of the uterus outwards, in the upper margins of the broad ligament towards the sides of the pelvis. They are about 4 inches long, and at their uterine ends are narrow. They then enlarge, forming the *ampulla*, and finally bend downwards to end in a *fimbriated margin*. One of the fimbriae is attached to the ovary. In structure the uterine tubes are covered by peritoneum, beneath this lies the muscular coat of longitudinal and circular fibres. The tubes are lined by ciliated epithelial cells.

The uterine tubes open into the peritoneum, and thus a passage from the vagina, through the uterus and tubes into the peritoneal cavity is formed, so that in the female the peritoneum is an open, not a closed sac and may be infected by organisms ascending through the genital tract.

The ovaries and uterine tubes are supplied with blood by the

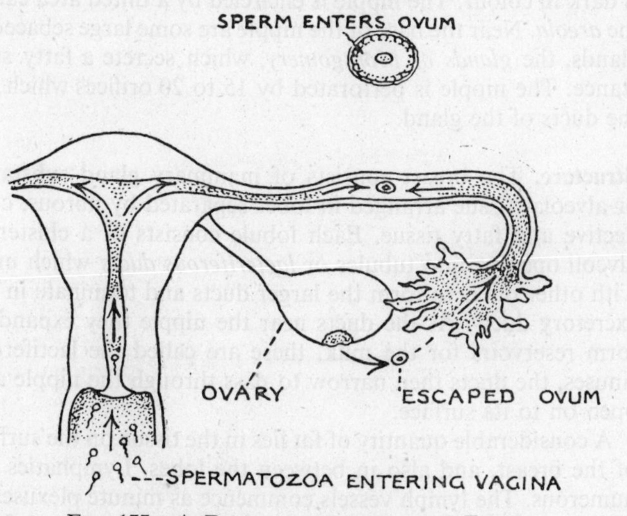

FIG. 177.—A DIAGRAM INDICATING THE ESCAPE OF AN OVUM FROM THE OVARY.

Arrows indicate its passage into and along the uterine tube. Spermatozoa are shown entering the vaginal vault and arrows indicate the direction taken by the male germ cell in search of the ovum.
Inset is shown a spermatozoon entering an ovum.

ovarian arteries, and the nerve supply is derived from the hypogastric and ovarian plexuses.

The *function* of the uterine tubes is to act as a passage from the ova from ovary to uterus (*see* page 281).

THE MAMMARY GLANDS

The *mammary glands* or *breasts* are accessory to the female reproductive organs and secrete the milk. In the male these glands are rudimentary. The breasts lie beneath the superficial fascia on the pectoral region between the sternum and axilla, and extend from about the second or third, to the sixth or seventh ribs. The weight and size of the breasts vary; they enlarge at puberty and increase in size during pregnancy and after delivery; they atrophy in old age.

The breasts are convex anteriorly with a prominence in the middle called the *nipple*, which consists of skin and muscle and is dark in colour. The nipple is encircled by a tinted area called the *areola*. Near the base of the nipple are some large sebaceous glands, the *glands of Montgomery*, which secrete a fatty substance. The nipple is perforated by 15 to 20 orifices which are the ducts of the gland.

Structure. The breast consists of mammary gland substance or alveolar tissue arranged in lobes separated by fibrous, connective and fatty tissue. Each lobule consists of a cluster of alveoli opening into tubules or *lacteriferous ducts* which unite with other ducts to form the larger ducts and terminate in the excretory ducts. As the ducts near the nipple they expand to form reservoirs for the milk, these are called the lactiferous sinuses, the ducts then narrow to pass through the nipple and open on to its surface.

A considerable quantity of fat lies in the tissue on the surface of the breast, and also in between the lobes. Lymphatics are numerous. The lymph vessels commence as minute plexuses in the interlobular spaces of the gland tissue, unite and form larger vessels, which pass to the pectoral group of the axillary glands, the internal mammary, and the subclavicular glands. The blood supply is derived from branches of the axillary, intercostal, and internal mammary arteries, and the nerve supply from the cutaneous nerves of the chest.

The Functional Activity of the Breasts. At birth the breast consists only of a rudimentary nipple from which a few ducts radiate. In the female development changes occur at puberty when there is increase in the gland tissue. At the commencement of the menstrual life of a girl slight enlargement of the breasts takes place and for a few days before each menstrual period the blood supply is increased; in some subjects this is

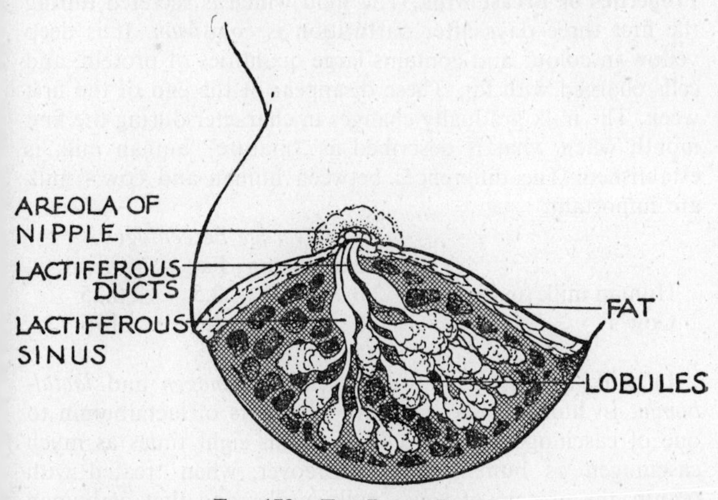

FIG. 178.—THE RIGHT BREAST.

more noticeable than in others, and gives rise to a sense of weight and slight congestion.

Gradually the breasts become fully developed and the deposit of fat in the structure results in permanent enlargement, varying with the individual. At the menopause, that is, the other end of the menstrual life of a woman, when the ovaries gradually cease to function, the breast tissue shrinks.

Secretion of milk in the breasts during the latter weeks of pregnancy is controlled by a hormone called *prolactin*, which is produced by the anterior lobe of the pituitary gland (*see* page 246).

The control of breast development is considered to be due to the activity of the ovarian hormones *oestrin* from the *ovarian* tissue and *progesterone* from the corpus luteum in the ovary. These hormones stimulate the development of the breasts during pregnancy. During the latter months of pregnancy the secretion of milk is stimulated by the anterior pituitary hormone called prolactin (*see* page 246). This hormone goes on acting during the period of lactation.

Properties of Breast Milk. The fluid which is secreted during the first three days after parturition is *colostrum*. It is deep yellow in colour and contains large quantities of protein, and cells charged with fat. These disappear at the end of the first week. The milk gradually changes in character during the first month when what is described as "mature" human milk is established. The differences between human and cow's milk are important.

	Average Percentage			
	Protein	Sugar	Fat	Mineral
Human milk (mature) .	2.0	7.0	2.5	0.25
Cow's ,, . .	4.0	4.0	4.0	0.75

In milk two proteins are present: *caseinogen* and *lactalbumin*. In human milk there are two parts of lactalbumin to one of caseinogen. Cow's milk contains eight times as much caseinogen as human milk. Moreover, when treated with rennin, the protein of cow's milk curdles and that of human milk forms a light precipitate which is much more digestible. Cow's milk contains more fat and minerals than human milk. The vitamin content of human milk depends on the diet of the mother. The milk is of the required temperature, it is sterile and it contains immunising factors. All these points are worthy of consideration when advocating the breast feeding of infants.

Disorders of the Breast. During lactation, in particular, a milk duct may become obstructed when a cyst which is called a galactocele may form. Infection may occur in any part of the breast, more usually during lactation. The breast tissue may be the site of either simple or malignant tumour. The latter is commoner in the breast than any other organ and therefore any irregularity, swelling or contraction of the breast should at once be seen by a surgeon. In any infection or tumour of the breast the axillary lymphatic glands may be affected. Both infection and carcinoma are spread by permeation of the surrounding structures and by infiltration of the lymphatics.

THE GENITO-URINARY TRACT IN THE MALE

The urinary tract in the female is quite separate from the genital tract, but in the male it is not so separated. The *male urethra* is from 7 to 9 inches long. It leaves the bladder and passes through the prostate gland, where it is known as the *prostatic urethra*; immediately below this the external sphincter is placed. The urethra curves at an angle of 90 degrees and passes along through the perineum to the penis.

The *testes* are the male organs of generation in which the spermatozoa are formed and the male sex hormones produced.

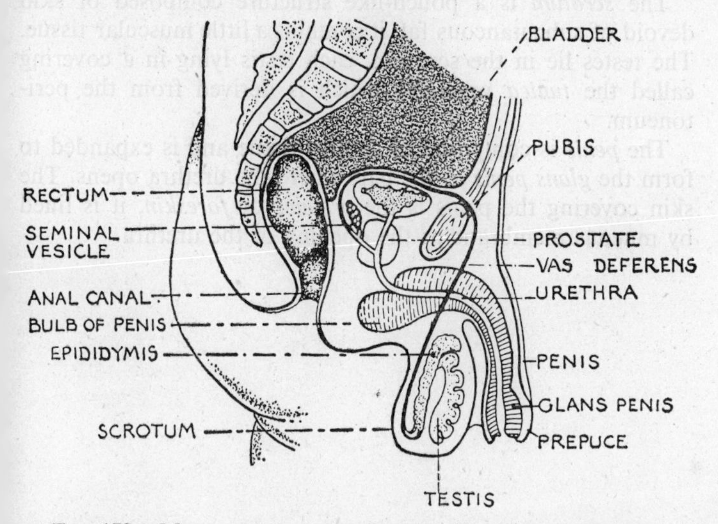

FIG. 179.—MALE REPRODUCTIVE ORGANS. THE GENITO-URINARY TRACT IN THE MALE.

The testes develop in the abdominal cavity and during foetal life descend through the right and left inguinal canals into the scrotum, where they lie obliquely suspended by the spermatic cords.

The *seminal vesicle* is a saccular organ which serves as a reservoir for the secretion of the testes. When this organ contracts the secretion is forced through a duct into the urethra.

The *epididymis* is a small organ composed of minute tubules lying near the testis and attached to it.

The *vas deferens* is a long tube passing from the lower aspect of the epididymis to the seminal vesicle. It ascends behind the testis, enters the spermatic cord, and reaches the abdominal cavity by means of the inguinal canal, and finally passes into the pelvis to join the seminal vesicle.

The *prostate gland* is about the size of a large walnut, it lies below the bladder, surrounding the urethra, and is composed of glands, ducts, and involuntary muscle. The glands of the prostate secrete a fluid which mingles with the secretion of the testes.

The *scrotum* is a pouch-like structure composed of skin devoid of subcutaneous fat, it contains a little muscular tissue. The testes lie in the scrotum, each testis lying in a covering called the *tunica vaginalis*, which is derived from the peritoneum.

The *penis* is composed of spongy tissue and is expanded to form the *glans penis* at the part where the urethra opens. The skin covering the penis is the *prepuce* or *foreskin*, it is lined by mucous membrane at the opening of the urethra.

Chapter 20

THE NERVOUS SYSTEM

The *Nervous System* is divided for convenience into two main parts: (1) the Central or Cerebrospinal system and (2) the Autonomic, which includes the sympathetic Nervous System.

The Cerebrospinal Nervous System. This consists of the *brain* and *spinal cord* and the nerves given off from these, the *peripheral nerves*. Nervous tissue forms one of the four groups of the elementary tissues of the body.

Nerve cells massed together form what is called the grey matter of this system, as is found in the cortex of the brain, and in the inner part of the spinal cord.

Nerve fibres or axons form the white matter. This difference in colour is due to the axons or conducting fibres being covered by a sheath of fatty matter, which serves to protect, nourish, and insulate the nerve fibres from each other (*see* Fig. 180). A nerve cell with its axon and other processes constitutes a *neurone*. Nerve fibres may be medullated or non-medullated. The cerebrospinal nerves are medullated but the sympathetic nerves are largely non-medullated.

The axon of a medullated nerve is covered and protected by the *medullary fatty sheath*. This sheath contains nuclei which lie between it and the outer covering—the *neurolemma*. The medullary sheath is interrupted at regular intervals along the course of the nerve by the *nodes of Ranvier*.

Medullated nerve fibres vary in size. Some of the largest of these pass to the skeletal muscles and some of the small ones pass to the blood vessels.

In the formation of a nerve trunk the nerve fibres are arranged in bundles called funiculi. Each *funiculus* is surrounded and held together by a connective tissue described as the *perineurium*. Fine strands from this tissue pass in between the individual nerve fibres conveying blood capillaries to them. These strands form a very delicate connective tissue called the *endoneurium*. The whole nerve trunk is surrounded by connective

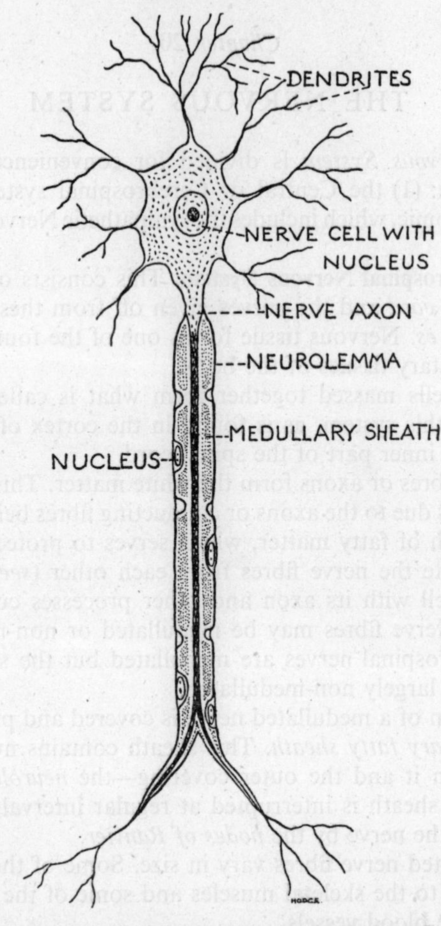

FIG. 180.—A MEDULLATED NERVE. THE AXON OR AXIS CYLINDER RUNS FROM THE CELL TO THE END OF THE NERVE FIBRE. IT IS SURROUNDED BY A FATTY SHEATH—THE MEDULLARY SHEATH—WHICH IS INTERRUPTED BY NODES OF RANVIER.

tissue called the *epineurium*, fat cells are contained in the epineurium.

A *nerve fibre* possesses the power of *conductivity* and *excitability*. It is capable of receiving and responding to stimuli from some outside agent, for example—the *stimulus* may be mechanical, electrical, chemical, or psychical; this gives rise to an *impulse* which is conducted along the nerve fibres. A nerve impulse is always conducted along a dendron to a cell, and from cell to axon. This is the *law of forward conduction.* An impulse may be passed along a series of neurones in this way.

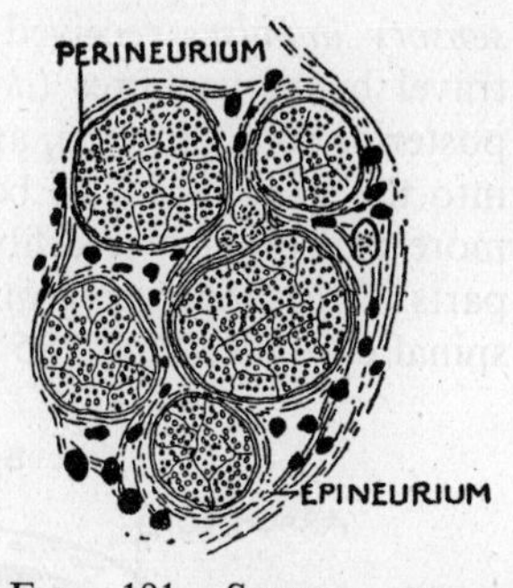

FIG. 181.—SECTION OF A NERVE TRUNK SHOWING SEVERAL FUNICULI SURROUNDED BY PERINEURIUM AND HELD TOGETHER BY EPINEURIUM. THE AREAS STAINED BLACK ARE FAT CELLS.

A *motor impulse* generated in one of the pyramidal cells of the motor area of the cortex, travels along the *axon* or nerve fibre, which, passing down the spinal cord, lies in the white matter; the axon arborizes with the dendrons of motor nerve cells in the anterior horn of the spinal cord. The impulse then passes to the axons of these cells, which form the motor fibres of the anterior root of a spinal nerve, and is conveyed to terminate in a muscle or other motor organ. On the other hand,

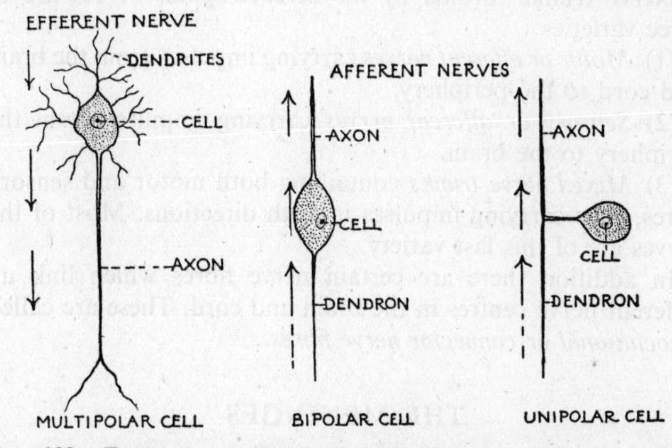

FIG. 182.—EXAMPLES OF EFFERENT AND AFFERENT NERVES. ARROWS INDICATE THE DIRECTION IN WHICH THE NERVE IMPULSE ALWAYS TRAVELS—FROM DENDRON TO CELL, AND FROM CELL TO AXON.

sensory impulses received by the nerve endings in the skin, travel by nerve fibres (*dendrons*) to the sensory cells in the posterior root ganglion, and thence by the axons of these cells into the spinal cord, to be relayed to the brain, along one or more neurones. Nerve fibres travelling to and from different parts of the brain are grouped together in definite tracts in the spinal cord (*see* Figs. 195 and 196).

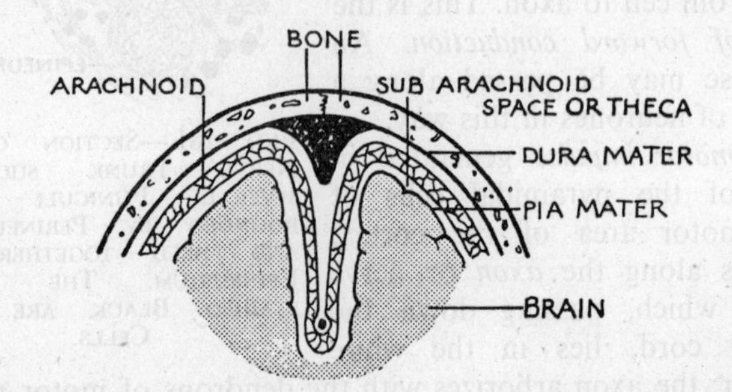

FIG. 183.—DIAGRAM OF A CORONAL SECTION OF THE CEREBRUM, SHOWING THE RELATIONS OF THE MENINGES TO THE SURFACE OF THE BRAIN.
The three Meninges are shown dipping in to the longitudinal fissure—central; the Pia Mater only, dips in between the convolutions.

Nerve trunks formed by the cerebro-spinal nerves are of three varieties:

(1) *Motor or efferent nerves* carrying impulses from the brain and cord to the periphery.

(2) *Sensory or afferent nerves* carrying impulses from the periphery to the brain.

(3) *Mixed nerve trunks* containing both motor and sensory fibres, thus carrying impulses in both directions. Most of the nerves are of this last variety.

In addition there are certain nerve fibres which link up different nerve centres in the brain and cord. These are called *associational or connector nerve fibres.*

THE MENINGES

The brain and spinal cord are surrounded by a threefold membrane, the *meninges,* which protect the delicate nerve structure, carry the blood vessels to it, and, by the secretion of a fluid, the *cerebro-spinal fluid*, minimize any blow or concussion. The meninges are in three layers.

The innermost layer or pia mater. This membrane dips in between all the fissures, ridges, and convolutions of the brain and cord, thus reaching every part of its surface. It supports

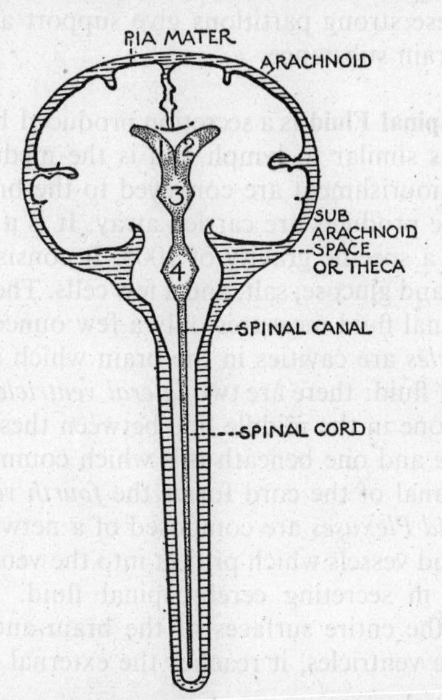

FIG. 184.—DIAGRAMMATIC SKETCH INDICATING THE SITUATION OF THE SPACES CONTAINING FLUID—THECA, VENTRICLES AND SPINAL CANAL WHICH LIES WITHIN AND AROUND THE BRAIN AND SPINAL CORD.
1 and 2. Right and Left Lateral Ventricles.
3 and 4. The Third and Fourth Ventricles.

the blood vessels, and by closely investing the nerve matter carries the blood vessels to it.

The arachnoid membrane. This is a fine transparent serous membrane. It secretes some of the cerebrospinal fluid which then lies between the pia mater and the arachnoid, in the subarachnoid space or *theca*.

The dura mater. The dura mater is the tough outer covering of the brain and cord. It is strong and fibrous, and acts as a lining to the cranial cavity and spinal canal. Portions of the dura mater form the venous sinuses of the brain (*see* page 166). The vertical partition formed by the dura mater, which separates the two cerebral hemispheres, is sickle-shaped, and is called the *falx cerebri.* A horizontal partition separating the cerebrum from the cerebellum is known as the *tentorium cerebelli.* These strong partitions give support and protection to the soft brain substance.

The Cerebrospinal Fluid is a secretion produced by the choroid plexuses. It is similar to lymph and is the medium by which oxygen and nourishment are conveyed to the brain and cord, and the waste products are carried away. It is a clear alkaline fluid, having a specific gravity of 1005. It consists of water, a little protein and glucose, salt, and a few cells. The total amount of cerebrospinal fluid measures only a few ounces.

The ventricles are cavities in the brain which are filled with cerebrospinal fluid: there are two *lateral ventricles*, one in each hemisphere; one in the middle line between these is called the *third ventricle* and one beneath this which communicates with the central canal of the cord forms the *fourth ventricle.*

The Choroid Plexuses are composed of a network of minute capillary blood vessels which project into the ventricles and are instrumental in secreting cerebrospinal fluid. Cerebrospinal fluid bathes the entire surfaces of the brain and spinal cord; formed in the ventricles, it reaches the external surface of the

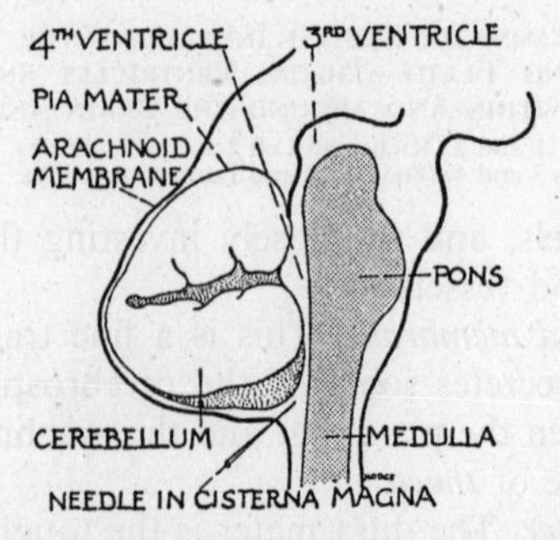

FIG. 185.—THE THIRD AND FOURTH VENTRICLES SEEN FROM THE LATERAL ASPECT IN SECTION (*see also* Fig. 184). NOTE POSITION OF CISTERNA MAGNA.

brain by means of tiny openings in the roof of the fourth ventricle and, lying in the subarachnoid space or theca, covers the outer surfaces of brain and cord.

Cerebrospinal fluid is contained also in the central canal of the spinal cord, which is continued downwards from the fourth ventricle. By this arrangement the delicate nerve matter of the brain and spinal cord lies between two layers of fluid—the internal layer of fluid being contained in the ventricles of the brain and central canal of the spinal cord and the external layer of fluid in the subarachnoid space. By means of these two 'water beds' the central nervous system is protected from shock and jarring.

Cerebrospinal fluid has a certain pressure. This can be demonstrated roughly by inserting a lumbar puncture needle when the fluid will be seen to drop out. The normal pressure is up to 120 m.m. of water measured by means of a manometer.

The functions of cerebrospinal fluid

(1) It acts as a buffer, protecting the brain and cord.
(2) It conveys nourishment to the nervous system.

THE DIFFERENT PARTS OF THE BRAIN

The brain fills the cavity of the skull. It is divided into the following parts:

The cerebrum or great brain,
The cerebellum or lesser brain,
The pons varolii or bridge of nerve matter, and
The medulla oblongata or spinal bulb.

The average weight of the adult brain is a little under three pounds.

The Cerebrum fills the top and front portions of the cranial cavity. The cortex or grey matter forms its surface and is arranged in irregular folds or convolutions, which have the effect of increasing the superficial area, as scalloping a piece of material increases the length of its exact edge.

The cerebrum is divided into two *cerebral hemispheres*, right and left, by a deep cleft or fissure, the *longitudinal fissure*.

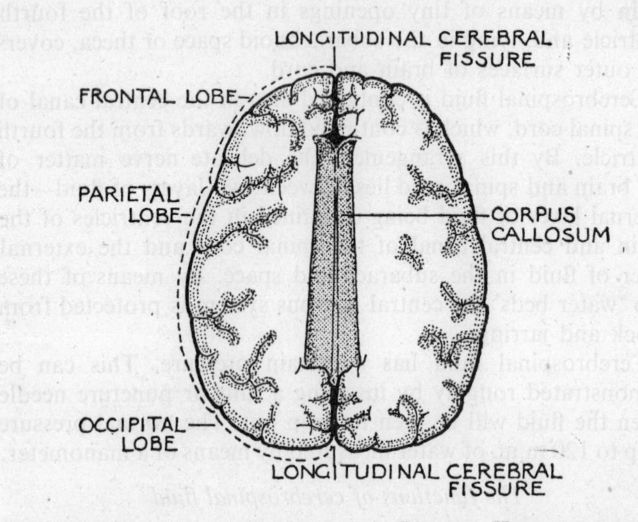

FIG. 186.—DIAGRAM OF A SECTION OF THE CEREBRAL HEMISPHERES, SHOWING THE ARRANGEMENT OF THE GREY AND WHITE MATTER.

Other clefts or fissures further divide or mark out parts of the surface. The *central sulcus or fissure of Rolando* runs in each hemisphere from the middle of the longitudinal fissure, downwards and forwards, dividing off the frontal lobes. The *lateral sulcus* or the *fissure of Sylvius* runs upwards and backwards from the base of the brain on either side, separating the temporal from the parietal lobes. A small area in front of the lateral fissure is concerned with speech. This is Broca's area; it lies on the left side of the brain in right-handed people and on the right side of the brain in those who are left-handed.

The surface of the brain is further mapped out in imaginary areas that correspond with the bones of the skull under which they lie, e.g. the frontal, temporo-sphenoidal, parietal, and occipital lobes.

The cerebrum is composed of grey and white matter. The grey matter or cortex lies superficially and is made up of nerve cells; the white matter is composed of the nerve fibres belonging to the cells of the cortex. The *lateral ventricles* form a central cavity in each cerebral hemisphere; these communicate with

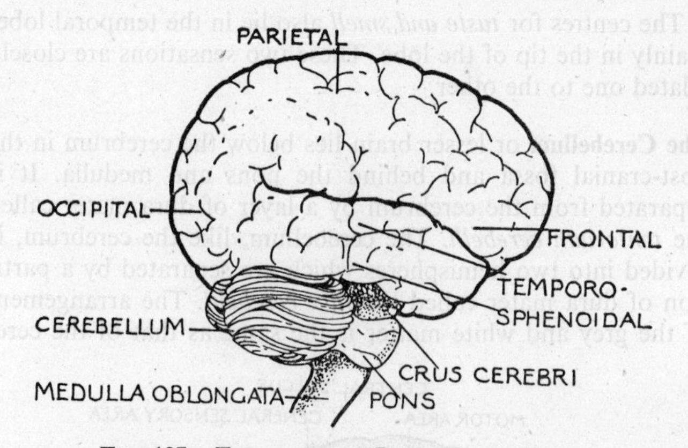

FIG. 187.—THE DIFFERENT PARTS OF THE BRAIN.
The positions of the cerebral lobes are indicated.

each other, and with the *third ventricle*, which lies just below and is more centrally placed, by means of a tiny aperture.

The functions of the cerebrum are the control of all voluntary movement, the discrimination of tactile sense, touch, texture, shape, etc. It contains the higher centres for speech, language, thought, intellect, memory, self-control (inhibition), consciousness, and the special senses. Different parts of the cerebrum dealing with special functions are named accordingly (*see* Figs. 188, 189).

The *motor centre* lies in front of the central sulcus or fissure of Rolando. It controls the movements of the body, the controlling areas are arranged from above downwards—toes, ankle, knee, hip, trunk, shoulder, elbow, wrist, fingers, eyes, mouth, lips and tongue.

The *sensory centre* lies behind the central sulcus. It is here that skin sensation is dealt with, and touch pressure, vibration, muscle and joint sense, and sensations of heat, cold and pain are interpreted.

The *visual centre* lies in the occipital lobe where visual images and impressions are interpreted.

The *auditory centre* lies in the temporal lobe, mainly in the under portion. It is here that sound impressions are received and their meaning interpreted.

The centres for *taste and smell* also lie in the temporal lobe, mainly in the tip of the lobe. These two sensations are closely related one to the other.

The Cerebellum or lesser brain lies below the cerebrum in the post-cranial fossa and behind the pons and medulla. It is separated from the cerebrum by a layer of dura mater called the *tentorium cerebelli.* The cerebellum, like the cerebrum, is divided into two hemispheres which are separated by a partition of dura mater called the *falx cerebelli.* The arrangement of the grey and white matter is the same as that of the cere-

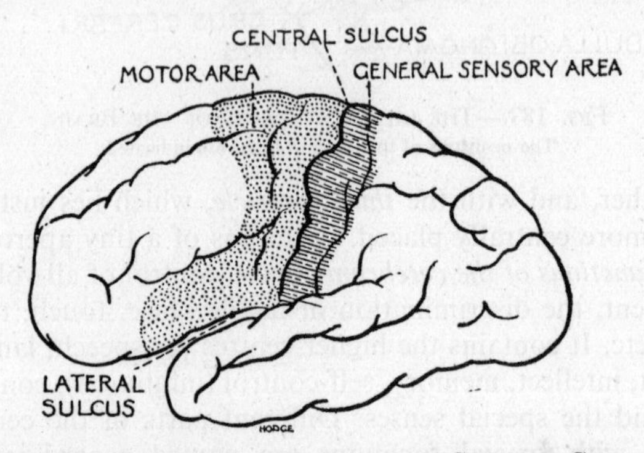

FIG. 188.—THE LATERAL ASPECT OF THE CEREBRAL CORTEX. THE CENTRAL SULCUS SEPARATES THE SENSORY AND MOTOR AREAS.

brum as regards position, but on section a peculiar arrangement of white and grey matter is seen, giving the appearance of the branches of a tree, to which the name *arbor vitae* is given. The surface of the cerebellum is ridged, not convoluted.

The functions of the cerebellum are the co-ordination of muscular movement, and the maintenance of balance and equilibrium.

The Pons Varolii is the bridge of nerve matter which connects the cerebrum and the medulla oblongata, and also connects both cerebellar hemispheres. Many nerve fibres cross here. Above the pons and beneath the cerebrum lies a part called the *mid-brain.*

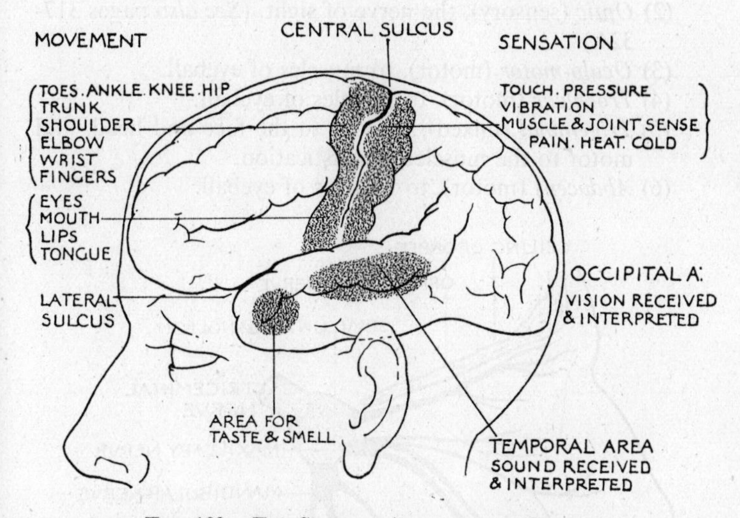

FIG. 189.—THE SENSORY AREAS OF THE BRAIN.

The Medulla Oblongata or spinal bulb is similar in structure to the spinal cord, but larger. It is continuous with the Pons Varolii and lies just inside the foramen magnum of the occipital bone, from where it is continued downwards as the spinal cord. Some of the tracts of nerve fibres cross here, e.g. most of the motor fibres cross as they pass to the spinal cord.

In addition to the crossing of fibres and the conducting of nerve fibres from and to the brain, the medulla oblongata controls the vital reflexes of breathing, cardiac action, swallowing and vomiting. Groups of cells form these various centres and are termed the respiratory centre, the cardiac centre, etc. Injury to the medulla is therefore liable to be instantly fatal.

The Cranial Nerves. There are twelve pairs of cranial nerves. Some are mixed nerves, i.e. both motor and sensory, some motor only, and some sensory nerves, e.g. the nerves of the special senses.

(1) *Olfactory* (sensory), the nerve of smell. (*See* also pages 316-317.)

(2) *Optic* (sensory), the nerve of sight. (*See also* pages 317-324.)
(3) *Oculo-motor* (motor), to muscles of eyeball.
(4) *Trochlear* (motor), to muscles of eyeball.
(5) *Trigeminal* (mixed), sensory to the face and head, and motor to the muscles of mastication.
(6) *Abducens* (motor), to muscles of eyeball.

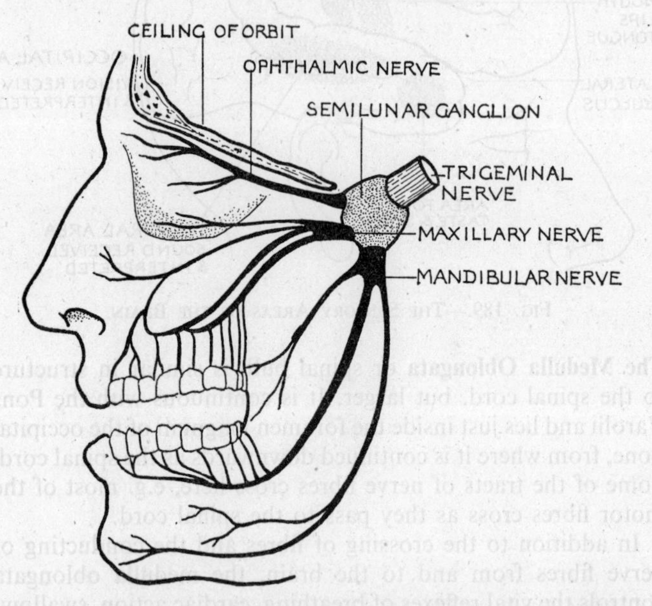

FIG. 190.—DISTRIBUTION OF THE TRIGEMINAL (5TH CRANIAL) NERVE TO THE STRUCTURES OF THE FACE.

(7) *Facial* (motor), to muscles of expression.
(8) *Auditory* or *Acoustic* (sensory), the nerve of hearing. This nerve is in two parts, the *cochlear nerve*, the true nerve of hearing, and the *vestibular nerve*, which is concerned with equilibrium. (See also page 327.)
(9) *Glosso-pharyngeal* (mixed), motor to the pharyngeal muscles, sensory to the tongue.
(10) *Pneumogastric* or *Vagus*. This nerve is composed of mixed afferent and efferent fibres, supplying the pharynx,

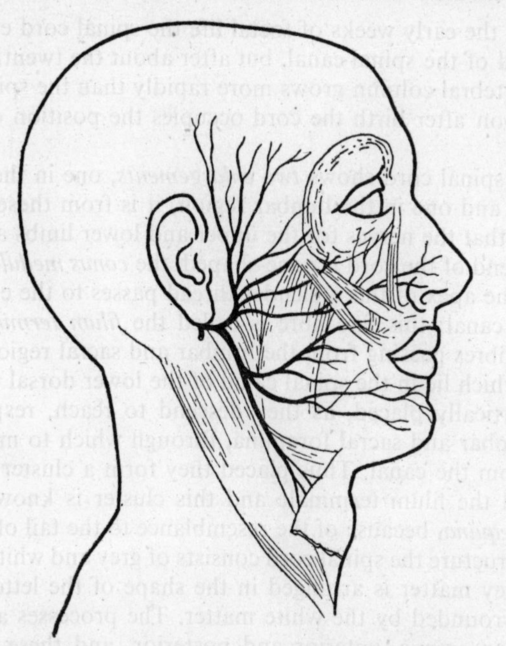

FIG. 191.—DISTRIBUTION OF THE FACIAL (7TH CRANIAL) NERVE TO THE MUSCLES OF THE FACE.

larynx, oesophagus, stomach, intestines, heart, lungs, and some of the solid abdominal organs. (*See also* Fig. 201.)

(11) *Spinal Accessory*. This nerve divides into two parts, one accompanies the vagus nerve, and the other is a motor nerve to the sterno-cleido-mastoid and trapezius muscles.

(12) *Hypoglossal* (motor), to the muscles of the tongue.

THE SPINAL CORD

The *Spinal Cord* is cylindrical in shape. It lies in the upper two-thirds of the neural canal of the vertebral column and extends from the foramen magnum of the occipital bone, to the first lumbar vertebra. The average length of the cord is 18 inches, and it is about $\frac{3}{4}$ inch thick. It is an interesting point that in the early weeks of foetal life the spinal cord extends to the end of the spinal canal, but after about the twentieth week the vertebral column grows more rapidly than the spinal cord, and soon after birth the cord occupies the position described above.

The spinal cord shows *two enlargements*, one in the cervical region and one in the lumbar region, it is from these enlargements that the nerves for the upper and lower limbs arise. The lower end of the cord is cone-shaped, the *conus medullaris*, and from the apex of this a slender thread passes to the end of the spinal canal; this fine fibre is called the *filum terminale*. The nerve fibres passing from the lumbar and sacral regions of the cord which lie in the spinal canal of the lower dorsal vertebrae are vertically placed, as they descend to reach, respectively, the lumbar and sacral foramina, through which to make their exit from the canal. Thus placed they form a cluster of fibres around the filum terminale and this cluster is known as the *cauda equina*, because of the resemblance to the tail of a horse.

In structure the spinal cord consists of grey and white matter. The grey matter is arranged in the shape of the letter H and lies surrounded by the white matter. The processes are called horns or *cornua*, anterior and posterior, and these are connected by a bridge of grey matter, in the middle of which is a small canal, the *central canal* of the spinal cord. This runs through the entire length of the cord communicating with the fourth ventricle of the brain, and contains cerebro-spinal fluid (*see* page 292).

The cord, although cylindrical in shape, is partly divided into right and left sides by two fissures, anterior and posterior. The anterior fissure is shallow, and the posterior is deep and narrow.

SPINAL NERVES

The thirty-one pairs of spinal nerves arise by two roots, anterior and posterior, corresponding with grooves at the sides of the cord. The anterior and posterior nerve roots then unite, to form the trunk of a spinal nerve. A pair of these nerves, one on each side, corresponds with each segment of the vertebral column. The thirty-one pairs of spinal nerves are divided into eight cervical, twelve dorsal, five lumbar, five sacral, and one coccygeal; these are all mixed nerves. The anterior nerve root is composed of motor or efferent fibres, the posterior root of sensory or afferent fibres. The posterior root has a small oval enlargement upon it which is called the *spinal ganglion*; immediately below this ganglion the two roots unite to form a

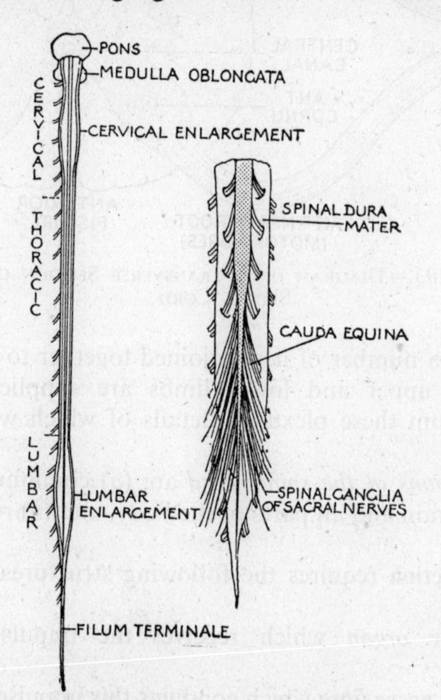

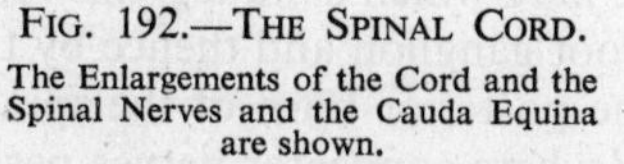

FIG. 192.—THE SPINAL CORD.
The Enlargements of the Cord and the Spinal Nerves and the Cauda Equina are shown.

spinal nerve. This union takes place before the nerve passes through the intervertebral foramen. Soon after the nerve emerges from this foramen, it divides again into anterior and posterior primary divisions. The posterior primary divisions supply the skin and muscles of the back, and the anterior divisions form branches which unite into *nerve plexuses* for the limbs and, in the thoracic region, form the *intercostal nerves*.

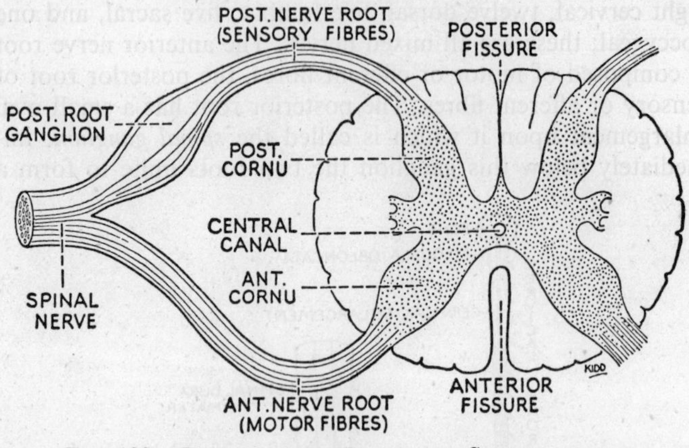

FIG. 193.—DIAGRAM OF A TRANSVERSE SECTION OF THE SPINAL CORD

A plexus is a number of nerves joined together to form a network. The upper and lower limbs are supplied by large branches from these plexuses, details of which will be given later.

The functions of the spinal cord are (*a*) communication between the brain and all parts of the body, and (*b*) reflex action.

A Reflex Action requires the following structures to bring it about.

A sensory organ which receives the impulse, e.g. the skin.

A sensory nerve fibre which conducts this impulse to the cells in the posterior root ganglion and thence by their fibres to the grey matter of the posterior horn of the spinal cord.

The spinal cord where connector nerves pass impulses on to the anterior horn of the cord.

A motor nerve cell in the anterior horn of the spinal cord which receives and transmits the impulse along motor nerve fibres.

A motor organ, e.g. a muscle, which, stimulated by the motor nerve impulse, performs the action.

These parts together constitute the *reflex arc.*

Reflex actions are part of the defence mechanism of the body, and take place much more rapidly than voluntary actions, e.g. the closing of the eye when irritated by dust, the movement of withdrawing the hand from some article accidentally touched if unpleasantly hot. Reflex actions can be inhibited by voluntary control, the hand instead of being withdrawn, may, for example, be held deliberately in contact with the hot surface.

In carrying impulses from and to the brain the spinal cord links the nervous system up with all parts of the body. This is done by means of the motor and sensory nerve paths. The motor

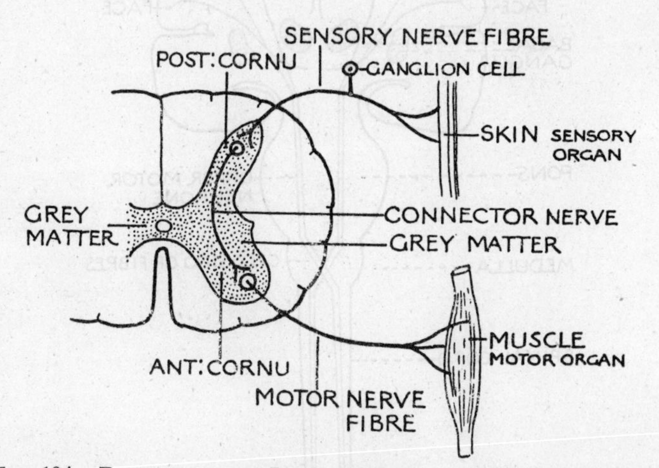

FIG. 194.—DIAGRAM OF THE PARTS REQUIRED IN THE FORMATION OF A REFLEX ARC.

paths lie in the anterior and lateral columns of the cord, the sensory paths mainly in the posterior columns.

The Motor Nerve Path consists of two neurones (for the formation of a neurone *see* page 287).

The upper motor neurone starts in a cell in the pre-Rolandic areas of the cortex of the brain, the fibres pass through the internal capsule, then through the pons and medulla where the majority of the fibres cross, and down through the columns of the spinal cord to terminate in the anterior horn of the cord by arborizing round a nerve cell there (*see* Fig. 195).

The lower motor neurone begins in a cell in the anterior horn of the spinal cord and passes out in the anterior root of a spinal nerve to be distributed to the periphery, ending in a motor organ such as a muscle.

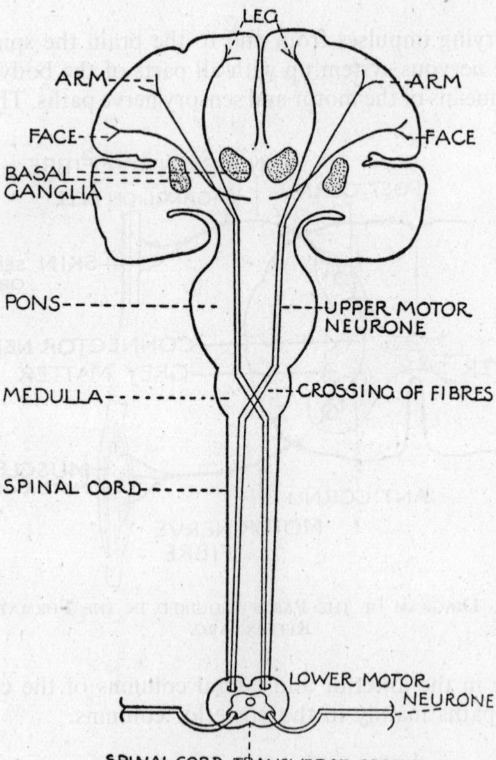

FIG. 195.—THE MOTOR NERVE TRACT. UPPER MOTOR NERVES COMMENCE IN THE CEREBRAL CORTEX AND PASS INTO THE SPINAL CORD, CROSSING AT THE MEDULLA.

LOWER MOTOR NERVES BEGIN AS CELLS IN THE GREY MATTER OF THE CORD, AND PASS OUT IN THE SPINAL NERVES TO SUPPLY THE MUSCLES AND OTHER STRUCTURES.

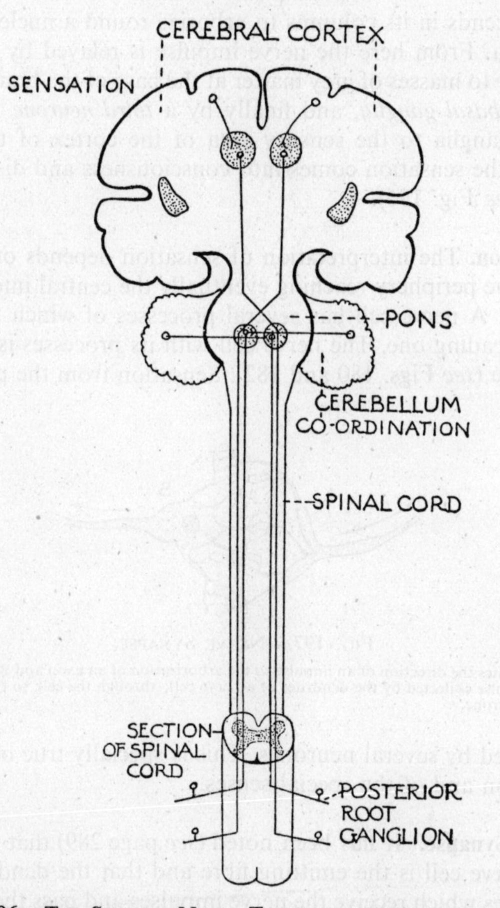

FIG. 196.—THE SENSORY NERVE TRACT IS RELAYED THREE TIMES:
From the Periphery to the Spinal Cord,
From the Grey Matter of the Spinal Cord or Medulla to the Basal Ganglia,
From thence to the post-Rolandic Sensory Area (*see* Fig. 189).

The Sensory Nerve Path consists of three neurones. The first element or *lower sensory neurone* begins in a cell in the ganglion of the posterior root of a spinal nerve; one branch, a dendron, passes to the periphery to reach some sensory organ such as the skin; the other branch, the axon, passes into the spinal cord and ascends in its columns to arborize round a nucleus in the medulla. From here the nerve impulse is relayed by a *second neurone* to masses of grey matter at the base of the brain known as the *basal ganglia*, and finally by a *third neurone* from the basal ganglia to the sensory area of the cortex of the brain where the sensation comes into consciousness and discrimination (*see* Fig. 196).

Sensation. The interpretation of sensation depends on stimuli from the periphery reaching eventually the central interpreting station. A nerve cell has several processes of which the axon is the leading one. The nerve cell with its processes is called a neurone (*see* Figs. 180 and 182). Sensation from the periphery

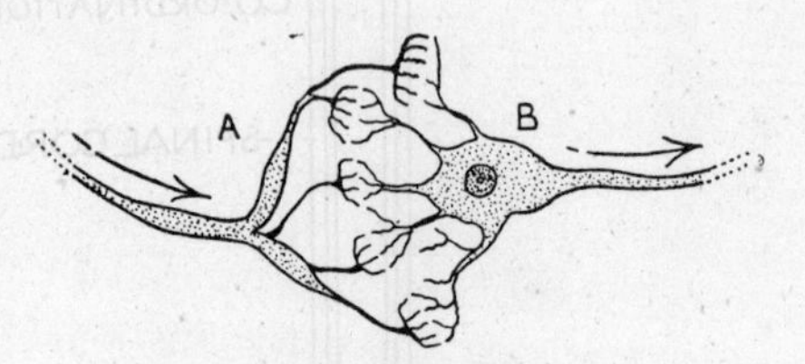

FIG. 197.—NERVE SYNAPSE.

A, indicates the direction of an impulse to the arborization of an axon and B, the passing of the impulse collected by the dendrites of a nerve cell, through the cell, to the axon of a second neurone.

is relayed by several neurones. This is specially true of surface sensation and of the special senses.

Nerve Synapse. It has been noted (*see* page 289) that the axon of a nerve cell is the emitting fibre and that the dendrites are the fibres which receive the nerve impulses and pass them on to the nerve cell. In the central nervous system impulses may be passed along relays of neurones. This is effected by the terminal arborizations of the axon of one neuron passing the impulse on to the dendrites of another axon. It is definitely considered that this process is effected without actual continuity of structure, without one structure touching another. There is continuity of the passage of the impulse without contact of the conducting fibres. *This process is called a synapse* (*see* Fig. 197).

THE MAIN NERVE PLEXUSES AND THEIR TRUNKS

The anterior primary divisions of the spinal nerves other than those which arise in the dorsal region and form the intercostal nerves, are arranged into four main plexuses.

The Cervical Plexus is formed by the first four cervical nerves. It lies in the neck beneath the sterno-mastoid muscle. Many branches arise from it, and because of their position and direction these are described as ascending, descending and connecting branches. The *phrenic nerves* which supply the diaphragm arise from this plexus.

The Brachial Plexus is formed by the four lower cervical nerves and the first dorsal nerve. It is placed in the neck from above the clavicle to the axilla. At first, three trunks are formed; these then divide and unite again to form three cords, outer, inner, and posterior cords. From these cords nerves arise which supply the arm, and some of the neck and chest muscles. The five main nerves from the brachial plexus are (1) *the circumflex*, which winds round the head of the humerus and supplies the deltoid muscle; (2) *the musculo-cutaneous*, which passes down

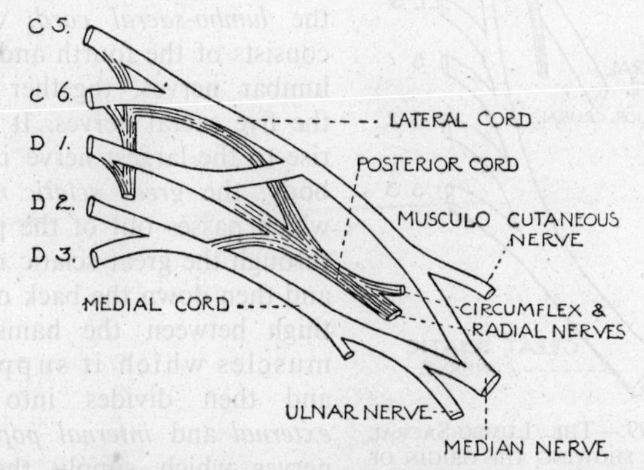

FIG. 198.—THE BRACHIAL PLEXUS (LEFT) SHOWING THE ORIGIN OF THE PRINCIPAL NERVES OF THE UPPER LIMB.

the inner side of the arm and supplies biceps; (3) *the radial* or *musculo-spiral*, which winds round the back of the humerus in the musculo-spiral groove, supplying triceps, and then divides into the posterior interosseous which supplies the extensors of the wrist and fingers, and which, when paralysed, results in wrist-drop. The radial nerve then continues its course as a sensory nerve to supply the skin over the radial aspect of the forearm; (4) *the median* nerve supplies the flexors and pronators of the wrist and fingers, and (5) *the ulnar* nerve passes down the inner side of the arm supplying the deep flexors of the wrist and the small muscles of the hand.

The Lumbar Plexus is formed by the first four lumbar nerves; it lies beside the lumbar spine in the psoas muscle, which it supplies. The main branches are the *femoral* or *anterior crural* and the *obturator nerves*. The anterior crural passes into the thigh beneath Poupart's ligament, to lie in Scarpa's triangle. It supplies the quadriceps extensor. The obturator passes into the thigh through the obturator foramen, and supplies the adductor muscles.

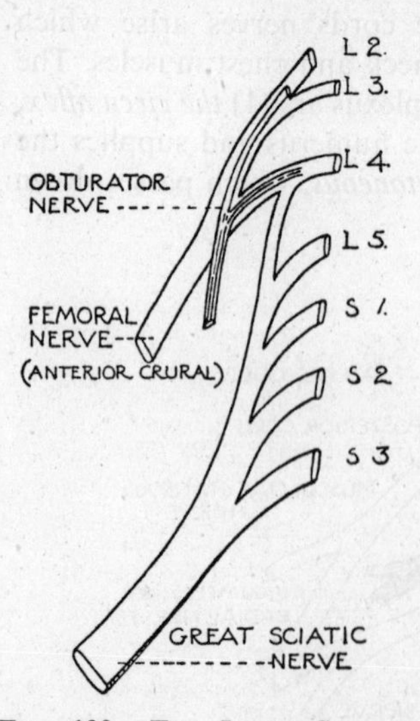

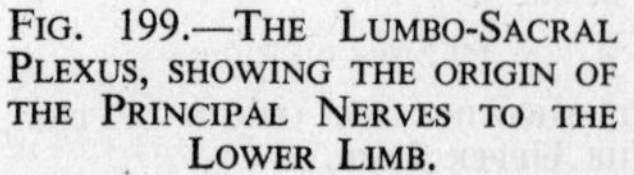
Fig. 199.—The Lumbo-Sacral Plexus, showing the origin of the Principal Nerves to the Lower Limb.

The Sacral Plexus is formed by the *lumbo-sacral cord*, which consists of the fourth and fifth lumbar nerves, together with the five sacral nerves. It gives rise to the largest nerve in the body, the *great sciatic nerve*, which passes out of the pelvis through the great sciatic notch and then down the back of the thigh between the hamstring muscles which it supplies, and then divides into the *external* and *internal popliteal* nerves which supply the leg and foot.

THE AUTONOMIC NERVOUS SYSTEM

The *autonomic nervous system* is dependent on the central nervous system with which it is connected by afferent and efferent nerves. It behaves as if part of the central nervous system had migrated from it in order to reach glands, blood vessels, the heart and lungs and the intestinal tract. Because the function of the autonomic nervous system deals mainly with involuntary or automatic nervous control of viscera it is sometimes called the *involuntary nervous system.* The autonomic nervous system is divided functionally into two parts (a) the *sympathetic system* which lies in front of the vertebral column and is associated and connected with the spinal cord by nerve fibres and (b) the *parasympathetic system* which is divided into two parts composed of the cranial and sacral autonomic nerves.

The Sympathetic System consists of a double chain of ganglionated cords extending from the base of the skull, lying in front of the vertebral column, to end in the pelvis opposite the coccyx as the ganglion impar. These ganglia are arranged in pairs and distributed from the following regions:

In the neck:	Three pairs of *cervical ganglia.*
In the chest:	Eleven pairs of *thoracic ganglia.*
In the loins:	Four pairs of *lumbar ganglia.*
In the pelvis:	Four pairs of *sacral ganglia.*
Front of coccyx:	The *ganglion impar.*

These ganglia are intimately connected with the central nervous system through the spinal cord by means of communicating branches—the *rami communicantes,* which pass outwards, from cord to ganglia, and inwards from ganglia to cord.

Other sympathetic ganglia are placed in relation to these two great chains of ganglia and with their fibres form the sympathetic plexuses (*see* Fig. 200).

(1) *The cardiac plexus* is placed near the base of the heart and sends branches to it and to the lungs.

(2) *The solar plexus* lies behind the stomach and supplies organs in the abdominal cavity.

(3) *The hypogastric plexus* lies in front of the sacrum and supplies organs in the pelvis.

Functions. Sympathetic nerves supply innervation to the muscle of the heart, the involuntary muscle of all blood vessels, and of viscera such as the stomach, pancreas, and intestines. It supplies motor secretory fibres to the sweat glands, motor fibres to the involuntary muscle in the skin—the arrectores pilorum—and maintains the tone of all muscle, including the tone of voluntary muscle.

SYMPATHETIC SYSTEMS

The Parasympathetic System. The *Cranial Autonomics* are the third, seventh, ninth and tenth cranial nerves. These form the means by which the para-sympathetic fibres pass out from the brain to the organs partly controlled by them.

By means of the *third cranial nerve*, the *oculo-motor nerve*, fibres reach the circular muscular fibres of the iris stimulating the movements which determine the size of the pupil of the eye.

By the *seventh nerve*, the *facial*, and the *ninth*, the *glosso-pharyngeal*, splanchnic fibres reach the salivary glands. These are motor secretory fibres which are efferent in character. Splanchnic afferent fibres concerned with taste are also conveyed by these nerves.

The *vagus* or *tenth cranial* nerve is the largest autonomic nerve. It has a very wide distribution and sends fibres to a number of glands and organs including the respiratory tract, the heart and great blood vessels, the oesophagus, stomach and intestine, and the liver and pancreas. This distribution is closely associated with that of the sympathetic fibres (*see* system of dual control of certain organs below).

The Sacral Parasympathetic Nerves pass out from the sacral region of the spinal cord. These form the pelvic splanchnic nerves and together with the sympathetic nerves form the pelvic plexuses which supply the colon, rectum and bladder (*see* Fig. 201).

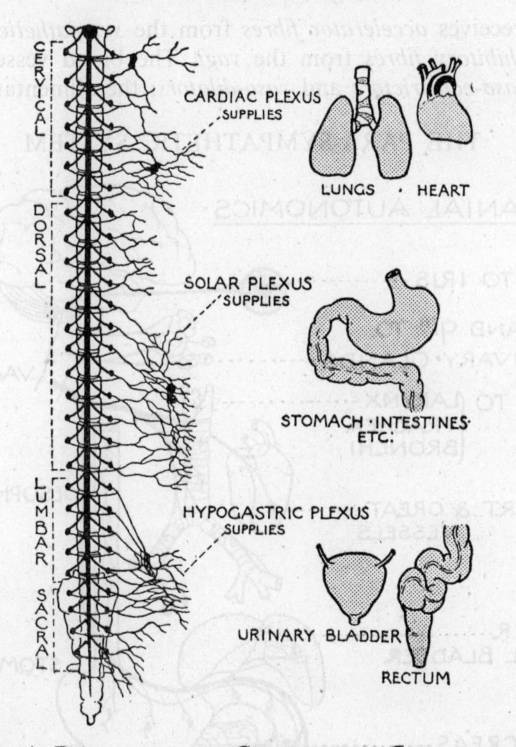

FIG. 200.—A DIAGRAM OF THE GANGLIONATED CORDS OF THE SYMPATHETIC SYSTEM, THE PRINCIPAL PLEXUSES, AND SOME OF THE ORGANS SUPPLIED BY THESE.

A System of Dual Control (sympathetic and autonomic). Although some organs and glands have only one source of supply, sympathetic or autonomic, these are in the minority; the majority have a dual supply, receiving some fibres from the sympathetic system and some from the cranial or sacral autonomic nerves. The activity of the organ being stimulated by one set of nerves and retarded or inhibited by the other set—each acting in antagonism to the other. In this way an exact adjustment is maintained between activity and rest, and the smooth rhythmic action of the internal organs, glands, blood vessels, and involuntary muscle is maintained. Thus the heart receives *accelerator fibres* from the *sympathetic nerves*, and *inhibitory fibres* from the *vagi*. The blood vessels have their *vaso-constrictors* and *vaso-dilators*; the alimentary canal

THE PARA-SYMPATHETIC SYSTEM

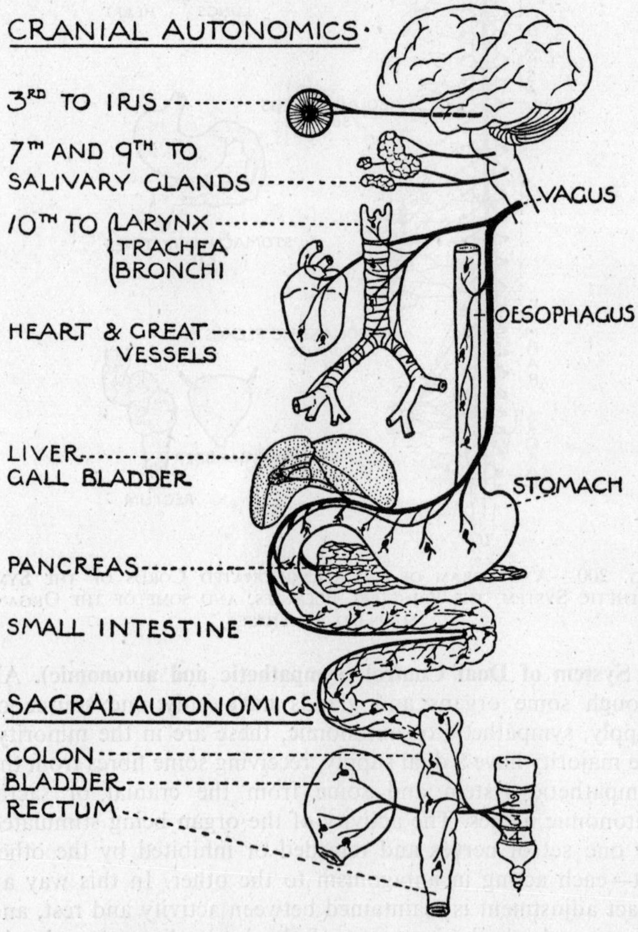

FIG. 201.—DIAGRAM OF THE ORGANS SUPPLIED BY THE CRANIAL AND SACRAL AUTONOMIC NERVES, AFTER GASKELL.

has accelerator and inhibitory nerves, which increase and decrease peristaltic movements respectively.

In addition to the efferent fibres, afferent or sensory fibres are described; little is known of their distribution, but it is thought that the viscera are in some way related by these nerves with definite patches of skin. Disease of some of the internal organs give rise to pain in the skin, which is described as *referred pain.*

The plan shown below gives some of the best examples of the dual control by sympathetic and autonomic nerves as it affects some organs.

Organ	*Action increased or Activated by:*	*Action depressed or Inhibited by:*
Heart . .	Sympathetic (rate increased)	Vagus (rate decreased)
Bronchi . .	Vagus (constricted)	Sympathetic (inhibited)
Stomach . .	Vagus (contracted)	Sympathetic (relaxed)
Intestine . .	Vagus (contracted)	Sympathetic (relaxed)
Bladder . .	Sacral autonomic (contracted)	Sympathetic (relaxed)
Pupil of eye (*iris*)	3rd cranial autonomic (contracted)	Sympathetic (dilated)

In the case of an organ which possesses a sphincter muscle such as the stomach in the *pyloric sphincter*, the intestine in the *ilio-colic sphincter*, and the bladder in the *internal urethral sphincter*, the nerve which causes contraction of the organ inhibits the sphincter and vice versa. For example, in the act of micturition the urethral sphincter is relaxed whilst the muscle in the wall of the bladder is contracted thus enabling the bladder to be emptied.

The nerve fibres from the different parts of the involuntary nervous system—sympathetic and autonomic—are conveyed to the different organs, and to the peripheral parts, such as the glands and muscles in the skin, by means of the blood vessels and the spinal nerves. In this way, by making a transport system of vessels and nerves, the involuntary nervous control reaches every tissue in the body.

Chapter 21

ORGANS OF SPECIAL SENSE

The organs of special sense are specially adapted end-organs for the reception of certain kinds of stimuli. The nerves which supply them form the means by which sensory impressions are carried from the sense organs to the brain, where sensation is interpreted. Some sense impressions arise outside the body such as those of touch, taste, sight, smell, and sound. Others arise from within and include hunger, thirst and pain.

In each case the sensory nerves are supplied with special nerve endings for collecting the stimuli of the particular sense with which each organ deals. We apparently taste with the nerve endings in the tongue, hear with those in the ear, and so on, but in reality it is the brain that appreciates these sensations.

The *sense of touch* has been described in the notes on the skin (page 259).

TASTE

The tongue is principally concerned in the special sense of taste. It is largely composed of muscle which is in two groups. The *intrinsic muscles of the tongue* perform all the delicate movements, and the *extrinsic muscles* which attach the tongue to the surrounding parts and perform the larger movements such as those which form an important part of mastication and swallowing. The food is turned about by the tongue, pressed against the palate and teeth, and finally passed into the pharynx.

The tongue lies in the floor of the mouth, at its *root* the vessels and nerves pass in and out, the *tip* and *margins of the tongue* are in contact with the lower teeth, and the *dorsum* is the arched surface on top of the tongue. When the tongue is turned up the under surface and the *frenulum* of the tongue, a soft ligamentous structure, which attaches the posterior part of the tongue to the floor of the mouth can be seen. The anterior portion of the tongue is free. When protruded the tip of the tongue becomes pointed but when lying in the floor of the mouth and relaxed, the tip is rounded.

The *mucous membrane of the tongue* is moist and pink in health. On the upper surface it has a velvety appearance and is covered by papillae, of which there are three varieties.

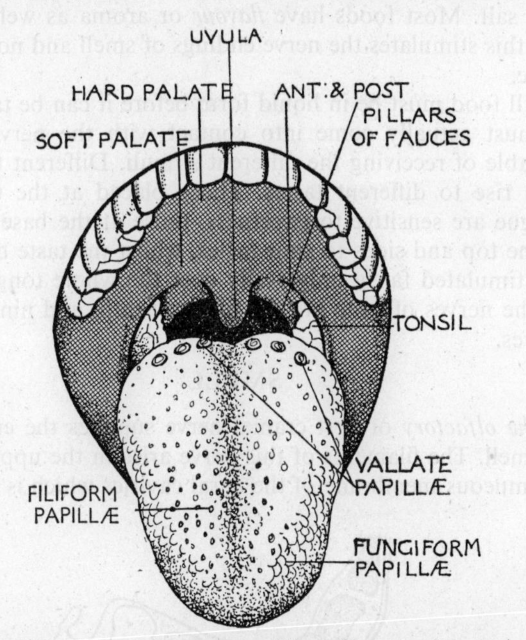

FIG. 202.—A DIAGRAM OF THE UPPER SURFACE (DORSUM) OF THE TONGUE.

Circumvallate papillae. Of these there are from eight to twelve placed at the base of the tongue. These are the largest and each one is surrounded by a little moat-like depression. These papillae are arranged in a V-shape at the back of the tongue.

Fungiform papillae are distributed over the tip and sides of the tongue, and are fungoid in shape.

Filiform papillae are the most abundant and are found over the whole surface of the tongue.

The end-organs of taste are the *taste buds*, which are very numerous in the walls of the circumvallate and fungiform papillae. The filiform papillae are concerned more with the sense of touch rather than actual taste. Taste buds are also contained in the mucous membrane of the palate and pharynx.

There are four true *sensations of taste*: sweet, bitter, sour, and salt. Most foods have *flavour* or aroma as well as taste, but this stimulates the nerve endings of smell and not those of taste.

All food must be in liquid form before it can be tasted, and it must actually come into contact with the nerve endings capable of receiving the different stimuli. Different taste buds give rise to different tastes. Those placed at the tip of the tongue are sensitive to sweetness, those at the base to bitter, at the top and sides to sour tastes, whilst the taste of salt can be stimulated fairly universally over the whole tongue.

The nerves of taste are the fifth, seventh, and ninth cranial nerves.

SMELL

The olfactory or first cranial nerve supplies the end-organs of smell. The filaments of this nerve arise in the upper part of the mucous membrane of the nasal cavities which is known as

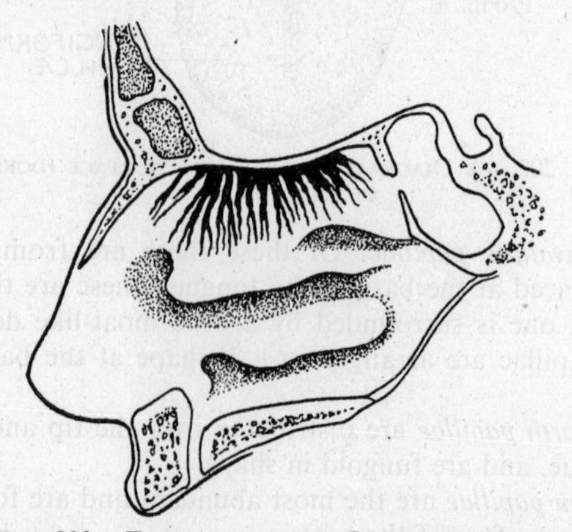

FIG. 203.—FILAMENTS OF THE OLFACTORY NERVES.

the *olfactory portion of the nose.* It is lined with highly specialized cells from which minute fibrils pass to arborize with fibres from the olfactory bulb. The *olfactory bulb* which is actually an outlying portion of the brain, is the slightly bulbous (enlarged) portion of the olfactory nerve tract which lies above the cribiform plate of the ethmoid bone. From the olfactory bulb sensation is passed along the *olfactory tract* by several relaying stations until it reaches the final receiving area in the olfactory centre which lies in the temporal lobe of the cerebral hemisphere where the sensation is interpreted.

The *sense of smell* is stimulated by gases inhaled or by small particles. It is a very delicate sense, and becomes easily deadened when exposed to any one odour for some time. Persons in a stuffy room rapidly become oblivious to the unpleasant odours, which strike others forcibly on entering the room from the fresh air. The sense of smell is also lessened if the nasal mucous membrane is very dry, very wet or swollen, as in a cold in the head. Smells are described as pleasant or unpleasant.

THE EYE AND THE SPECIAL SENSE OF SIGHT

The *optic* or second cranial nerve is the sensory nerve of sight. The nerve arises from the ganglion cells in the retina (*see also* Fig. 207) which converge to form the optic nerve. When the fibres reach the *optic chiasma* half of the fibres converge to reach the opposite side of the *optic tract.* By means of this arrangement of fibres each optic nerve is related to both sides of the brain. The *visual centre* lies in the cortex of the occipital lobe of the brain (*see also* page 297). The eyeball is the organ

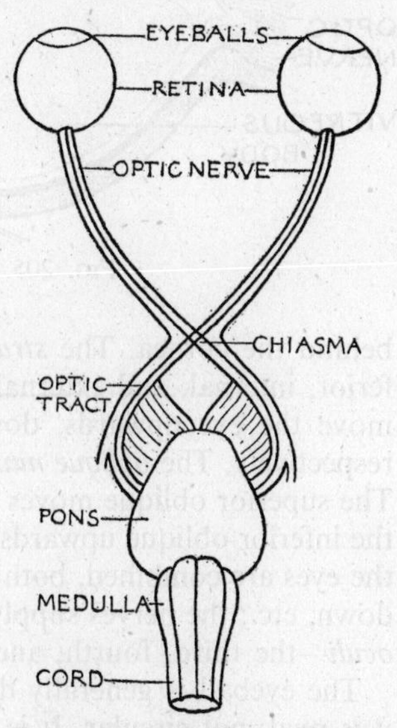

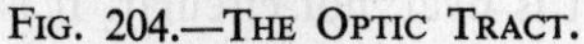
FIG. 204.—THE OPTIC TRACT.

of sight. It is contained in the orbit (*see* page 48), and protected by appendages such as the eyelids, eyebrows, conjunctiva, and the lacrimal apparatus.

THE EYEBALL

The *eyeball* is moved by six muscles, four straight and two oblique. These lie inside the orbit passing from the bony walls of the orbit to be attached to the sclerotic coat of the eye

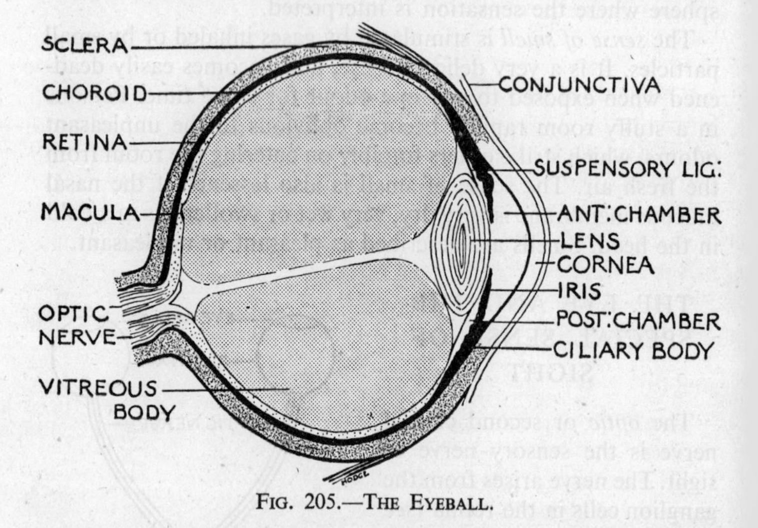

FIG. 205.—THE EYEBALL.

behind the cornea. The *straight muscles* are the superior, inferior, internal, and external rectus muscles of the eye. These move the eye upwards, downwards, inwards, and outwards respectively. The *oblique muscles* are the inferior and superior. The superior oblique moves the eye downwards and outwards. the inferior oblique upwards and outwards. The movements of the eyes are combined, both eyes move to right or left, up and down, etc.; the nerves supplying these muscles are the *motores oculi*—the third, fourth, and sixth cranial nerves.

The eyeball is generally described as a globe or sphere but it is oval, not circular. It is about an inch in diameter, transparent in front, and composed of three layers, outer fibrous, middle vascular and inner nervous.

The sclera is the tough outer fibrous coat. It forms the *white of the eye* and is continuous in front with a transparent window-membrane, the *cornea*. The sclera protects the delicate structures of the eye and helps to maintain the shape of the eyeball.

The choroid or middle vascular coat contains the blood vessels, which are the ramifications of the ophthalmic artery, a branch of the internal carotid. The vascular coat forms the *iris* with the central opening or *pupil* of the eye. The pigmented layer behind the iris gives it colour and determines whether the eye is blue, black, brown, grey, etc. The choroid is continuous in front with the iris and just behind the iris this coat is thickened to form the ciliary body.

The *ciliary body* lies between the choroid and the iris. It contains circular muscle fibres and radiating fibres; contraction of the former contracts the pupil of the eye.

The retina is the inner nervous coat of the eye, composed of a number of layers of fibres, nerve cells, rods and cones (*see* Fig. 207), all of which are included in the construction of the retina which is the delicate nerve tissue conducting the nerve impulses from without inwards to the *optic disc* which is the point where the optic nerve leaves the eyeball. This is a *blind spot*, as it possesses no retina. The most acutely sensitive part of the retina is the *macula*, which lies just external to the optic disc, and exactly opposite the centre of the pupil.

In examining the eyeball from front to back the following parts are seen (please consult Fig. 205).

Cornea, the transparent front portion continuous with the dense white sclera. It consists of several layers. The superficial layer is stratified epithelium continuous with the conjunctiva.

Anterior chamber, between cornea and iris.

Iris, the coloured curtain in front of the lens which is continuous with the choroid coat. The iris contains two sets of involuntary or plain muscle fibres—one set contracts the size of the pupil and the other set dilates the pupil.

Pupil, the dark central spot which is an opening in the iris through which light reaches the retina.

Posterior chamber, between iris and lens. Both anterior and posterior chambers are filled with the *aqueous humour*.

Aqueous humour of the eye. This fluid is derived from the ciliary body and it is re-absorbed into the blood stream at the angle between the iris and cornea by a tiny vein known as the canal of Schlemm.

Lens, a bi-convex transparent body made up of several layers. It lies just behind the iris. It has both in front and behind a membrane, known as the *suspensory ligament*, by which the lens is attached to the ciliary body. When the suspensory ligament is slackened, the lens recoils and becomes thicker, when the ligament is taut the lens flattens. Slackening of the lens is controlled by contraction of the ciliary muscle.

Vitreous humour. The remaining back portion of the eyeball, extending from the lens to the retina is filled with a jelly-like albuminous fluid—the vitreous humour of the eye, which serves to give it shape and firmness and to keep the retina in contact with the choroid and sclerotic coats.

Function of the Eye. The eye is the special organ of sight. It is constructed to receive the stimuli of rays of light on the retina, and by means of the optic nerves, to transmit these to the visual centres of the brain for interpretation.

The cornea acts as a transparent window protecting the delicate structures behind it, and helping to focus images on to the retina. It does not contain any blood vessels.

The iris, with its central opening, the pupil, is a movable disc, which acts as a curtain to protect the retina, controlling the amount of light entering the eye.

The lens is the principal organ of focus, bending rays of light reflected from objects seen, to a clear image on the retina. The lens is contained in an elastic capsule, attached to the ciliary body of the choroid by a suspensory ligament. By means of the ciliary muscle the anterior surface of the lens is made more or less convex, to focus near or distant objects. This is visual *accommodation.*

The pigmented choroid coat darkens the inner chamber of the eye, comparable to the blackened interior of a photographic camera.

The retina is the nervous mechanism of sight. It contains the endings of the optic nerves, and is comparable to a sensitive photographic plate.

When an image is perceived, rays of light from the object seen pass through the cornea, aqueous humour, lens, and vitreous body to stimulate the nerve endings in the retina. The most sensitive part of the retina is the yellow spot or macula. The stimuli received by the retina pass along the optic tracts to the visual areas of the brain, to be interpreted. Both areas receive messages from both eyes, thus giving perspective and contour.

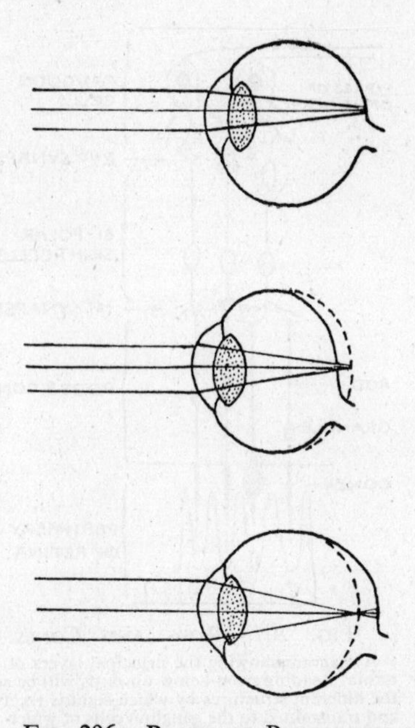

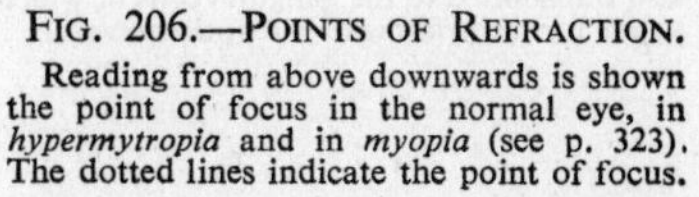

FIG. 206.—POINTS OF REFRACTION.

Reading from above downwards is shown the point of focus in the normal eye, in *hypermytropia* and in *myopia* (see p. 323). The dotted lines indicate the point of focus.

In an ordinary camera one lens is provided. In the eye, whilst the crystalline lens is very important in focusing the image on the retina, there are in all four structures acting as lenses: (1) the cornea, (2) the aqueous humour, (3) the crystalline lens, (4) the vitreous body.

As is all interpretation of sensation from the surface, a number of relaying stations are concerned with the transmission of the sensation which in this case is sight. A number of these relaying stations are in the retina as can be seen by studying Fig. 207. Internal to the periphery of the retina are layers of rods and cones which are highly specialised sight cells

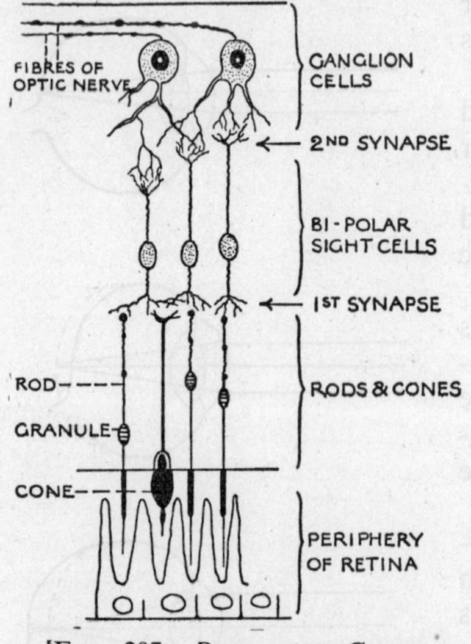

FIG. 207.—RODS AND CONES.

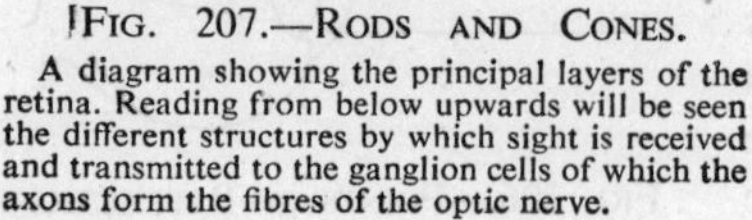
A diagram showing the principal layers of the retina. Reading from below upwards will be seen the different structures by which sight is received and transmitted to the ganglion cells of which the axons form the fibres of the optic nerve.

sensitive to light. The circular interruptions in these are termed granules. The proximal end of the rods and cones form the first synapse with a layer of bi-polar cells, still in the retina. The second processes of these cells form the second nerve synapse with large ganglion cells, also in the retina. The axons of these cells form the fibres of the optic nerve. These pass backwards, first reaching the lower centre in special bodies near the thalamus, and finally reaching the special visual centre in the occipital lobe of the cerebral hemisphere where sight is interpreted.

APPENDAGES OF THE EYE

Eyebrows. These are two arches of thick skin from which hairs grow. The eyebrows are attached to muscles beneath, and serve to protect the eye from too great light.

Eyelids. These are two plates, the *tarsal plates*, which are composed of very dense tissue resembling cartilage, covered by skin and lined with conjunctiva. The tissue beneath the skin does not contain fat. The upper eyelid is larger than the lower, and is raised by the *levator palpebrae* muscle. The lids are closed by a circular muscle, the *orbicularis palpebrae*. Eyelashes are attached to the free margins of the lids, and protect the eyes from dust and light.

Refracting function of the Eye. As already mentioned the rays of light falling upon the eye which will bring an image to focus on the retina pass through and are altered by the cornea, lens, aqueous and vitreous bodies, but the lens is the principal organ bending rays of light to focus an image on the retina. In the normal eye these rays converge to strike a point on the retina as illustrated in Fig. 206 where the image is focused.

Abnormalities of Refraction which result in defects of visual accommodation occur either as the result of alteration in the shape of the eyeball or abnormalities of the lens. In *Hypermetropia* or long sight the eye is short from back to front and therefore the lens focuses the image *behind the retina*, whilst *in myopia* or short sight the eyeball is longer than normal from back to front and the lens focuses the image *in front of the retina.*

Astigmatism is an error of refraction which occurs when rays of light fall upon lines on the retina and not on sharp points. This is due to alteration in the curves of the lens and is corrected by spectacles with lenses which are convex in the direction which is lacking in the abnormal lens and so make good the deficiency.

Presbyopia is the term used to describe the defect of accommodation which occurs in advancing age. The lens loses its

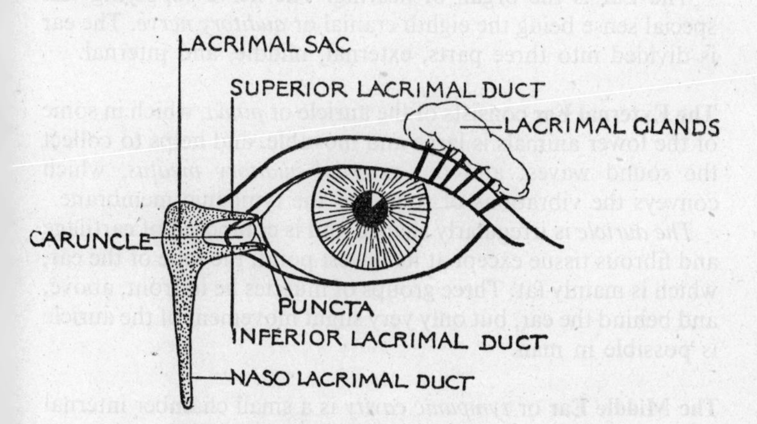

FIG. 208.—A DIAGRAM OF THE LACRIMAL APPARATUS.

elasticity and becomes less resilient and fails to focus the image of a near object. Distant vision is unimpaired. The subject with presbyopia is seen to hold a paper a distance away in order to be able to read it. This defect is corrected by providing convex lenses.

Conjunctiva. This is the mucous membrane lining the eyelids and covering the front of the sclera. When the lids are closed the conjunctiva forms a closed sac.

Lacrimal Apparatus. The lacrimal glands are compound racemose glands, situated at the upper outer corner of the orbital cavity and secrete the *tears*, which at the upper and outer margins of the eye are poured into the conjunctival sac from the ducts of the lacrimal glands. As the eyelids move in blinking, the tears are distributed across the surface of the eyeball. A considerable amount of this fluid is evaporated and any excess passes from the inner angle of the eye into the lacrimal ducts and then by the naso-lacrimal duct into the nose. The flow of tears is increased by irritants (tear gases, for example) and by emotion.

THE EAR

The Ear is the organ of hearing. The nerve supplying this special sense being the eighth cranial or *auditory nerve*. The ear is divided into three parts, external, middle, and internal.

The External Ear consists of the auricle or *pinna*, which in some of the lower animals is large and movable, and helps to collect the sound waves; and the *external auditory meatus*, which conveys the vibrations of sound to the tympanic membrane.

The auricle is irregularly shaped and is composed of cartilage and fibrous tissue except at its lowest point, the lobe of the ear, which is mainly fat. Three groups of muscles lie in front, above, and behind the ear, but only very slight movement of the auricle is possible in man.

The Middle Ear or *tympanic cavity* is a small chamber internal to the tympanic membrane or ear drum, which separates it

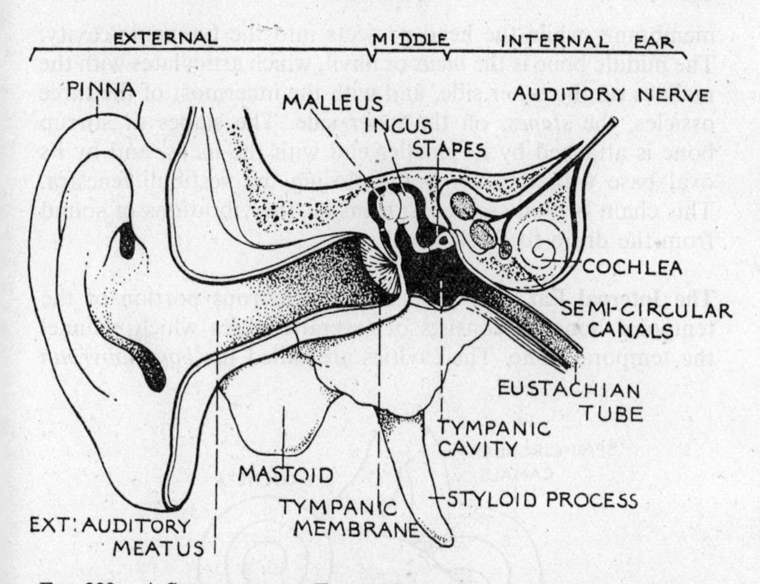

FIG. 209.—A SECTION OF THE EAR SHOWING THE PARTS WHICH COMPOSE THE EXTERNAL, MIDDLE AND INNER EAR.

from the external auditory meatus. It has bony and membranous walls, and communicates behind by means of an opening called the *aditus* with the mastoid antrum in the mastoid process; and, through the naso-pharynx, with the Eustachian tubes, one on each side which provide a means of communication with the air. The tympanic cavity always contains air. The opening of the Eustachian tube is closed normally, but opens each time swallowing occurs. In this way the pressure of the air in the tympanic cavity is kept the same as that of the atmosphere, and injuries and deafness due to greater or less pressure are avoided. It is this communication with the naso-pharynx that allows infection to spread from the nose or throat to the middle ear.

The auditory ossicles are three small bones arranged across the middle ear, like a chain reaching from the tympanic membrane to the inner ear. The external bone is the *malleus*, shaped like a hammer, the handle of which is attached to the tympanic membrane, while the head projects into the tympanic cavity. The middle bone is the *incus* or anvil, which articulates with the malleus on the outer side, and with the innermost of the three ossicles, the *stapes*, on the inner side. The stapes or stirrup bone is attached by its smaller end with the incus, and by its oval base with the membrane closing the vestibuli fenestra. This chain of bone serves to transmit the vibrations of sound from the drum to the internal ear.

The Internal Ear is contained in the petrous portion of the temporal bone. It consists of several cavities which channel the temporal bone. The cavities are called the *bony labyrinth*

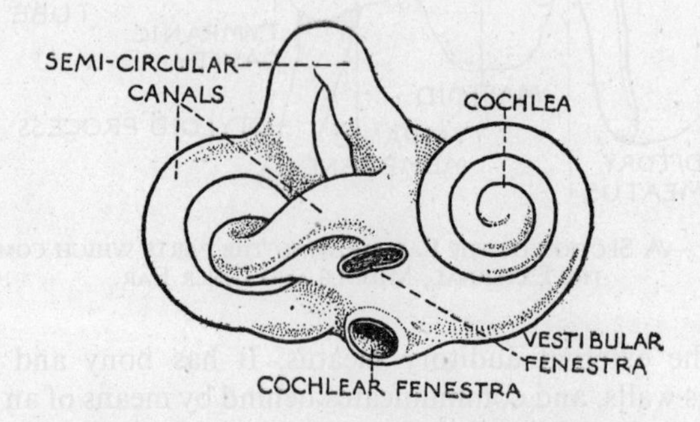

FIG. 210.—THE BONY LABYRINTH OF THE EAR SHOWING THE VESTIBULAR AND COCHLEAR FENESTRAE.

and are lined with membrane, which forms the *membranous labyrinth*. These membranous channels contain fluid and the nerve endings for hearing and balance. (*See* below.)

The bony labyrinth consists of three parts.

The vestibule, which is a central part with which all the others communicate, as doors may open out of the vestibule of a house.

The semicircular canals, these communicate with the vestibule. There are three of them, superior, posterior, and external; the latter is situated horizontally and all three of the canals lie at right angles to each other. Each canal has a swelling at one end called the *ampulla*. (It is by movements of the fluid stimulating special nerve endings within the ampullae that we are made conscious of our position. The function of this part of the internal ear is to assist the cerebellum in the control of the equilibrium, and the sense of the position of the body.)

The cochlea. This is a spiral tube twisted on itself and resembling a snail-shell. The coils are arranged round a central bony cone-shaped axis called the *modiolus*. The tube begins at the fenestra ovalis, and ends at the cochlear fenestra, and contains fluid called the *perilymph*.

Within each of these is a *membranous counterpart* to which are attached the endings of the auditory nerve. The fluid within the membranous labyrinth is called *endolymph*, the fluid outside it and within the bony labyrinth is the *perilymph*. There are two windows in this bony enclosure, (1) the *fenestra vestibuli* (also called ovalis, as it is oval in shape) is closed by the stapes, (2) the *fenestra cochleae* (also called rotunda, as it is round) is closed by a membrane. Both these are directed towards the middle ear. The purpose of these windows in the bony labyrinth is to allow the vibrations transmitted from the middle ear to occur in the perilymph (fluid being practically incompressible). Vibrations of the perilymph are transmitted to the endolymph and so activate the nerve endings of the auditory nerve.

The Auditory Nerve is in two portions, one collecting sensations from the vestibular portion of the inner ear is concerned with equilibrium. The fibres from this pass to the vestibular nuclei at the junction of the pons and medulla and then on to the cerebellum. The cochlear portion of the auditory nerve is the *true nerve of hearing*. Its fibres are first relayed to a special nucleus immediately behind the thalamus and thence to the final receiving centre in the cerebral cortex which lies in the under portion of the temporal lobe of the cerebrum.

Hearing. Sound is due to vibrations of atmosphere known as sound waves, varying in rate and volume. Sound waves pass along the external auditory canal and cause the tympanic membrane to vibrate. The malleus is attached to this membrane, and the vibration is transmitted through it to the incus and stapes. By movement on each other these bones magnify the vibrations, which are then communicated through the vestibular fenestra to the perilymph. Vibrations of the perilymph are transmitted through the membrane to the endolymph in the canal of the cochlea, *and the stimuli reach the nerve endings in the organ of Corti, to be conveyed to the brain by the auditory nerve.*

The sensation of hearing is interpreted by the brain as a pleasant or unpleasant sound, or one of noise or music. These terms are used in their widest sense. Irregular sound waves produce noise, regular rhythmic waves produce pleasant musical sounds. Sound travels at the rate of 375 yards a second in still air of 60° F.

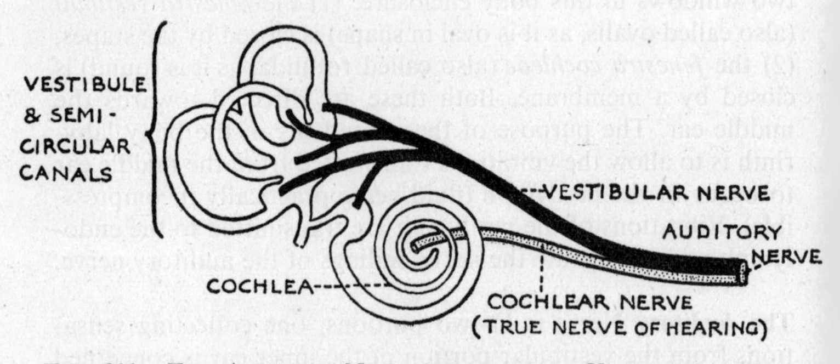

FIG. 211.—THE AUDITORY NERVE SHOWING THE VESTIBULAR AND COCHLEAR PORTIONS.

Balance. *The vestibular nerve* distributed to the semi-circular canals conveys to the brain the impulses generated there by alteration in the position of the fluid in these canals which have so much to do with the knowledge of the sense of the position of the head in relation to the body. If a person is suddenly thrown to one side, the tendency is for the head to bend towards the opposite side in order to maintain balance so that weight is adjusted, the erect position maintained, and a fall is prevented. It is the change in the position of the fluid in the semicircular canals which stimulates the impulse, obeyed as a reflex, by the quick response of the body to transfer weight and maintain equilibrium.

Chapter 22

SHORT NOTES ON SURFACE ANATOMY

Surface anatomy includes the study of the form and marking of the surface of the human body. The various bony points serve as landmarks; and the position of many of the organs and internal structures are described in relation to these points.

Some Points of Surface Anatomy of the Head. A line drawn from the external occipital protuberance of the occipital bone,

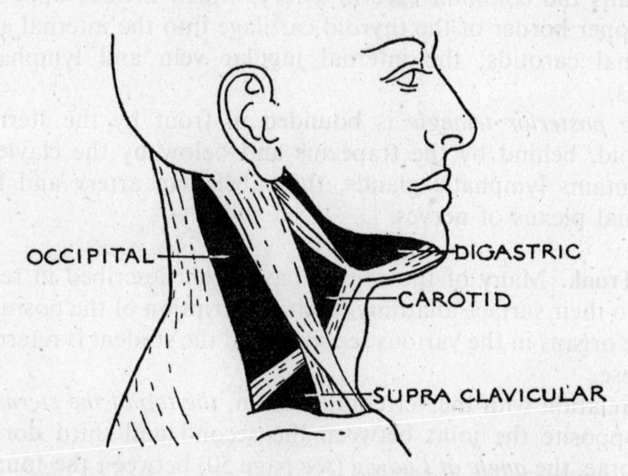

FIG. 212.—THE POSITION OF THE TRIANGLES OF THE NECK.

forwards over the top of the skull, to a point at the centre of the base of the nose, marks the position of the *longitudinal fissure* separating the cerebral hemispheres, and also the position of the *superior longitudinal sinus* of the dura mater.

The fissure of Rolando is marked by taking a point from about an inch in front of the middle of the line described above, and carrying it downwards and forwards towards the ear.

The mastoid process can be felt behind the ear.

The parotid gland lies below the zygomatic process of the temporal bone, and between it and the angle of the mandible. Its duct can be seen opening into the mouth opposite the second upper molar tooth.

The facial artery passes over the body of the mandible, anterior to the angle.

The temporal artery crosses the zygomatic process of the temporal bone, in front of the ear.

The Neck. The region of the neck is divided into two triangles.

The anterior triangle, which is bounded behind by the anterior border of the sterno-mastoid muscle, above by the ramus of the mandible, and in front by the middle line of the neck. It contains the common carotid artery, which divides opposite the upper border of the thyroid cartilage into the internal and external carotids; the internal jugular vein and lymphatic glands.

The posterior triangle is bounded in front by the sterno-mastoid, behind by the trapezius and below by the clavicle. It contains lymphatic glands, the subclavian artery and the brachial plexus of nerves.

The Trunk. Many of the organs have been described in relation to their surface anatomy, in the description of the position of the organs in the various sections, and the student is referred to these.

In relation with the vertebral column, *the top of the sternum* lies opposite the joint between the second and third dorsal vertebrae, the *angle of Ludwig* (*see* page 50) between the fourth and fifth and the articulation between the body of the sternum and the ensiform process lies about the level of the joint between the ninth and tenth dorsal vertebrae.

The vertebral border of the scapula lies opposite the second to about the seventh dorsal vertebra. The *highest point of crest of the ilium lies in a line with the joint between the third and fourth lumbar vertebrae* and is taken as a guide to this position in performing lumbar puncture.

For the division of the abdomen into regions, *see* page 195.

The caecum lies in the right iliac fossa, the vermiform appendix is attached to it at about the junction of the right lateral vertical line, and the line joining the anterior superior spines.

McBurney's point is described as the usual point of the site of maximum pain in appendicitis. It is found by drawing a line from the umbilicus to the anterior superior iliac spine; the line is divided into two, and McBurney's point is described as being on the outer half of the line.

The Extremities. Many of the points are dealt with in the various chapters. The different bony points can be felt on palpation. In the upper extremity, the axilla and ante-cubital space are described on pages 130–132.

The tendons crossing the wrist can be readily felt and seen; the extensor tendons passing to the thumb form the *anatomical snuff-box*. The styloid process of the radius can be felt in the floor of this space, and the radial artery crosses it. In the lower extremity, for Scarpa's triangle and the popliteal space, *see* pages 133. For position of arteries, *see* Chapter 9.

Nelaton's line is an imaginary line drawn from the anterior superior iliac spine, backwards to the tuberosity of the ischium. It cuts through the centre of the hip joint, and across the top of the great trochanter.

The great sciatic nerve, after passing out from the pelvis, enters the thigh between the tuberosity of the ischium and the great trochanter.

The bones of the foot can be easily felt and the arrangement of the different arches determined (*see* pages 85–88). The *tubercle of the navicular* lies on the inner side of the foot, and a line drawn outwards across the dorsum of the foot, slightly behind this point, represents the position of the mid-tarsal joints.

APPENDIX

Question papers set in Part I of the Preliminary State Examination in Anatomy and Physiology during the past three years.

JUNE 1947

Elementary Anatomy and Physiology

1. Give an account of the anatomy and function of the liver. (*See* pages 214–219.)
2. Describe the femur. What are its functions? (*See* pages 77–81.)
3. What is a ductless gland? Name three and give an account of the functions of one of them. (*See* pages 245–252.)
4. Describe the composition and functions of blood. (*See* pages 144–151.)
5. Give an account of the large intestine. Describe its functions. (*See* pages 208–210.)

FEBRUARY 1947

Elementary Anatomy and Physiology

1. Describe the shoulder girdle. What are the chief muscles attached to it? (*See* pages 63–67 and figs. 76, 79.)
2. Give an account of the structure and function of the heart. (*See* pages 134–142.)
3. What is a food? What are the essential components of a normal diet? (*See* pages 178–185.)
4. Describe the physiology of respiration. (*See* pages 232–234.)
5. Describe the spinal cord. What are its functions? (*See* pages 299–303.)

OCTOBER 1946

Elementary Anatomy and Physiology

1. Give a description of the Spinal Column. (*See* pages 52, 59 and 60.)
2. Describe the chief muscles concerned in Respiration. (*See* page 237. *See also* 110 and 111.)
3. Describe the digestion and utilization of carbohydrates in the body. (*See* pages 194–5, 205–207 and 241.)
4. What are the functions of
   (*a*) The Thyroid Gland;
   (*b*) The Bone Marrow;
   (*c*) The Vagus Nerve?
   (*See* pages 247–248, 35 and 298–299 and fig. 211.)

JUNE 1946

Elementary Anatomy and Physiology

1. Describe the anatomy of the small and large intestines. (*See* pages 201 and 208.)
2. Give the names and position of the chief blood vessels of the limbs. (*See* pages 160–169.)
3. Describe the function of the kidneys. (*See* pages 264–266.)
4. Give an account of the mechanism of heat regulation in the body. (*See* pages 243–244 and 258.)

FEBRUARY 1946

Elementary Anatomy and Physiology

1. Describe the contents of the female pelvis. (*For contents see* page 272. *See also* pages 267, 208, and 275–281.)
2. Give a brief account of the human teeth. (*See* page 190.)
3. What are the functions of
   (*a*) the gastric juice;
   (*b*) the medula oblongata;
   (*c*) the lymph glands?
   (*See* pages 199, 297 and 174.)
4. Describe the various types of muscle tissue and their mode of action. (*See* pages 27–30. *See also* page 104.)

SEPTEMBER 1945

Elementary Anatomy and Physiology

1. How is blood carried to the heart from the abdominal organs? (*See portal circulation*, page 143, *inferior vena cava*, page 171, and the *systematic circulation*, pages 141 and 142.)
2. Give an account of the bony and muscular boundaries of the thorax. Details of individual bones are not required. (*See* pages 49–50 and 227.)
3. What are the essentials of a normal diet? (*See* pages 184–185.)
4. What are the functions of
   (*a*) the pituitary gland;
   (*b*) the spleen;
   (*c*) the ovary?
   (*See* pages 246, 252 and 278.)

APRIL 1945

Elementary Anatomy and Physiology

1. Give an account of the Ankle Joint. (*See* page 102.)
2. Describe briefly the contents of the Skull. (*See Meninges*, page 290, *parts of brain*, pages 293–297, *venous sinuses*, page 166, and *Circle of Willis*, page 161.)
3. Describe the various ways in which the waste products of the body are excreted. (*By the kidneys*, see pages 264–269, *by the skin*, page 257, *by the colon*, page 210, and *from the, lungs*, page 233.)
4. Give an account of the functions of
   (*a*) The Thoracic Duct;
   (*b*) the white blood cells;
   (*c*) the Gall Bladder.
   (*See* pages 147, 175, and 219–220.)

INDEX

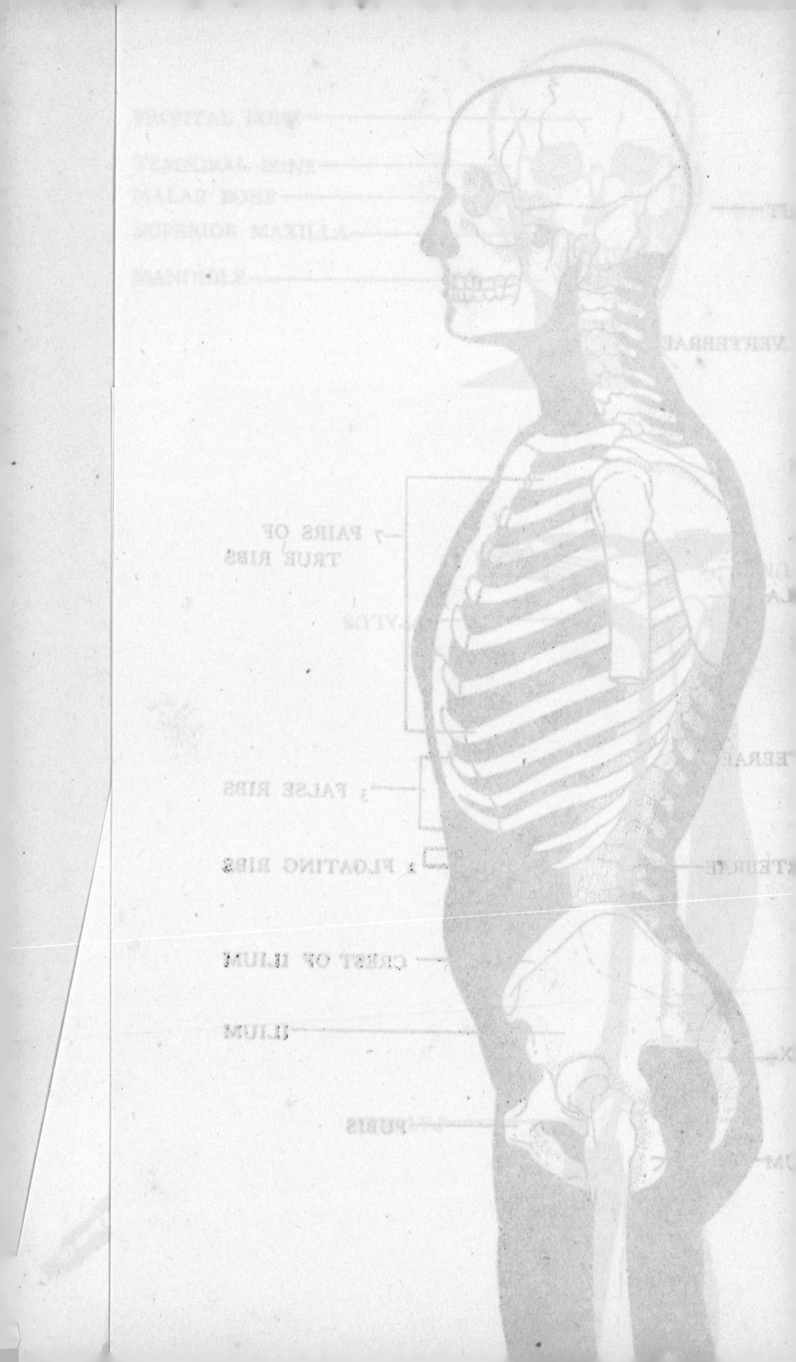

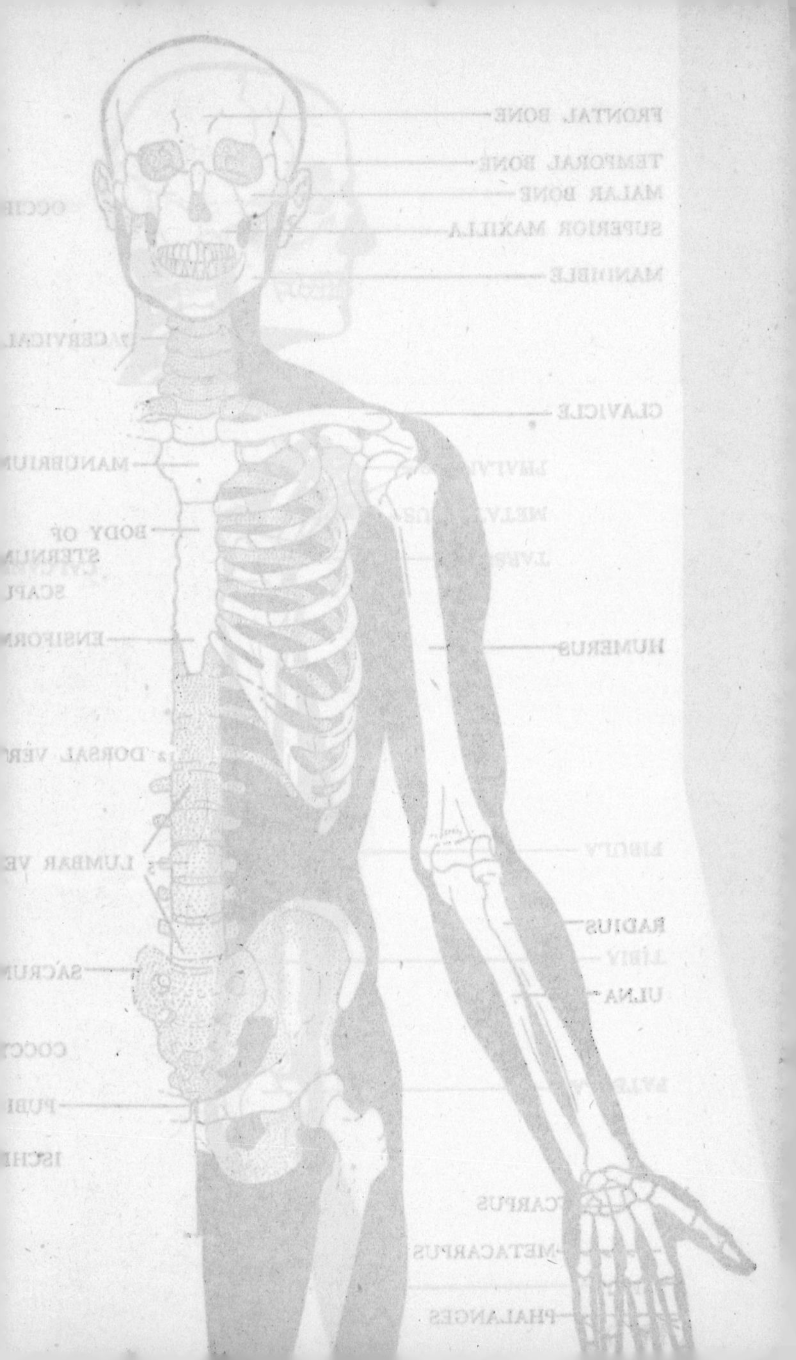
FRONTAL BONE
TEMPORAL BONE
MALAR BONE
SUPERIOR MAXILLA
MANDIBLE
7 CERVICAL
CLAVICLE
MANUBRIU
BODY OF
STERNU
SCAPU
ENSIFOR
HUMERUS
12 DORSAL VER
5 LUMBAR VE
RADIUS
SACRU
ULNA
COCC
PUB
ISCH
CARPUS
METACARPUS
PHALANGES